Modern Studies in Philosophy is a series of anthologies presenting contemporary interpretations and evaluations of the works of major philosophers. The editors have selected articles designed to show the systematic structure of the thought of these philosophers, and to reveal the relevance of their views to the problems of current interest. These volumes are intended to be contributions to contemporary debates as well as to the history of philosophy; they not only trace the origins of many problems important to modern philosophy, but also introduce major philosophers as interlocutors in current discussions.

Modern Studies in Philosophy is prepared under the general editorship of Amelie Oksenberg Rorty, Livingston College, Rutgers University.

DAVID F. PEARS is Tutor in Philosophy at Christ Church, Oxford, England. He is the author of *Bertrand Russell and the British Tradition in Philosophy* and of *Ludwig Wittgenstein* in *Modern Masters* series edited by Frank Kermode; and the editor of *The Nature of Metaphysics* and of *David Hume: A Symposium* and of *Freedom and the Will.*

Modern Studies in Philosophy

BERTRAND RUSSELL

A Collection of Critical Essays

EDITED BY

D. F. PEARS

1972
ANCHOR BOOKS
Doubleday & Company, Inc.
Garden City, New York

PREFACE

This collection of articles is not concerned with Bertrand Russell's life, but only with his philosophy. Anyone who wishes to find out what kind of man he was and what he achieved outside philosophy should read his *Autobiography*. His range and influence were prodigious. At one end of his spectrum there is his abstract work on the foundations of logic and mathematics. But this is closely connected with his metaphysics, philosophy of science, and theory of knowledge. So when we move toward those parts of his philosophy that have a more evident bearing on human life and experience, we do not feel any sharp discontinuities. His thinking is more integrated than is usual for a philosopher of his range, particularly in this century. Even when its practical consequences are greatest, in morals and politics, we are still kept aware of its theoretical basis.

There is no need for me to give a general account of his philosophy. This is provided by four of the articles in this volume. A. J. Ayer's *An Appraisal of Bertrand Russell's Philosophy* contains the most comprehensive survey. W. V. Quine's *Remarks for a Memorial Symposium* is briefer and more informal because it was written as a speech rather than as a lecture or article. G. Kreisel's *Bertrand Russell's Logic* was delivered on a similar occasion, and may serve as a short introduction to Russell's work on the foundations of logic and mathematics. Finally, D. H. Monro's *Russell's Moral Theories* provides, within the compass of an article, a synoptic view of Russell's leading ideas in morals and politics.

All the other articles are more confined in their scope, and a few involve technicalities. I hope that, taken together, they will give a reasonably comprehensive picture of Russell's philosophy, at least in its more theoretical aspects. It would be possible and valuable to produce a collection of articles which focused on the practical side of his thought, and left the theory in the background. But this collection has been put together on the opposite plan, and D. H. Monro's article is the only one exclusively about morals and politics.

There are fifteen articles, and seven of them are concerned with the philosophy of logic and mathematics. If this emphasis needs justification, it is justified by the way in which Russell became involved in philosophy and by the proportion of his early work that is devoted to logic and mathematics. As he explains in *My Philosophical Development,* he came to philosophy through mathematics, and his greatest early works are *The Principles of Mathematics,* and the book which he wrote in collaboration with A. N. Whitehead, *Principia Mathematica.*

The remaining articles belong somewhere in the middle of Russell's spectrum. They deal with his metaphysics, philosophy of science, theory of knowledge, and philosophy of mind. The influence of his work in these areas has been and still is very great, and I wish that there had been space to cover it more fully. However, nothing in this collection makes any claim to approach completeness, except H. Ruja's bibliography. This should be valuable to students of Russell because it is the first comprehensive bibliography of his philosophical writings, and it includes important contemporary reviews of them.

When this volume was being prepared, six of the contributions to it had either already appeared or were about to appear elsewhere. I wish to thank their authors for allowing me to reprint them, and the publishers of books and editors of journals, in which they came or were about to come out, for adding their permission. I am particularly grateful to those authors whose contributions have not appeared in print before—a long list, which makes this a largely new book: C. S. Chihara, C. A. Fritz, Jr., J. Hintikka, G. Kreisel, G. Maxwell, W. V. Quine (*Remarks for a Memorial Symposium*), Anthony Quinton, H. Ruja, and J. Vuillemin—a list to which my own name might have been added had I not been the editor.

CONTENTS

REMARKS FOR A MEMORIAL
SYMPOSIUM

W. V. Quine

Russell's godless godfather—as Sir Alfred Ayer put it
two weeks ago—was John Stuart Mill. Russell's life
coincides with an era in the history of philosophy that
detaches itself rather neatly, and can be defined in
any of three almost equivalent ways: philosophy since
John Stuart Mill; or, the past hundred years in philosophy; or, most significantly, the Age of Russell. We
have now reached the end of the era. *Eheu fugaces.*

Russell's life was long. Moreover, it was as broad
as it was long. Off at one edge of Russell's broad spectrum, he was a logic-chopping technician, a mathematician's philosopher and philosopher's mathematician.
At the other edge of his spectrum he was a social reformer advocating revision of the structure of the
family and of sexual mores and was even communi-
cating with the world's political leaders, doing what
he could to decide the fate of empires.

Within this broad spectrum of Russell's there is also
that broad bright zone of philosophy and science en-
tertainingly written for the thoughtful layman. I think
of such books as *The A.B.C. of Relativity, Sceptical
Essays, The Scientific Outlook, In Praise of Idleness,
Why I Am Not a Christian.* In these books an insidious
combination of irreverent banter and deep dedication
was Russell's invitation to philosophy. It is remarkable
that through some of his writing for lay readers Russell
lent glamour to the austerest side of philosophy, his
symbolic logic and philosophy of mathematics. This is

This paper was written for the memorial symposium on
Bertrand Russell at Brandeis University, February, 1970, but
was not delivered due to the postponement of the symposium.

the part of philosophy that promises least in a box-office kind of way, but still it is the part that lends itself most strikingly to the aha effect: the sense of seeing things fall into place. The editors of the Modern Library made no mistake when in arranging their 1927 volume of *Selected Papers of Bertrand Russell* they chose a chapter from the *Introduction to Mathematical Philosophy* as the concluding essay. It was the chapter entitled "Definition of Number," and it built up to this climax:

> The number of a class is the class of all those classes that are similar to it. . . . A number is anything which is the number of some class.

What was the impact of this upon the unspoiled reader? Something of mystery, something of novelty, something of profundity, something of illumination. One of Russell's major contributions to mathematical logic was his drawing power: he made the subject attractive to a succession of lively and inquiring younger minds. We are apt to overlook this, faced with Russell's many more conspicuous and direct contributions to mathematical logic.

Russell inducted some of us into the mainstream of philosophy, the theory of knowledge, by a devious and even paradoxical route. He first fired our interest in the least likely, most esoteric end of philosophy, the philosophy of mathematics; and his charismatic powers were helped in this, as I have said, by its being a domain that lends itself peculiarly well to the aha effect. Then, when we had marveled for a while at those illuminations, we were encouraged by Russell's more centrally philosophical writings to hope for further and comparable illumination in domains where illumination was even more to be prized: in the philosophy of natural knowledge itself. The authentic scientific ring of Russell's logic echoed in his epistemology of natural knowledge. The echo was especially clear in 1914, in *Our Knowledge of the External World*. That book fired some of us, and surely Carnap for one, with new hopes for phenomenalism.

Russell's work in logic had, if I am right, this curious power to draw people into philosophy. It also had, if Jules Vuillemin is right, the power to set the tone of twentieth-century philosophy itself.

There is no missing the relevance of *Our Knowledge of the External World* and *The Philosophy of Logical Atomism* and *The Analysis of Matter* and *The Analysis of Mind* to the Western scientific philosophy of the century. And there is no missing the prior influence of Russell's logic, in turn, upon these influential philosophical works of Russell. Also some of the influence of Russell's logic upon the philosophy of the Age of Russell is more obvious and direct, needing no mediation through other and more broadly philosophical writings of his. One thinks, first of all, of Russell's theory of descriptions; one thinks also of the theory of types.

Russell produced the theory of types as a cure for the paradoxes. Russell also had discovered the disease that the types were to cure. True, Burali-Forti's paradox antedated Russell's; but Burali-Forti just supposed it was a proof that the infinite ordinals were not in a linear order. Cantor found that it was a paradox, and that a somewhat simpler paradox could be gotten for infinite cardinal numbers. But all of this seemed to be the kind of thing that none of us needed to worry about who had had better judgment than to tangle with infinite numbers in the first place; and who wants infinite numbers? It was Russell, in 1901, who cut Cantor's paradox down to size, thereby producing a simple and basic paradox from which none of us could excuse ourselves, for all our scorn of infinite numbers. Seven years later he came up with his cure, the theory of types.

During his seven-year quest he surveyed alternative courses too. He considered an expedient that had al-

ready been hinted by König and even by Cantor: that
of banning the infinite classes of largest size, and retaining those of all the smaller infinite sizes. Zermelo
soon came out with a fully worked-out set theory
along this line. In fact he came out with it in the very
same year, 1908, in which Russell came out with his
theory of types. Zermelo's system and its variants have,
in the long run, carried the field in mathematical set
theory—if the years since 1908 count as a long run.
(Having run them myself, I doubt that they do.)

But however that may be, it was Russell's theory
of types that counted for philosophy. For the essential method of the theory of types invited further applications. The theory of types eliminated the paradoxes by cautery; it burned the morbid combinations
of symbols out of the language. It counted them
meaningless. This expedient was resumed twenty
years later by the logical positivists in Vienna who
had found other morbid tissue to eliminate: not paradox, this time, but metaphysics. Gilbert Ryle continued
in this vein, scouting what he called category mistakes.
Here the inspiration of the theory of types is especially
evident, Ryle's categories being a continuation or generalization of Russell's idea of logical types. Between
Russell and Ryle, moreover, there is in this matter of
categories a middleman to notice: Husserl. His doctrine of grammatical or syntactical categories, dating
from 1913, may have inspired Ryle and may have
been inspired by Russell's theory of types. This idea
of Husserl's, moreover, has been reaching us also
through another long and notable channel: Husserl to
Lesniewski to Ajdukiewicz to Geach. Geach has lately
been improving and exploiting the device in ways
that bid fair, I think, to raise the current level of structural linguistics.

Russell's logical theory of descriptions was philosophically important both for its direct bearing on philosophical issues having to do with meaning and reference, and for its illustrative value as a paradigm of

philosophical analysis. Russell's theory of logical types established new trends at once in the metaphysics of ontological categories, in the antimetaphysics of logical positivism, and, overspilling philosophy at the far edge, in structural linguistics. Is it any wonder that Vuillemin sees Russell's work in logic as "inaugurating contemporary philosophy"?

There is more to this point. The logical work of Russell that Vuillemin is concerned with, in *La Première Philosophie de Russell*,[1] is Russell's *Principles of Mathematics*. "The *Principles* inaugurate contemporary philosophy"; so writes Vuillemin (p. 333). Yet the *Principles* appeared in 1903, antedating both the theory of descriptions and the theory of types. It even antedated Russell's logically illuminating phase altogether, the phase that seduced us with that sense of new-found clarity. The *Principles*, as Vuillemin remarks, "was never in fashion." It is the more remarkable, then, that this prelogical logic of Russell's, this morass of half-formulated problems, should already contain the embryo of twentieth-century philosophy.

In the Age of Russell, if Vuillemin is right, philosophy itself has gone the way that each of us has gone who was lured to philosophy by Russell's logic. "The whole of Anglo-Saxon philosophy has undergone Russell's influence," Vuillemin writes (p. 332 f.), "for better or worse. This is, moreover, the only living philosophy today. It is sufficient praise of an author to state that a philosophy that ignores him is a dead philosophy."

[1] Colin, 1968.

AN APPRAISAL OF BERTRAND
RUSSELL'S PHILOSOPHY

A. J. Ayer

By the last quarter of the nineteenth century, British philosophy had fallen very largely under the spell of Hegel. The British Hegelians, of whom F. H. Bradley at Oxford and J. E. McTaggart at Cambridge were the most distinguished, were perhaps not very orthodox disciples of the master—Bradley in particular found it difficult to free himself entirely from the legacy of British empiricism—but with their belief in the Absolute, their characterization of the material world as mere appearance, and their denial of the reality of space and time, they committed themselves to metaphysics in a way that British philosophers have fought shy of, both before and since. That the present century has seen a return to the older and sounder empiricist tradition, and its development in a more rigorous form, is very largely due to the work of Bertrand Russell. What is called the analytical movement in philosophy, which in one form or another has fashioned the philosophical climate at least in English-speaking countries during the last quarter of a century, is in a great measure the fruit of his ideas.

As he relates in *My Philosophical Development*, there was a period in Lord Russell's youth when he himself, under the influence of Bradley's writings, was a Hegelian idealist. He was, however, very soon converted by his Cambridge friend and colleague, G. E. Moore, to a form of Platonic realism. This conversion

This essay first appeared in *Bertrand Russell: Philosopher of the Century*, ed. by Ralph Schoenman, London: Allen & Unwin, 1967; Boston: Little, Brown and Co., 1968. It is reprinted by permission of the author, the editor, and the publishers.

was made easier by the fact that Russell had first been led to take an interest in philosophy by his desire to find some reason for believing in the truth of mathematics; and he soon came to see that if he was to regard the propositions of mathematics as having objective validity, he would have to reject the fundamental idealist doctrine that the objects of knowledge are conditioned by their being known. Besides, Hegelian idealism looked askance on relational judgements which it regarded as incoherent; and Russell was convinced that the propositions of mathematics are irreducibly relational. For the same reason he rejected the view which is attributed to Aristotle and to Leibniz that all propositions are of the subject-predicate form. In the earliest of his philosophical books, *A Critical Examination of the Philosophy of Leibniz,* which appeared in 1900, Russell made a convincing attempt to show that the assumption of this logical doctrine can be made to account for the main features of Leibniz's metaphysics.

Two current explanations of the nature of mathematical propositions were the Kantian view that they were synthetic *a priori* truths, and at the other extreme the view of John Stuart Mill that they were empirical generalizations, which owed their security to their having been found to be supported by a very large number of instances. But neither of these explanations satisfied Russell. He did not then reject the notion of the synthetic *a priori,* as he came to do later, but the use that was made of it in this instance seemed to him not to explain enough; at the same time, the idea that the propositions of mathematics were empirical generalizations appeared to him untenable, because it implied the denial of their necessity.

Russell's own radical solution was to reduce mathematics to logic. In order to achieve this, he had to show that the fundamental terms of mathematics could be defined by means of purely logical concepts, but more importantly he had to transform logic itself. He

had to elaborate a system of logic which would
be rigorous and rich enough to allow the propositions
of mathematics to be incorporated in it. The first part
of this undertaking was carried out in the *Principles of
Mathematics*, which appeared in 1903. The second
led to *Principia Mathematica*, which extended to three
large volumes, of which the first came out in 1910, the
second in 1912, and the third in 1913. A comparatively untechnical account of the main ideas of these
works was given by Russell in his *Introduction to
Mathematical Philosophy*, which he wrote while in
prison as the result of his agitation against the First
World War, and published in 1919.

In his idea that mathematics could be reduced to
logic, Russell had been anticipated by the German
mathematician, Gottlob Frege. Though Frege's work
had been published over twenty years before, it was
very little known, and Russell arrived independently
at very similar results. In their definition of the natural
numbers, for example, both Russell and Frege made
use of the concept of a one-one relation; that is, a relation which is such that if it holds between any two
terms x and y, no other term but x is so related to y,
and x bears the relation to no other term but y. Two
classes are said to be similar if their members can be
correlated by a one-one relation. Then the number of
a class is defined as the class of all those classes that
are similar to it, and a cardinal number is defined as
anything which is the number of some class. This
definition is not circular as the notion of a one-one relation can be introduced in purely logical terms, without any reference to numbers. On the other hand, if
the definition is to apply to every cardinal number, it
seems to require that there be no upper limit to the
number of things that can be classified; and it may be
disputed whether this is a principle of logic.

At the time that he wrote the *Principles of Mathematics* Russell was still very much of a Platonic realist.
He spoke of 'whatever may be an object of thought'

as a term, and maintained that 'every term has being, i.e. *is* in some sense'. This committed him to a belief in the reality not only of universals, propositions, and classes, but of everything that was denoted by any substantival expression. His assumption was that if such an expression was meaningful, there must in some sense be an object to which it referred. This worked well enough in the case of proper names like 'Napoleon' or descriptions like 'the author of Waverley' which denoted objects which were known to exist: yet it hardly seems credible that there should in any sense *be* such objects as the present King of France, or the golden mountain, or the round square. At the same time, so far as the analysis of their meaning went, there appeared to be no justification for drawing a distinction between expressions like 'the present King of France' and expressions like 'the author of Waverley'. It was just a contingent, historical, fact that one of these succeeded in its reference and the other did not.

Russell's solution of this difficulty is to be found in his famous Theory of Descriptions. This theory was designed to show that even in their referential usage expressions of the form 'the so-and-so' do not function as names. It does not follow from the fact that they are meaningful that there is any object which they mean. Russell's way of showing this was to give a rule for translating sentences in which the definite descriptive phrase occurs, in such a way that the phrase no longer even looks as though it were a name. So, to take his own favourite example, the statement 'the author of Waverley was Scott' becomes in his translation a conjunction of the three statements: 'At least one person wrote Waverley': 'At most one person wrote Waverley': and 'It is not the case that anyone both wrote Waverley and was not identical with Scott'. To put it symbolically, as Russell himself preferred to do, the theory is that to say that something which has *f* has *g*, where *f* is the property concealed in the definite description and g is a property attributed to what it describes, is to say that there is an x such that (1) x has f, (2) for all y, if y has f, y is identical with x, and (3) x has g. Thus any description of the subject goes into the predicate, and only what Russell called a logically proper name, that is a pure demonstrative, can serve to designate the value of the variable x.

This theory, which the Cambridge philosopher, F. P. Ramsey, called a paradigm of philosophy, has recently had its critics. One objection to it is that there are many cases in which the literal application of Russell's rule yields unwelcome results. If I say 'The policeman on the corner told me where to go', I am surely not implying that there exists only one policeman or only one corner. The point about cases of this kind is that the definite description does not individuate the object to which it refers; it is assumed that the means of identifying the object are supplied by the context. Nevertheless the object will have a unique set of properties which could be specified: and if they are specified, then Russell's analysis will apply. Another objection is that the existence claim which is involved in the use of a definite description is not implicitly stated by it, as Russell assumes, but rather pre-supposed. It is alleged that we should not ordinarily say that a sentence like 'The present King of France is bald' was used to make a false statement: we should say rather that since there is no present King of France the question of truth or falsehood did not arise. It does not seem to me, however, that this is a question upon which the appeal to ordinary usage is at all decisive; and there are obvious advantages in construing sentences of this kind in such a way that they do make statements which have a truth-value.

A more serious criticism is that Russell starts from a false premise. The theory is intended to show how it is possible for a descriptive expression to be meaningful, even though there is nothing which it denotes: and it does this in effect by maintaining that these expressions are not referential. The underlying assumption is then that the meaning of a referential expression is to be identified with its denotation; and it is argued that, even in the case of proper names, this theory of meaning is mistaken. I agree that it is mistaken, and, therefore, that the reasoning which appears to have led Russell to the theory of descriptions can be criticized. However, the fact that it was designed to meet an avoidable difficulty does not invalidate the theory itself.

It was not only in the field of the theory of descriptions that Russell came to be sceptical of the generous ontology which he had admitted in the *Principles of Mathematics*. In his later works he thought it unnecessary to attribute real existence either to classes or to propositions: he held them rather to be logical fictions, in the sense that they could be analysed in terms of entities of a more concrete sort. On the other hand, he has always felt bound to admit the existence of universals. He has allowed, it may be wrongly, that one can go so far in dispensing with universals as to reduce them all to the single relation of resemblance; but since he takes the view that resemblance itself is a universal, he does not think that the nominalists achieve their aim.

It is not possible, within the limits of a general sketch of Russell's philosophy, to assess the scope and originality of *Principia Mathematica*. There is in any case no doubt that it played a very important part in the development of mathematical logic. The break with Aristotelian logic consisted not so much in the use of a special notation, as in the greater generality of Russell's and Whitehead's system, and above all in their attempt to make it rigorously formal. Other systems of logic have since been developed which lay claim to greater formal rigour, but they have in a large measure been inspired by Russell's and Whitehead's work.

One very important outcome of Russell's concern

with the problems of mathematical logic was his invention of the Theory of Types. The need for this theory arose out of his discovery of a contradiction in the theory of classes: a discovery which made Frege say, when the news of it was communicated to him by Russell, that the whole foundation of mathematics had been undermined. This contradiction is fairly easy to set out. Most classes appear not to be members of themselves: for example, the class of men is plainly not itself a man. On the other hand, some classes do appear to be members of themselves. For example, the class of all the things that can be counted would itself appear to be a thing that can be counted. Now consider the class of all classes that are not members of themselves. Is it or is it not a member of itself? If it is, it is not, and if it is not, it is.

Similar contradictions appear in other fields. A notorious example is the paradox of Epimenides the Cretan, who said that all Cretans were liars. Another well-known paradox, which belongs to the same family as that of the liar, arises out of the fact that some, but not all, adjectives are predicable of themselves. For instance, the word 'short' is short but the word 'long' is not long. Let us call those that are so predicable 'autological' and those that are not 'heterological'. Then is the word 'heterological' predicable of itself? Once again, if it is, it is not, and if it is not, it is.

Russell's solution of these antimonies was to arrange objects into a hierarchy of types, with the consequence that what may be true or false of the objects of one type cannot be meaningfully asserted about those of another. In particular, if a given class is the extension of a given predicate, only nonsense results if the predicate is applied to that class. So, it is not false but nonsensical to say that the class of men is human: the question whether the word 'heterological' is itself autological or heterological is a meaningless question. Even when a predicate does appear to characterize objects of different types, it does not have the same meaning in each case. Thus a predicate like 'being countable' becomes, as Russell puts it, systematically ambiguous.

The theory of types, of which I have here given only an outline, has a certain *ad hoc* air about it. It is hard to maintain that all forms of self-reference are logically vicious: and there seems to be no sure method for deciding when it is legitimate and when it is not. For this reason attempts have since been made to find a less restrictive means of avoiding the paradoxes. All the same, the theory of types has had an important historical influence. It called attention, in a very striking way, to the fact that a sentence may be grammatically well-formed and yet fail to express a meaningful statement. Among other things, it helped to set the stage for the Logical Positivists who rejected metaphysics on the ground that metaphysical doctrines were not even false but literally nonsensical. This is indeed a view that goes back to Hume, but Russell's work was taken as giving it logical support.

It follows from the theory of types that the statements which come lowest in the hierarchy refer to individuals; and it follows from the theory of descriptions that the individuals which, in Russell's phrase, make up the furniture of the world are designated by logically proper names. But, since logically proper names are pure demonstratives, it would appear that the only individuals which they can designate are those that are directly observable. In this way Russell's logic was integrated with his theory of knowledge.

The distinction between knowledge by acquaintance and knowledge by description, which is an outcome of the theory of descriptions, was developed by Russell in his *Problems of Philosophy*, which appeared in 1912. This book was written for the Home University Library and is still as good an introduction to philosophy as there is. It approaches the theory of knowledge from an empiricist standpoint: its guiding principle being that every proposition which we can

understand must be composed of constituents with
which we are acquainted. Thus Russell held that we
are acquainted with universals. We are also acquainted with particulars, but only with a limited class
of them: namely those which are directly given to us
in experience. In their case, he took it to follow from
the fact that one was acquainted with a particular
object, both that the object really existed and that it
had the properties which it appeared to have. On this
view, we can indeed surmise that particulars of other
types exist: but we can only refer to them indirectly
as objects which stand in certain relations to those
with which we are acquainted. Thus, when an object
is known by acquaintance, its existence is not open to
doubt; but the existence of objects which are known
only by description is problematic.

At that time Russell believed that the particulars
with which it was possible to be acquainted were
one's own self and one's own private thoughts, feelings, images and sense-data; these might be past as
well as present, since he allowed memory to be a form
of direct acquaintance. By 1921, when he published
The Analysis of Mind, he had come round to the view
that the existence of the objects, or events, which we
claim to remember is not known to us directly but
only inferred from our present memory-images; and
he also rejected the idea that one could be acquainted
with oneself, on the ground that the self did not exist
as a separate entity. On the other hand, he has never
given up the view that the objects with which we are
directly acquainted in perception are our own private
sense-data. The sense-datum theory has indeed met
with considerable opposition in recent times, as part
of a general reaction against allowing the existence
of private entities. If Russell adhered to it, it was
mainly because he thought that the alternative of supposing that we are directly acquainted with physical
objects was obviously untenable. His main argument
against naïve realism is most succinctly put in the *In-*

quiry into Meaning and Truth, which appeared in 1940. 'We all start from "naïve realism", i.e. the doctrine that things are what they seem. We think that grass is green, that stones are hard and that snow is cold. But physics assures us that the greenness of grass, the hardness of stones, and the coldness of snow are not the greenness, hardness, and coldness that we know in our own experience, but something very different. The observer, when he seems to himself to be observing a stone, is really, if physics is to be believed, observing the effect of the stone upon himself. . . . Naïve realism leads to physics, and physics, if true, shows that naïve realism is false. Therefore naïve realism, if true, is false; therefore it is false.'[1]

This implies a causal theory of perception, with which Russell began and to which he reverted. There was, however, a period in which in obedience to the principle 'wherever possible substitute constructions out of known entities for inferences to unknown entities', a principle which he has called the supreme maxim in scientific philosophy, he gave up the causal theory, at any rate in its conventional form, in favour of the phenomenalist position that physical objects are logical constructions out of actual and possible sense-data. This is a reformulation of John Stuart Mill's view that physical objects are permanent possibilities of sensation; the form in which it presents it is that statements about physical objects can be faithfully translated into statements about sense-data.

Russell developed this view in *Our Knowledge of the External World* which was published in 1914, and in two of the essays collected in *Mysticism and Logic* which appeared in 1918. The materials out of which he tried to construct physical objects were not limited to the actual sense-data with which any single observer was acquainted. Russell also brought in the sense-data sensed by other persons and even unsensed

[1] p. 15.

sense-data, to which he gave the name of sensibilia. The only way in which a sensibile was supposed to differ from a sense-datum was in its not being actually sensed. Roughly speaking, Russell's theory was that at any given moment each observer perceives a private three-dimensional world with its own private space, or spaces, since Russell distinguishes the space of sight from the space of touch. He calls these private worlds perspectives. In addition to these perceived perspectives, there exists also an infinite number of unperceived perspectives, namely all those that an observer would perceive if he were in the appropriate state and in the appropriate position. The constituents of the unperceived perspectives are sensibilia. A physical object is then defined as a class of sensibilia, where sensibilia are taken as including sense-data; it is in fact identified with those sensibilia, or sense-data, which are commonly regarded as its actual and possible appearances. Since the three-dimensional perspectives are themselves arranged in a three-dimensional order, physical space is one of six dimensions. Russell does not work out this theory in full detail, but it is clear that it encounters very serious difficulties, even if one is willing to assume that sensibilia and unperceived perspectives literally exist.

In the *Reply to Criticisms* which Russell wrote for *The Philosophy of Bertrand Russell,* a volume in the Library of Living Philosophers, which was published in 1944, he remarked that he did not see why this theory should preclude him from regarding physical objects as causes of sense-data. His ground for this presumably was that the causal relations which are supposed to hold between physical objects and sense-data may themselves be capable of being analysed in terms of correlations among sensibilia. This is substantially the position which he took in the *Analysis of Mind,* where he develops a theory about mind and matter which is akin to the neutral monism of William James. The theory is that both mind and matter are logical constructions out of elements, primarily sense-data, which are themselves neither mental nor physical. Apart from the fact that certain elements, such as images and feelings, enter only into the constitution of minds, what chiefly distinguishes mind from matter, in this view, is the operation of different causal laws. Thus the same sense-data when correlated according to the laws of physics constitute physical objects and when correlated according to the laws of psychology help to constitute minds. In their mental aspect, they engage among other things, in what Russell called mnemic causation, a kind of action at a distance by which experiences produce subsequent memory-images. A consequence of this view is that Russell rejects the notion not only of the self, but also of consciousness, as a substantial entity. On the other hand, while he has dallied with behaviourism, he has never denied the existence of states of consciousness which are not definable in physical terms.

An interesting feature of Russell's more recent writings on the subject of perception is that he locates sense-data, or percepts as he now prefers to call them, in the percipient's brain. He does not mean by this that when we think that we are perceiving the world around us, we are, in any literal sense, really observing only our own brains. His argument is rather that an event's position in space-time is determined by its causal relations and that 'the causal and temporal connections of percepts with events in afferent and efferent nerves gives percepts a position in the brain of the observer'.[2] If this still sounds paradoxical it has to be remembered that for Russell the brain itself is a construction out of sensible events. It is one of the perspectives from which the world is viewed and it is via the perspectives which constitute their point of view, rather than the physical objects which are con-

[2] *The Philosophy of Bertrand Russell*: Reply to Criticisms, p. 705.

structed out of them, that actual percepts acquire their own location in physical space.

The view that the world consists in the last resort of sensible events is a feature of the doctrine of Logical Atomism which Russell, under the influence of his pupil Ludwig Wittgenstein put forward in the years following the First World War. It was expounded by him in some lectures which were first published in the *Monist* in 1918 and 1919 under the title of 'The Philosophy of Logical Atomism', and have since been reprinted in a collection of essays called *Logic and Knowledge,* which appeared in 1956; and there is also an essay called 'Logical Atomism' which Russell contributed to the first series of Contemporary British Philosophy in 1924. While making a strong plea for the method of logical analysis, considered primarily as an application of Ockham's razor, in accordance with the principle of substituting logical constructions for inferred entities, the lectures were largely concerned with the problem of truth. In his earlier writings on the subject of truth, at a time when he believed in the objective reality of propositions, Russell had taken the view that truth and falsehood were unanalysable properties by which propositions were simply characterized. Propositions, he held, were true or false just as roses may be red or white. It was not long, however, before he came, with reason, to regard this theory as obscurantist and he accordingly abandoned it in favour of a correspondence theory of truth.

In Russell's exposition of Logical Atomism, as in Wittgenstein's *Tractatus Logico-Philosophicus*, the correspondence theory is given a very literal interpretation. Russell conceived of sensible events as entering into what he called atomic facts; and these atomic facts were designated, as it were photographically, by elementary propositions. The truth of all higher-order propositions depended upon the truth of these elementary propositions and the truth of these elementary propositions consisted in their structural correspondence with atomic facts. Russell devoted much ingenuity to the elaboration of this theory, but it depends upon a pictorial theory of meaning which both he and Wittgenstein subsequently found to be untenable.

Russell reverted to the problem of truth both in his *Inquiry into Meaning and Truth* and in *My Philosophical Development*, which was published in 1959. He still adheres in these works to a correspondence theory in so far as he holds that propositions are made true by facts, but he no longer thinks that truth consists in a relation of structural correspondence, and he prefers to regard the truth of propositions as derivative from the truth of beliefs. Roughly speaking, his view is that a belief is accounted true if the state of affairs which is taken as verifying it is found by observation to exist, and false if its 'verifier' is found not to exist. This is in line also with his rejection of a pictorial in favour of a causal theory of meaning.

Russell remained a Logical Atomist in the sense of thinking that the world consists of a number of particulars. But in the *Inquiry into Meaning and Truth* he gives this position a new aspect by identifying these particulars with what are ordinarily called qualities. Here again his motive is one of economy, supported by the desire to eliminate the dubious notion of substance. Accordingly he follows Berkeley in treating the things of common sense as collections of qualities, which are united by what he calls a relation of compresence. There are some difficulties in this theory, which centre mainly upon the interpretation of the relation of compresence: but I think it quite possible that they can be overcome.

This view of the nature of particulars is retained in Russell's *Human Knowledge: Its Scope and Limits*, which was published in 1948. Otherwise, this book is of interest chiefly for its attempt to deal with the problem of induction. Russell takes the unfashionable view that inductive reasoning stands in need of justification, and he elaborates a set of principles which he thinks would be sufficient for this purpose. He does not, however, think that any of these principles can be known to be true.

There are many other aspects of philosophy to which Russell contributed. He wrote extensively on ethics, on political philosophy, on social philosophy and the philosophy of education, on the history of philosophy and the philosophy of history. But while this section of his work contains some of the best of Russell's writing, it has not the same theoretical interest as his work in the field of logic and the theory of knowledge. In moral philosophy, he began by sharing G. E. Moore's view that 'good' was an objective unanalysable non-natural quality, but he was later persuaded that ethical judgements are not objectively either true or false, but are rather expressive of attitudes. Though he accepted this conclusion intellectually, he confessed to disliking it on emotional grounds. His own ethical standpoint appears to have been mainly utilitarian. He believed that the proper concern of ethics is to find out what people want and how their ends can be attained. At the same time it is clear that he attached an intrinsic value to such things as justice and liberty and the pursuit of truth.

While he had an extensive knowledge of history, of which he made effective use, Russell's approach to social questions was more moral than historical. In the *History of Western Philosophy*, which he published in 1946, he did indeed set out to relate philosophical ideas to the social conditions under which they were produced, but for the most part the exposition of the ideas and the description of the social background proceed side by side: no very serious attempt is made to integrate them. As might be expected, his history of philosophy is most illuminating when it treats of the philosophers to whom he is most sympathetic; in particular, Leibniz and the British empiricists.

To my mind, the best of Russell's political writings

is his book on the *Principles of Social Reconstruction*, which appeared in 1916 at the height of his campaign against the First World War. It is anarchist in temper and it reflects the distrust of institutions, and especially of the power of the State, that always coloured his political thinking. Not only in politics, but also in the sphere of education, he was a consistent advocate of liberty. Though he is more keenly aware of the irrational features in human conduct, his outlook on moral, political and social questions bears a fairly close affinity to that of John Stuart Mill.

In the course of his long career, Russell, as we have seen, held quite a large variety of philosophical opinions. This has sometimes been used as an argument against him, especially by those who publish very little for fear of being discovered to be wrong. But the fact is that, while he fairly often changed his views on points of detail, his approach to philosophy was remarkably consistent. His aim was always to try to find reasons for accepted beliefs, whether in the field of mathematics, the natural or social sciences, or common sense. He was a consistent sceptic, not in the sense that he denied our claims to knowledge, but that he questioned them. He adhered also to a single method, the method of starting with propositions which are the least susceptible to doubt, and trying to reconstruct the edifice of knowledge on this basis, with as few assumptions as possible. When he changed his views, the reason was usually either that he thought he could make do with even fewer assumptions, or else that he had pared them down too far, so that the basis from which he was working was not adequate to the facts. The result of his using this method has been that his justifications usually take the form of analyses; it is thus that he has come to furnish so much of the inspiration for the analytic movement in contemporary philosophy. Even so, he himself was not interested in analysis for its own sake, but only as a method of proof. In this, as in the power and elegance of his literary style, he continues the main tradition of British Empiricism. He is, and is likely to remain, its outstanding representative in the twentieth century.

RUSSELL'S LOGICAL ATOMISM

D. F. Pears

Russell's logical atomism is a difficult theory to interpret. One source of the difficulty is the sketchiness of his exposition. At the time when he was developing the theory he was so sure that it must be true in one form or another, that he was not very concerned to say precisely in what form it is true. Wittgenstein's version of the theory is obscure for the same reason. But that is less surprising, because Wittgenstein, unlike Russell, did not claim that he was yet in a position to indicate the simple things that he took to be the ultimate constituents of the world. Another source of the obscurity of Russell's version of the theory is its versatility. It is offered as the answer to so many different questions. It is a theory of meaning for nonlogical words, but, because it is an empiricist theory, it is especially concerned with the ways in which their meanings are learned and remembered. This concern makes it necessary for the theory to include answers to certain questions in epistemology and the philosophy of mind. If the meanings of some nonlogical words are the things that they signify, what kinds of knowledge do we have of those things, and in what form does our knowledge of them persist in our minds? The theory also includes, at least implicitly, an account of the identification and reidentification of things, because this is an essential part of a theory of meaning that equates any meanings with things signified.

The interpretation of so versatile a theory should start from its primary task, which is to explain the fact that nonlogical words have meanings. Considered from

This paper was written for this volume, and is here published for the first time. It will also appear in *Russell's Logical Atomism*, ed. by D. F. Pears, London: Collins, 1972.

this point of view, logical atomism claims that everyday language may be analyzed into a better language,
which will disclose the real structure of the facts with
which everyday language is concerned. This language
is not better in practice because it is too cumbersome
to be used, but only in theory, because it yields the
kind of understanding of the world that philosophers
seek. Russell characterizes it in the following way: "In
a logically perfect language there will be one word
and no more for every simple object, and everything
that is not simple will be expressed by a combination
of words, by a combination derived, of course, from
the words for the simple things that enter in, one word
for each simple component. A language of that sort
will be completely analytic and will show at a glance
the logical structure of the facts asserted or denied.
The language that is set forth in *Principia Mathematica* is intended to be a language of that sort. It is a
language that has only syntax and no vocabulary whatsoever. Barring the omission of a vocabulary I maintain that it is quite a nice language. It aims at being
the sort of language that, if you add a vocabulary,
would be a logically perfect language. Actual languages are not logically perfect in this sense and they
cannot possibly be, if they are to serve the purposes
of everyday life."[1]

The vocabulary that has to be added will be a list
of nonlogical words. Russell assumed that, if any of
these nonlogical words has meanings, some of them
must signify existent things. This is a reasonable assumption since, if none of them signified existent
things, the whole vocabulary, whatever the connections between its elements, would lack any connection
with anything outside itself. However, it would not
follow that any specific subset of nonlogical words

[1] "The Philosophy of Logical Atomism," in *Essays in Logic
and Knowledge*, ed. by R. C. Marsh, London: Allen & Unwin,
1956, pp. 197–98.

must signify existent things. Before he draws this conclusion, Russell brings in the syntactical distinction between analyzable and unanalyzable expressions. An analyzable expression may or may not signify an existent thing, and, if it does, the existence of the thing will amount to no more than the existence and appropriate combination of its elements, and such things are logical fictions. But an unanalyzable, or simple expression must signify an existent thing, and in such a case Russell equates the meaning of the expression with the thing itself, and the thing is a genuine constituent of the world.

This theory of meaning is founded on two very general ideas: the idea that nonlogical expressions may be divided into the analyzable and the unanalyzable, and the idea that they have meanings if, and only if, either they or the expressions that appear in their analyses (if any) signify existent things. This is a theory that can be applied to different vocabularies, and to a given vocabulary in different ways. Moore applied it to the vocabulary of ethics. When Russell and Wittgenstein applied it to the vocabulary of factual language, they reached different results, because they used different criteria of analyzability.

In "The Philosophy of Logical Atomism," which contains the most detailed exposition of Russell's version of the theory, he uses it as a guide to the real structure of factual discourse and of the world of facts. This is equally true of the version of the theory that Wittgenstein developed in *Tractatus Logico-Philosophicus*. The two versions diverge because Wittgenstein required that fully analyzed propositions be logically independent of one another, whereas Russell uses a less stringent criterion of unanalyzability. This difference between the two theories affects their application to factual discourse. Russell is able to arrange a quick marriage between his version of the theory and his empiricism: sense-data are the simple particulars that are signified by fully analyzed singular expressions, and some of their qualities and relations are the simple universals that are signified by fully analyzed general expressions. But the universals that Russell regarded as simple—specific shades of color, for example—did not pass Wittgenstein's test for simplicity, because they are capable of producing logical incompatibilities between the propositions in which they are mentioned. Consequently, Wittgenstein could not connect his logical atomism with factual discourse in the same way as Russell, and, though he was convinced that the connection could be made somehow, he never succeeded in making it. He believed that it would be made when the analysis of factual propositions had been taken further than he had taken it, and elementary propositions, unanalyzable even by his stringent criterion, had been discovered. He offers no reason for supposing that they would be discovered among propositions about physical objects rather than among propositions about sense-data. That pair of alternatives is left open by him, like all other questions about elementary propositions except the question, what criterion of unanalyzability they must satisfy.

This difference between the two philosophers' versions of logical atomism must not be exaggerated. It would be a mistake to suggest that Russell rests his case for his version solely on its suitability to his empiricism. The truth is that, like Wittgenstein, he argues for the theory on general grounds of logic and meaning, and it is not clear how much additional confirmation he supposes to accrue from its application to sense-datum propositions. In fact, he occasionally expresses doubts about the details of this application, but his doubts do not undermine his belief in the theory itself. For example, in his later essay "Logical Atomism" he says: "When I speak of simples, I ought to explain that I am not speaking of something experienced as such, but known only inferentially as the limit of analysis. It is quite possible that, by greater logical skill, the need for assuming them could be avoided. A logical language will not lead to error if its simple symbols (i.e., those not having any parts that are symbols, or any significant structure) all stand for objects of some one type, even if these objects are not simple. The only drawback to such a language is that it is incapable of dealing with anything simpler than the objects which it represents by simple symbols. But I confess it seems obvious to me (as it did to Leibniz) that what is complex must be composed of simples, though the number of constituents may be infinite."[2]

We should, therefore, distinguish between the theory itself and the accretions derived from its adaptation to Russell's empiricism. The main ideas in the theory itself are the two that have already been isolated: the idea that nonlogical expressions may be divided into the analyzable and the unanalyzable, and the idea that they have meanings if, and only if either they or the expressions in their analyses signify existent things. In "The Philosophy of Logical Atomism" he presents these two ideas as part and parcel of his empiricism, and it is best to begin with this presentation of the theory because it is the most extensive one in his writings. We can then remove the empiricist accretions and see what is left.

Considered as a contribution to empiricism, Russell's logical atomism is directly related to Hume's psychological atomism. Russell asks how people achieve understanding of propositions, and his answer, which connects his theory of meaning with his theory of knowledge, is that "every proposition which we can understand must be composed wholly of constituents with which we are acquainted."[3] This principle may

2 *Essays in Logic and Knowledge,* p. 337, cf., *My Philosophical Development,* pp. 221–23: "I on occasion spoke of atomic facts as the final residue in analysis, but it was never an essential part of . . . [my] analytical philosophy . . . to suppose that such facts were attainable."

3 *Problems of Philosophy,* p. 58.

be compared with Hume's principle, that every idea to which a person can attach significance must either be a replica of a sense-impression that he has had, or else be analyzable into simpler ideas that are replicas of sense-impressions that he has had. If Hume's ideas are taken as the counterparts, not of Russell's propositions, but of the expressions, singular and general, that occur in them, a close relationship can be seen between the two empiricist systems. In both alike, complexes are analyzable and simple elements are unanalyzable. In both alike, simple elements will lack significance unless they are correlated with existent things—sense-impressions, if they are Humean simple ideas, and if they are Russellian, simple words, the things that they signify. Naturally, there are also big differences between the two systems, and perhaps the most important one is that Hume did not think that any singular ideas are simple, whereas Russell did think that some singular expressions are simple, *viz.,* logically proper names.

Russell's theory of logically proper names is certainly the most paradoxical part of his logical atomism. He adopted it because he believed that in the end non-logical words, whether they be general or singular, must signify existent things, and that the end must be reached at some level of analysis. In the passage that has just been quoted from "Logical Atomism" he only says that this seems obvious to him, and in a discussion at the end of the second lecture in "The Philosophy of Logical Atomism,"[4] he concedes that it may not be true: "I think it is perfectly possible to suppose that complex things are capable of analysis *ad infinitum,* and that you never reach the simple. I do not think it is true, but it is a thing that one might argue, certainly. I do myself think that complexes—I do not like to talk of complexes—but that facts are composed of simples, but I admit that that is a difficult argu-

[4] *Essays in Logic and Knowledge,* p. 202.

ment, and it might be that analysis could go on forever." It is hard to know how definite a view can be extracted from these two passages. He seems to have felt unsure about the kind of argument that Wittgenstein uses for the thesis that the analysis of nonlogical words must terminate at some level—the argument that "the naming of complexes presupposes propositions, while propositions presuppose the naming of simples."[5]

However, these doubts do not seem to have undermined Russell's belief that there must be a level at which the analysis of nonlogical words will terminate (whether this is the "must" of obviousness or of cogent argument). At that level, propositions will be composed entirely of simple general expressions and logically proper names. Both these types of expression will have meanings that cannot be expressed in words, so that, if someone wished to learn their meanings, ostension would be his teacher's only resource. From here it is a short step to the thesis that the meanings of simple expressions are the things that they signify. Although it is correct to characterize this thesis as one that confuses the meaning of a name with its bearer, this is not a very explanatory characterization of it. When Russell's logical atomism is taken with its empiricist accretions, it would be more explanatory to say that he adopted a theory of meaning which is not implausible in its application to general expressions ("red" means that color), extended it to singular expressions, and so ran into all the difficulties that beset the notion of individual substances. But it would be essential to add that he also assimilated logically proper names to demonstratives.

There are two kinds of difficulty that his theory encounters. There are difficulties in his description of a

[5] Russell's *Introduction to Tractatus Logico-Philosophicus*, p. xiii. See *Tractatus Logico-Philosophicus* 2.02–2.0212 and 3.23–3.24.

logically perfect, or fully analyzed language, and the best known difficulty of this kind is the one that has just been mentioned. There are also difficulties in his account of the analysis that is supposed to reveal the logically perfect language underlying everyday language.

His analysis relies on two different logical devices, the replacement of complex general expressions by definitionally equivalent strings of simple general expressions, and the replacement of complex singular expressions by definite descriptions of the simple particulars constituting the original complexes and statements about the ways in which they are combined. Both devices are independent of his empiricism, but both pick up empiricist accretions when they are used in his analysis of factual propositions.

The first type of analysis is the less problematic of the two, but it has its problems. For example, there are cases where a definition of an apparently simple general word might help someone to learn its meaning, but could not complete the lesson by itself. Russell considers a case of this kind in "The Philosophy of Logical Atomism:" after claiming that " 'red' could not be understood except by seeing red things," he says that, "if you define 'red' as 'the color with the greatest wavelength,' you are not giving the actual meaning of the word at all; you are simply giving a true description, which is quite a different thing, and the propositions which result are different propositions from those in which the word 'red' occurs. In that sense the word 'red' cannot be defined. In the sense of analysis you cannot define 'red'."[6] Russell refuses to allow that this definition "the color with the greatest wave-length" is an analysis of "red," on the ground that if a proposition p contains the word "red," and if q is the result of substituting it for "red" in p, then a person might understand p without understanding q, and *vice versa*.

[6] *Essays in Logic and Knowledge*, pp. 194–95.

Consequently, though this definition might help someone to learn the meaning of the word "red"—once equipped with it, he could go off and try to achieve acquaintance with the color with the greatest wavelength—it could not serve as a complete pedagogic substitute for acquaintance.

Russell need not have presented this point in empiricist terms. For he could have made it even if he had refrained from identifying simple qualities and relations with certain familiar qualities and relations of sense-data. He need not even have connected the point with the learning of meanings. He could simply have argued that the meanings of the two propositions, p and q, are different. However, in fact he does present the point in empiricist terms, and he evidently regards the analysis of a general expression as a formula that successfully captures its meaning, the test of success being to ask whether someone who is told the analysis, and understands the words in it will grasp the meaning of the *analyzandum* without more ado.

It is possible that Russell's preoccupation with the learning of meanings provides the explanation of the difference, already noted, between his criterion of unanalyzability and Wittgenstein's. Russell may have had the following idea: a definitional connection between two general words, such as "red" and "green," does not provide the analysis of either of them, if it is not sufficient by itself to teach the meaning of one of them to someone who knows the meaning of the other. It does not even provide part of the analysis of either of them if it is not sufficient by itself to teach part of the meaning of one of them to someone who knows the meaning of the other. For someone might have complete knowledge of the meaning of the word "red" even if he did not know the meaning of "not green," and so teaching a person the meaning of "not green" would not be teaching him part of the meaning of the word "red." If, influenced by this idea, Russell believed that "not green" is not part of the meaning of "red," although it is definitionally connected with it, that might explain why, unlike Wittgenstein, he allows that "This is red" is a fully analyzed proposition.

Apart from the difficulties of this line of thought, the attribution of it to Russell is speculative because this part of his theory is sketchily presented. There is also another quite different, but at least equally plausible explanation of his choice of criterion for unanalyzability. Unlike Wittgenstein, he seems to have been more concerned with the actual world than with alternative possible worlds, and so more concerned with the structure of facts, and especially of known facts, than with the structure of possibilities. Consequently, he may not have required the logical independence of all atomic propositions, but only of all true atomic propositions. If this was his view, it would explain why he did not think that the logical incompatibilities between "red" and "green" and between other similar pairs of words for properties and relations rule out the atomicity of propositions containing such words. However, it is uncertain whether this was his view, because the best evidence for attributing it to him is inconclusive: "Whether an atomic proposition, such as 'This is red,' or 'This is before that,' is to be asserted or denied can only be known empirically. Perhaps one atomic fact may sometimes be capable of being inferred from another, though this seems very doubtful; but in any case it cannot be inferred from premises no one of which is an atomic fact. It follows that, if atomic facts are to be known at all, some at least must be known without inference."[7] This passage, which is slanted toward knowledge of atomic facts, suggests that he may only have required the logical independence of all true atomic propositions, but was not absolutely sure even about this point. If this is so, it produces a big difference between his atomic propositions and Wittgenstein's elementary

[7] *Our Knowledge of the External World*, pp. 62–63.

propositions, all of which had to be logically independent of one another.

Russell's analysis of complex singular expressions runs into several difficulties which are connected with the difficulty that has just been pointed out in his analysis of complex general expressions. The difficult thing is to give a coherent way of determining which true descriptions of X will count as analyses of "X."

Russell's procedure is to replace complex singular expressions by definite descriptions of the simple particulars constituting the original complexes. In the most straightforward kind of case the original complex will consist of a single simple particular possessing simple qualities, and the definite description will mention all these simple qualities, and identify the simple particular as the one that possesses them. It is evident that a particular identified in this way will be simple in the following sense: no fact will be embedded in it and so, unlike, for example, a number, it will have no essential nature. It follows that, if it is named, its name will be a logically proper name, devoid of descriptive content. The meaning of this name, according to Russell, is the particular that it signifies, and it can be learned only through acquaintance with that particular.

When Russell uses this procedure in the analysis of complex singular expressions in factual language, he is almost exclusively concerned with a less straightforward kind of case, *viz.*, complexes consisting not of single simple particulars, but of sets of simple particulars. This is because everyday factual language mentions things that endure through time, whereas he identifies simple particulars with momentary sense-data: ". . . Substance, in the sense of something that is continuously identical in the same desk, is not given to you. Therefore, in all cases where you seem to have a continuous entity persisting through changes, what you have to do is to ask yourself what makes you consider the successive appearances as belonging to the same thing. When you have found out what makes you take the view that they belong to the same thing, you will then see that that which has made you say so is all that is *certainly* there in the way of unity. Anything that there may be over and above that I shall recognize as something that I cannot know. What I can know is that there is a certain series of appearances linked together, and the series of these appearances I shall define as being a desk. In that way the desk is reduced to being a logical fiction, because a series is a logical fiction. In that way all the ordinary objects of daily life are extruded from the world of what there is, and in their place as what there is, you find a number of passing particulars of the kind that one is immediately conscious of in sense."[8]

This passage raises many questions about the theory of logical fictions or logical constructions. Does the existence of a desk really amount to no more than the existence and appropriate combination of such simple elements as sense-data? And what will happen to the predicate in whatever proposition about the desk is being analyzed? Presumably, it will often have to undergo a thorough transformation in the course of the analysis.

But these problems about the application of Russell's logical atomism are peripheral to the theory itself. The problem that was raised earlier is the central one. How are we to determine when a true description of X counts as an analysis of "X"?

Russell categorically denies that a true description of a quality is an analysis of the word for the quality. He denies this even when the description is a general scientific one, which might be used as a criterion. It is then difficult for him to maintain that the way to analyze a complex singular expression is to replace it by a definite description of a simple particular. Sup-

[8] "The Philosophy of Logical Atomism," *Essays in Logic and Knowledge*, p. 273.

pose, for example, that a person, John, were a simple particular possessing, as a matter of contingent fact, various qualities and standing in various relations to other simple particulars. Then the difficulty is to see how Russell could use these contingent facts in order to construct a definite description of the particular that would yield an analysis of a proposition about John when it was substituted for his name. Since they are all contingent facts, any of them might not have been the case, and, though it might be impossible to understand which person had been meant by "John" if none of them had been the case, this provides no support for the thesis that at least one of the propositions that result from replacing "John" with a definite description drawn from those facts is logically equivalent to the original proposition. Of course, the form that this difficulty takes in Russell's theory is more elaborate because he treats persons and material objects as serial complexes consisting of large numbers of particulars. However, the logical problem is the same. The history of a complex individual is a contingent matter, and so, if variations in its history involve variations in the atomic facts about the simple particulars that constitute it, it follows that, though its name will be connected with definite descriptions of those particulars, this will not be a connection of meaning. It will be a connection revealed by the speaker's answers to the question "Whom did you mean?" It will not hold in all possible worlds, but only in those that are compatible with his knowledge who John is.[9]

The same difficulty besets the final stage in Russell's analysis of complex singular expressions. It is not sufficient for his purpose merely to replace them by definite descriptions of the simple particulars that constitute them. If a fully analyzed proposition mentions simple particulars only by their names, it seems that

[9] See J. Hintikka, "Knowledge by Acquaintance—Individuation by Acquaintance," the next paper in this volume.

the final stage in his analysis must be to substitute logically proper names for bound variables. But this substitution raises the same problem again. The connection between one of these definite descriptions and the particular that satisfies it will not be a connection of meaning. It will be a contingent connection, and, though the speaker may know that it holds, and may mean *a* when he uses the definite description, any higher estimate of the strength of the connection would be an exaggeration.

But in this case Russell has a way of dealing with the problem. He admits that this last connection is contingent, and accepts the consequence that the analysis of a complex singular expression cannot move from a definite description of a simple particular to its logically proper name. He then distinguishes between two different analyses of the same factual sentence. Someone who was acquainted with the simple particulars that constitute the complex mentioned in the sentence would use an analysis that contained their logically proper names; whereas someone who lacked that acquaintance would use an analysis that contained definite descriptions of them. The connection between these two analyses is not identity of meaning, and therefore the original sentence is capable of expressing two different propositions. The relation between the two analyses is that the first says what we would like to be able to mean, but the second says all that we can legitimately mean when we lack the requisite acquaintance.[10] It is evident that any other solution to this problem would upset Russell's thesis that logically proper names have no descriptive content, and simple particulars have no essential natures.

However, this solution has an air of arbitrariness. If an ordinary proper name and a set of definite descriptions of all the simple particulars that are involved

[10] *Mysticism and Logic,* p. 218.

are interchangeable without any change in the sense of the proposition in which they occur, why should this not be so for a logically proper name and the definite description of its simple particular? This question forces us to examine problems of the first of the two kinds that were distinguished earlier, *viz.*, problems about the terminus of analysis rather than problems about the process of analysis. For Russell's answer to the charge of arbitrariness would be that logically proper names, devoid of any descriptive content, are theoretically indispensable, and the only way to assess this answer is to look more closely at his account of singular expressions in a logically perfect language.

The theoretical reason for postulating simple particulars is that, when a complex singular expression is fully analyzed, there must be one or more particulars to carry the qualities and relations mentioned in its analysis, and these particulars will be simple because all qualities and relations will have been stripped off them. We may use the existential quantifier when we refer to them, but the truth of our existential propositions will imply the possibility of referring to them in a more intimate way which does not use quantifiers and predicative expressions, but is modeled on the practice of attaching proper names to things, or, better, on the use of demonstratives. Russell is impressed by the second of these two models because it requires some kind of confrontation, and so is appropriate to his empiricism.[11] However, his logically proper names are not entirely like demonstratives. For demonstratives may be understood as relational definite descriptions, but logically proper names have no descriptive content, and their meanings are the things they signify.[12] It follows that a logically proper name would be meaningless, if there

[11] "The Philosophy of Logical Atomism," *Essays in Logic and Knowledge*, p. 201.

[12] "On the Nature of Acquaintance," *ibid.*, p. 168.

were no particular that it signified: "*a* exists" is a kind
of tautology, and "*a* does not exist" is a kind of contradiction. Since there is this connection of meaning
between "*a*" and its particular, it ought also to follow
that "*a*" signifies the same particular in all possible
worlds, like a standard name. But though Wittgenstein
accepted this corollary,[13] Russell's attitude to it is
not clear.

This theory of singular expressions in a logically
perfect language raises many problems, some of which
are concerned with its application, while others are
concerned with its abstract structure. Russell applied
the theory to sense-data and connected it with his
epistemology of acquaintance. If we removed these
empiricist accretions, we would be left with the pure
theory, which is what Wittgenstein presents in the
Tractatus.

In its pure form the theory seems to have two paradoxical implications. Since the connection between "*a*"
and its simple particular is a connection of meaning
which holds in all possible worlds, it seems to follow
both that the particular must exist, and that "*a*" could
not have signified a different one. The second of these
two implications suggests that there is a method of
identifying the same simple particular in different possible worlds, and perhaps also that there is a method
of reidentifying the same simple particular in the actual world. This last suggestion would be canceled
if simple particulars were momentary. So it is canceled
by Russell's thesis that simple particulars are sense-
data. But what effect does this thesis have on the other
apparent implications of the pure theory?

Russell accepts the first implication, that a simple
particular signified by a logically proper name must
exist. But this is a parodoxical view, which was later
demolished by Moore and Wittgenstein.[14] If someone

[13] *Tractatus Logico-Philosophicus* 2.022–3.

[14] Moore objects to this part of the theory of logically proper

has a sense-datum and dubs it *"a,"* it might not have existed, because—to take the clearest kind of case, which avoids the problem of identity—he might have been unconscious at the time. Evidently, Russell ought to have confined himself to making the following two points: First, if a particular is dubbed *"a,"* it is a pragmatic contradiction to continue with the words ". . . does not exist," because the convention is that the meanings of *"a," "b," "c,"* etc., are the particulars that they signify; second, if the dubbing is *correct,* the particular must exist.

It might appear that the second stipulation about the correctness of the dubbing is entirely general and not specifically connected with the theory of simple particulars: to dub correctly is to dub an existing particular, and it does not matter whether the particular is simple or complex, so long as it exists. But this would miss Russell's second point. His second point is, at least, and ought to be no more than that the use of a logically proper name *"a"* is correct if and only if the particular dubbed *"a"* not only exists, but also is the right kind of particular. It must be a simple particular. If it were not a simple particular, *"a,"* contrary to the convention, would not be a logically proper name, but a complex singular expression, susceptible to analysis, and therefore capable of filling the blank in ". . . does not exist." Of course, the speaker may think he knows that a complex exists, and so attempt a dubbing. But Russell's second point is, at least, and ought to be no more than that, when the speaker dubs it *"a,"* he needs to know not only that it exists but also that it is simple. Otherwise his dubbing will be incorrect. Of course, this second point will not work any

names in "Is Existence a Predicate?" *Proceedings of the Aristotelian Society,* Supplementary Vol. XV, reprinted in Flew, ed., "Logic and Language," First Series. In *Philosophical Investigations* §§ 38–59, Wittgenstein also objects to its extension to so-called simple general expressions.

wonders. It is merely a point about the correct way of wrapping up one's knowledge in words.

In fact, Russell goes beyond those two legitimate points, and says that a sense-datum that is dubbed "*a*" must exist. He says this because he treats the connection between "*a*" and its particular as a connection of meaning, and such connections hold in all possible worlds. But, though it is correct to treat analytic statements as valid in all possible worlds, this treatment requires that they lack existential import. Russell is violating this requirement when he assimilates the "*a*"-*a* connection to a connection asserted by an analytic statement. The remedy is to modify the theory in one of two ways. Either it must be radically revised, and logically proper names must be treated exactly like demonstratives: *i.e.*, they must be given ordinary token-reflexive senses and contingent references. Or, alternatively, if Russell insists that they have their actual references necessarily, then he must draw the line between language and the world in a different way. The usual procedure is to abstract actual connections of meaning from the actual world, and to use them as a framework for constructing possible worlds. Russell's theory, if he adheres to it, requires him to follow a different procedure. He must treat the class of connections of meaning to which the "*a*"-*a* connection belongs as a class whose membership may vary from one possible world to another. If in a given language it is quasi-analytic that "*a*" signifies an existing simple particular, then he must allow that it is a contingent fact that this is quasi-analytic in that language. The possible worlds in which this connection holds are only a subclass of all possible worlds.

However, Russell does not adopt either of these two remedies, and when he applies his theory to the sense-datum language, he says nothing to mitigate the implausibility of the thesis that a simple particular that is signified by a logically proper name must exist. This is probably another illustration of the fact that he is more concerned with the actual world than with alternative possible worlds. Certainly the existence of a sense-datum can hardly be doubted by the person who supposes that he is having it, and this may have reassured Russell. For a person will be absolutely certain that his sense-datum exists before he attaches a logically proper name to it. But this consideration ought not to have been reassuring. For it still remains true that the sense-datum might not have existed. In any case, the theory of logically proper names requires not only that the sense-datum exist, but also that it be a simple particular.

In one or two passages which have already been quoted, Russell shows that he did not always feel confident that sense-data do meet the requirement of simplicity. Officially, he applies his logical atomism to the sense-datum language. But he sometimes has doubts about the details of this application. However, behind these doubts stands his confidence in the theory itself. Like Wittgenstein, he was convinced that it must apply to factual language at some level of analysis.

Russell never discusses the second paradoxical implication of the pure form of the theory—the implication that "*a*" could not have signified a different particular. Taken strictly, the theory must have this implication, because the "*a*"-*a* connection is a connection of meaning. It is the sort of connection of meaning that is more deeply rooted in the natures of things than any other, because "*a*" fastens on to *a* without the mediation of any descriptions. But precisely for this reason the natures of the particulars signified by logically proper names are inexpressible. The theory is the limiting case of essentialism. If the particulars are simple, what their names capture must be zero-essences.

There are various reasons why Russell never discusses the implication that "*a*" could not have signified a different particular. In general, he is more concerned with the actual world than with alternative possible worlds. It is also especially difficult in the case of a sense-datum to see how the speculation that "*a*" might have signified a different particular could even be raised, and it may be for this reason that Russell never considered it.

The difficulty of raising the question about a sense-datum may be brought out by a contrast. In order to get a contrasting case where the speculation is easy, we only need to substitute a material object or a person for the sense-datum. For example, if I observe a man crossing my garden, and say, "That man is trespassing," I could speculate that that man, whoever he is, might have been a different man. If, in the spirit of Russell's theory, I used the letter "*a*" instead of the demonstrative "That man," I could still indulge in the speculation which would now be expressed in the form, "*a* might have been a different man." The convention governing the use of "*a*" would be that such letters are used only once, like ideal names, and then in the presence of the object, like demonstratives. Such a letter, therefore, would signify an object in a momentary personal perceptual perspective,[15] and, since the object with which my speculation is concerned is a person, it is a very natural speculation. People endure through time, and a different person might have been observed by me crossing my garden at that moment. To say this is merely to go backwards in time and construct an alternative possible world in which a different man sets out from his home and eventually crosses my garden. This is a case of the very common branching kind, in which a segment of the actual world and a diverging segment of an alternative possible world grow (in this case backwards) out of a common segment of the actual world (in this case a segment observed by me).

[15] The remainder of this paper is strongly influenced by J. Hintikka, *op. cit.* The debts are too numerous to be listed individually.

When "*a*" signifies a sense-datum, there is a striking contrast which can be appreciated if in the previous example we treat *a* not as an object in a momentary personal perspective, but rather as a momentary personal perspective of an object. If that is what a sense-datum is, there seems to be no foothold for the speculation that "*a*" might have signified a different sense-datum (except in a trivial sense). It certainly could not mean anything like what it meant when *a* was a person. For sense-data do not endure through time, visiting different people at different stages in their histories. So the speculation about the sense-datum could not be meant as speculation of the usual branching kind. The idea could not be that *a* might have had a different history, and so might have been a different sense-datum. We could, of course, speculate that it might have played a different role in the history of its owner—e.g., "That pain might not have been a symptom of pleurisy": but we would not continue, "and so it might have been a (numerically) different pain." So the difficulty of setting up this kind of speculation about a sense-datum in an intelligible form may have led Russell to neglect the whole question of whether "*a*" could have signified a different simple particular. If this is right, he neglects it for the same reason that he neglects the question how simple particulars are to be reidentified in the actual world. Since sense-data do not endure through time, certain questions of identity do not arise about them.

However, such considerations do not eliminate the underlying difficulty. If the speculation that "*a*" might have signified a different simple particular cannot be raised about sense-data, that might perhaps justify Russell in ignoring the problem so long as he equates simple particulars with sense-data. But if the theory of logically proper names is developed in its pure form, the question whether "*a*" might have signified a different simple particular cannot be ignored, and is difficult to answer. This is not a direct criticism of

Russell's theory since he did not develop it in its pure form. But it suggests a line of thought which might explain the bafflement that is commonly produced by Russell's thesis that logically proper names signify absolutely simple particulars.

The fact that the question cannot be ignored comes out very clearly in Wittgenstein's presentation of the pure theory in the *Tractatus:* "It is obvious that an imagined world, however different it may be from the real one, must have *something*—a form—in common with it. Objects constitute this unalterable form."[16] Later, in *Philosophical Investigations* he suggested that he had regarded these objects as indestructible.[17] It would follow that he attributed temporal duration to them, so that questions of identity could arise about them at least in cases of branching possible worlds. But quite apart from the details of Wittgenstein's theory, there is no doubt that he did consider the question whether "*a*" would signify the same object in all possible worlds, and that his answer to it was affirmative.

The difficulty is that if we say that "*a*" would signify the same simple particular in all possible worlds, we must produce some criterion of identity for the particular. But we could not get a criterion of identity for a particular unless we assigned it to a type, so that we could say that it is the same so and so again. Otherwise, whatever descriptions it satisfied, it still might not be the same particular. It is only through its type that descriptions can get the kind of grip on it that they need if they are going to work as its criterion

---

[16] *Tractatus Logico-Philosophicus* 2.022–2.023. This passage, taken by itself, might mean only that there must be some objects in any world. But Wittgenstein's discussion of solipsism in 5.6 ff. shows that he believed that a specific set of objects is common to my actual world and any alternative possible world that I can imagine.

[17] *Philosophical Investigations* § 55.

of identity. However, if simple particulars are assignable to types, it follows that they have essences, and that their names are not devoid of descriptive content after all. So there seems to be a dilemma here for the logical atomist. Either he must give up the thesis that "*a*" signifies the same simple particular in all possible worlds, or he must relax his logical atomism in order to get a criterion of identity that would make this thesis intelligible.

Let me go over this dilemma in detail. It is easy to see that the only criteria of identity that reach into possible worlds involve descriptions. In a branching case it is evident that the properties and relations of the particular(s)—including spatio-temporal properties and relations—would provide the only basis for an identity statement. This is even more evident in a case where the two segments cannot be traced backwards or forwards to a common segment that would help us to answer the question of identity. It would be an illusion to suppose that a person could answer such a question by imagining that he retained only his strictly nondescriptive acquaintance with the particular in other possible worlds.

But from what source will the logical atomist get the descriptions that he needs in order to construct a criterion of identity for a simple particular? The answer to this question depends on how extreme his logical atomism is. If, like Russell, he empties his simple singular expressions of all descriptive content, then he will have no source from which to derive the requisite descriptions. This can be seen if we develop the previous example a little further. The hypothesis is that, instead of saying "That man," I use the letter "*a*" as the logically proper name of my visual sense-datum at that moment. The question is whether Russell's theory of logically proper names allows him to use a descriptive criterion of identity for that sense-datum. We need not be deterred from asking this question because he had reasons for avoiding such problems of identity about sense-data. What we want to know is whether the use of a descriptive criterion of identity for them is consistent with his account of logically proper names. Now there are many descriptions available for use in a criterion of identity of the sense-datum: it was visual, had a certain character, occurred at a certain time in my history, etc. But anyone who uses these descriptions in order to construct a criterion of identity must have classified the particular as a visual sense-datum, and he will be identifying it as the same visual sense-datum. So he will have to concede that the particular has an essence, and that its name has descriptive content. But in that case its name cannot be a logically proper name. If Russell rejects this horn of the dilemma and insists that its name really is devoid of all descriptive content, he will be unable to make the identity statement intelligible. All content will have been squeezed out of the statement, because *"a"* fastens onto *a* without the mediation of any descriptions. Logically proper names entirely lack the descriptive foothold which is exploited by such standard names as numerals.

Wittgenstein seems to have been aware of the difficulty presented by this dilemma. In the *Proto-Tractatus* (3.201412) he says that if something that is signified by a singular expression belongs to a certain type, so that restrictions have to be put on the kind of thing that can be said about it, it follows that the singular expression is not fully analyzed. This remark does not appear in the *Tractatus,* probably because he saw the objections to pushing his logical atomism to the extreme point and depriving objects of essences that would distinguish their types from one another. Certainly there are a number of remarks in the *Tractatus* which can be read as implying that objects have such distinctive essences, and that raises the question of whether the argument used by Wittgenstein in support of his logical atomism is compatible with this less extreme version of the theory.[18]

Whatever Wittgenstein's view may have been, it is clear that Russell's view was that simple particulars have no essences. This makes it impossible to deal with the question whether "*a*" would signify the same particular in all possible worlds. Although Russell has reasons for avoiding this question, it is unavoidable for anyone who tries to develop the pure form of his theory.

The most natural line of escape from these difficulties is to modify Russell's theory in the first of the two ways that were mentioned earlier. Logically proper names ought to be treated exactly like demonstratives, and given ordinary token-reflexive senses and contingent references.

If we look finally at Russell's theory of knowledge by acquaintance, we shall find ourselves driven on a parallel path to the same conclusion. Perceptual acquaintance with a simple particular is, according to him, a species of knowledge that cannot be expressed in a proposition. Such a particular may be described, but it itself is amenable to only one kind of verbalization: its zero-essence may be captured by a logically proper name. The mode of operation of a logically proper name is in one way like that of a demonstrative: its attachment to the thing perceived is not mediated by any non-token-reflexive description of that thing. But in another way its mode of operation is unlike that of a demonstrative: its attachment to the thing perceived is not even mediated by any token-reflexive description of that thing. For a logically proper name is devoid of all descriptive content. In spite of this, it is credited with a meaning. So its mean-

---

[18] Hidé Ishiguro argues for an affirmative answer to this question in "Use and Reference of Names," in *Studies in the Philosophy of Wittgenstein*, London: Routledge & Kegan Paul; New York: Humanities Press Inc., 1969.

ing has to be the particular that it signifies, just as the
meaning of the simple word "red" has to be the quality
that it signifies. If Russell had adhered strictly to the
analogy between a logically proper name and a simple
general word, he would have allowed that a person
may use a logically proper name of a simple particular
even when he is no longer perceiving it. For his acquaintance with it, which was originally perceptual,
would persist as a memory, like his acquaintance with
the color red. However, at a certain point Russell
abandons this analogy because he feels the pull of the
other analogy—the analogy between a logically proper
name and a demonstrative. If a demonstrative were
carried off from the scene of its original use and in-
serted in a memory-statement, it would have to retain
its connection with the original percept somehow or
other. But it seems that this connection could be retained only through the descriptions of the percept
or equivalent images that the speaker is still able to
produce. The suggestion that logically proper names
point right through all such material at the simple
particulars themselves may seem plausible when they
are actually being perceived, but it loses all plausibility when they are only being remembered. For
nothing that could happen later in the speaker's mind
could possibly serve as a phenomenological basis for
such a suggestion. There is of course a difference between memories based directly on personal perception and hearsay memories. However, memories of
the former class are distinguished by their causal gen-
esis and perhaps by their phenomenology, but certainly not by the complete detachment of their singular references from any descriptions.

There is, however, one exceptional type of memory
that requires special treatment. A person's memory
of something that he has just that moment perceived
often seems to retain the immediacy of the perception
itself. So Russell allows that acquaintance with perceived simple particulars persists at least for the dura-

tion of the specious present. He may even allow that it persists longer.[19] Even if he does allow this, he certainly shows a tendency to restrict it to the duration of the specious present. The explanation of this tendency is undoubtedly the pull of the analogy between logically proper names and demonstratives. However, though this explains the tendency, it does not justify it. Though the thesis, that logically proper names point through all descriptions at the simple particulars themselves, is just about as plausible in the case of immediate memory as it is in the case of perception, it certainly does not follow that it is true in either case.

The only way to understand Russell's theory of logically proper names is to appreciate the force of the two conflicting analogies on which it is based. Strict adherence to the analogy with simple general words would have led to a totally implausible account of knowledge by acquaintance. If perception of a simple particular allows a person to capture its zero-essence in a logically proper name, then his later memory of it will be a zero-memory: nothing that occurred later in his mind could count as a rehearsal of such a memory. So the only test of his claim to remember a simple particular in this way would be his reidentification of it, and this test would be available only if the theory were applied to things which, unlike sense-data, are amenable to reidentification. But then his reidentification of a simple particular would be a case of zero-recognition: he would not be able to say how he reidentified it, or even as what kind of thing he reidentified it. What a gift!

So the difficulties inherent in Russell's theory of knowledge by acquaintance drive us to the same con-

[19] I argued that he did allow this in *Bertrand Russell and the British Tradition in Philosophy*. J. O. Urmson argues against this interpretation in his review of my book; *Philosophical Review*, Vol. 19, December 1969.

clusion as the difficulties inherent in his theory of logically proper names. The most natural way to circum-
vent both sets of difficulties is to treat logically proper
names exactly like demonstratives, giving them ordinary token-reflexive senses and contingent references. This, of course, amounts to an abandonment of
Russell's distinctive contribution to philosophical
atomism. For his account of simple general expressions
was not new.

It might appear that, if Russell's account of logically
proper names is wrong, his whole theory of language
is undermined. But this is not so. The views about the
structure of language, which once led him to postulate logically proper names, are capable of being developed in a different direction, and have since been
developed in a different direction both by him and by
others. If we deny the necessity of a basic class of singular expressions that are devoid of all descriptive
content and take their references as their meanings,
we may still insist that someone who uses a singular
expression must know its meaning. But this will no
longer be a stipulation about its reference. The only
stipulation about its reference that would need to be
made is that the speaker must know which thing or
person he means. This, of course, brings in descriptions. But, as we have seen, acquaintance with a particular always involves descriptions. Once this is realized, it is a short step to the thesis that the speaker
may, and must, know which thing he means when
he is not perceptually acquainted with it just as much
as he is perceptually acquainted with it.

Russell, in fact, rejects the thesis that the speaker
may know which thing he means even when he is
not perceptually acquainted with it. His rejection of
it is unintelligible unless it is seen as a consequence
of the analogy between logically proper names and
simple general expressions. What he says is that perceptual acquaintance is the only possible source of

the speaker's knowledge of which thing he means.[20] That is plainly false. The most that Russell could plausibly say is that it is the best source of this knowledge. But what reason is there for going even as far as this? There would have been none if he had not been impressed by the analogy between logically proper names and simple general expressions. It was this analogy that pushed him to the conclusion that the meanings of some singular expressions are their referents, and so can be learned only by acquaintance.

[20] "Knowledge by Acquaintance and Knowledge by Description," *Proceedings of the Aristotelian Society*, Vol. XI, pp. 117–19 (*Mysticism and Logic*, pp. 219–21). See J. McDowell's discussion of this passage in "Identity Mistakes: Plato and the Logical Atomists," *Proceedings of the Aristotelian Society*, 1969/70, and J. Hintikka, *op. cit.*, in this volume.

KNOWLEDGE BY ACQUAINTANCE—
INDIVIDUATION BY ACQUAINTANCE

Jaakko Hintikka

The purpose of this paper is to try to see what the logical gist of Bertrand Russell's doctrine of knowledge by acquaintance is. I take the outlines of what Russell says on this topic as being familiar enough.[1] What is not equally clear is how Russell's doctrine is to be understood and evaluated. At least this was not clear to myself before I came upon some ideas in the semantics of propositional attitudes which suddenly made the logic of Russell's views—if not their correctness—perspicuously clear. Hoping that this clarity is not an illusion, I shall try to capture and preserve it by conveying it to others.[2]

By propositional attitudes I mean here the same sorts of things as Russell—knowledge, belief, wish, hope, etc.[3] The boundaries of this class of concepts are *prima facie* somewhat unclear. For instance, memory and especially perception seem to be concerned with an entirely different sort of relation of a man to his past or present environment than typical propositional attitudes—a relation much less propositional and at least partly causal and genetic.[4] Yet for the purposes of my semantical analysis they are on a par with knowledge and belief.

Sometimes propositional attitudes are characterized by saying that the verbs expressing them can be used with a that-construction and a personal subject.[5] Yet this is not the only construction in which they—or at

This essay is also being published in Rudolf Haller, ed., *Jenseits von Sein und Nichtsein*, Graz: Akademische Druck- und Verlaganstalt, 1971 or 1972. Notes appear at the end of this paper, on p. 75.

least some of them—occur. Interrogative constructions
(knowing who, remembering when, perceiving where,
etc.) do not appear too far removed from the that-
construction, and I have argued elsewhere at some
length that they can be reduced (apart from minor
qualifications) to the that-construction plus quantification over suitable entities.[6] For instance,

   (1)   *a* knows (remembers, perceives) who did B

may be paraphrased as

   (1)*   (Ex) *a* knows (remembers, perceives) that *x*
   did B

with the bound variable *x* assumed to range over
persons.

However, many verbs for propositional attitudes
also have a direct object construction. This might even
seem to be *sui generis,* apart from such harmless uses
of the direct object construction to do odd jobs for
other constructions as "knowing the answer" for
"knowing what the answer is," etc. Especially in the
case of perception, the direct object construction might
also seem to express the primary use of the concept
involved. This easily makes perception appear rather
unpropositional. Perhaps this does not make much difference between different propositional attitudes,
however, for the ubiquity and importance of the direct
object construction with other verbs easily encourages
us to think that what they express is also typically a
relation between a person and an object or a set of
objects, rather than a relation involving a person and
a proposition (or something else equally propositional). These objects are then so called in a double
sense, for they will be the objects of the attitude in
question. One of the most important questions in this
area is precisely whether this is the right view of the

objects of knowledge, belief, memory, and perception. It is not surprising to see profound thinkers like Husserl turning the question about the nature of this "intentional" relationship of our acts of perception, belief, desire, etc., to their objects into one of the main problems of their philosophy.

At the stage of his philosophical biography with which we are here concerned, Russell subscribes to a closely related view as applied to judgment. "A judgment, as an occurrence, I take to be a relation of a mind to several entities, namely, the entities which compose what it judged," Russell writes.[7] This theory of judgment was, according to Russell's own account, one of the main bases of his views concerning the nature of knowledge by acquaintance, and in particular concerning its primacy over knowledge by description. In any case, it is not much of an exaggeration to say that Russell's thinking around 1910 was dominated by something of a contrast between the kind of knowledge expressible by a propositional construction and the kind expressible by the direct object construction. For instance, in *Our Knowledge of the External World* he contrasts "acquaintance" and "knowledge about." The latter is "knowledge of propositions, which is not necessarily involved in acquaintance with the constituents of the propositions." (*Op. cit.*, London: Allen & Unwin, 1914, p. 145; Humanities Press, Inc., New York.)

The direct object construction with "knows" is especially interesting for our purposes here because what it expresses can both idiomatically and fairly accurately be said to be just acquaintance. In other words,

(2) a knows b

(where b is an individual) and

(3) a is acquainted with b

may be taken to be near-synonyms, if we disregard the social overtones of "is acquainted with." Russell makes liberal use of the direct object construction with "knows" in expounding his views on "knowledge by acquaintance." (He also calls acquaintance [a special kind of] knowledge of things; see *The Problems of Philosophy*, p. 46.) To a considerable extent, studying the nature of acquaintance will therefore mean studying the logic of such expressions as (2) and (3).

Recent logical and philosophical work on propositional attitudes—which is largely an upshot of the development of a satisfactory semantics (model theory) for modal logics—overwhelmingly suggests, however, that the key to their nature does not lie with the direct object construction but with the overtly propositional aspects of their logical behavior. Although the theories that have been developed here are not without their subtleties, the basic ideas are almost ridiculously simple.[8]

They can be uncovered by asking: What is it to specify what somebody knows (believes, remembers, perceives, etc.)? The obvious, and correct, answer is to say: We have to specify what is compatible with what he knows (and by implication what is incompatible with it). Now the force of the first "what" here is not restricted to the sundry aspects of what there actually is and what actually happens. We have to specify also what unrealized states of affairs and courses of events would still have been compatible with his knowledge in contradistinction to those which his knowledge is powerful enough to exclude. For simplicity of terminology and for vividness of imagery, I propose to dub all these realized and unrealized states of affairs and courses of events *possible worlds*.[9] Technically, specifying what a knows (in a world W) means specifying which possible worlds are alternatives (more fully, epistemic a-alternatives) to W, i.e., compatible with what a knows in W.

The same account applies at once to other propositional attitudes. One main qualification to keep in mind here is that in the context of some notions (e.g., perception), a "possible world" is a possible momentary *state of affairs*, while in the case of others (e.g., knowledge) it often, and maybe typically, has to be interpreted as a possible *course of events* (a possible "world history").

The crucial point is that in discussing people's propositional attitudes, we have to consider several possible worlds within the same "logical specious present." This immediately shows, among other things, that there is nothing surprising or disconcerting in the breakdown of the usual laws of identity and quantification whenever propositional attitudes are at issue. For instance, if we are discussing what a knows (and fails to know), the truth of "$b = c$" does not guarantee substitutivity *salva veritate*. For its truth means that the terms "b" and "c" pick out the same individual in the actual world, which does not preclude their referring to different objects in some relevant alien worlds, i.e., in some of the epistemic a-alternatives to the actual world.

Likewise, we cannot "existentially generalize" with respect to (say) the term "b" in "$F(b)$" so as to obtain "$(Ex)F(x)$," for "b" may refer to different individuals in different possible worlds under consideration, therefore giving us no foothold for maintaining that, for some particular individual x, it is true that $F(x)$ as "$(Ex)F(x)$" says. For instance, I can believe certain things about (say) the next Governor of California without there being any particular person of whom I believe them, *viz.*, if the phrase "the next Governor of California" picks out different politicians under the different courses of events I believe to be possible. Similar examples can be given in terms of proper names instead of definite descriptions.

Existential generalization with respect to "b" in (say) "$F(b)$" is legitimate if and only if "b" picks out one and the same individual in all the relevant possible worlds. These worlds are the ones as a member of which we are considering b in "$F(b)$." They are indicated by the way "b" occurs in "$F(b)$" (by the *modal profile* of "$F(b)$" with respect to "b"). If "b" occurs only outside the scope of all epistemic, doxastic, etc., operators, we are considering b as the member of the actual world only. If "b" occurs within the scope of "a knows that," we are considering b as a member of the "epistemic alternatives" to the actual world (with respect to a). If "b" occurs within the scope of two operators, b is considered as a member of certain alternatives to alternatives, and so on.

The simplest—and yet fully representative—situation is one in which "b" occurs only within the scope of "a knows that." Then the relevant possible worlds are the epistemic a-alternatives to the actual world. Since something is true in all these worlds if and only if it is known by a to be true, the uniqueness of reference of "b" in these several worlds is naturally expressed by

(4) (Ex) a knows that $(x = b)$

whose colloquial counterpart was already found to be

(5) a knows who b is.

This is the extra premise needed to guarantee uniqueness of reference here, and hence amenability to existential generalization.

All this is conditional on the assumption that the relevant possible worlds are those compatible with what a actually knows. For other situations and other concepts, we have similar or parallel premises. In the parallel cases for belief, memory, and perception, they are of the form

(6) (Ex) a believes (remembers, perceives) that $(x = b)$

whose vernacular counterparts are

> (7)   *a* has an opinion as to (remembers, perceives) who *b* is.

Philosophers have occasionally played with the tempting idea that there are some singular terms which *for conceptual reasons* cannot but refer to one individual, i.e., which pick out this individual in *all* possible worlds (insofar as they pick out anything at all). Such terms would presumably satisfy *all* "uniqueness premises" of form (6) as well as all other, more general uniqueness requirements. They are called by Russell *logically proper names*.[10] It seems to me, however, that this idea is a chimera and that the realistic procedure is usually to relativize one's discussion to some fixed set of alternatives to some given possible world.[11] Conditions (4)–(7) illustrate what the uniqueness of reference amounts to in such restricted circumstances. In some situations, we may have to consider other sets of possible worlds, perhaps alternatives to alternatives to the actual world. In each case, only a relatively small subset of the set of all possible worlds is considered, however. What the uniqueness premises for all the different cases look like can almost be gathered from what we have already said, and is discussed in some detail in my essay, "Existential Presuppositions and Uniqueness Presuppositions," in *Models for Modalities* (note 2 above), pp. 112–47. These uniqueness premises express the conditions on which the usual quantificational modes of inference, in particular existential generalization, apply to free singular terms in different contexts.

So far, so good. There is a pervasive assumption at work here, however, which has to be brought to the open. We have been speaking freely of a singular term's picking out *different individuals* (or *the same individual*) in different possible worlds. This clearly presupposes that we can *cross-identify*, i.e., tell (in principle) whether an inhabitant of one possible world is or is not the same as a given inhabitant of another. We cannot make sense of quantification (in a context in which we are overtly or tacitly considering several possible worlds) unless and until we can cross-identify between these possible worlds. Such considerations, however tacit, are from a logician's point of view unavoidable as soon as we quantify into a propositional-attitude context, i.e., bind a variable to a quantifier across a verb expressing a propositional attitude.

Since we can make sense of such expressions as (4)–(7) which blatantly involve quantification into a propositional attitude, we obviously can do this (up to a point at least) in our conceptual repertoire. But precisely how do we manage this neat trick? The depths of this profound question cannot be fathomed here. The best I can do is to register two claims for which I have argued at length elsewhere:

(A) Cross-identification relies on the properties and interrelations of individuals in the two worlds we are considering. In other words, it amounts to a comparison between these worlds.[12]

(B) In the context of perception, memory, knowledge, cross-identification can take place in two different ways.[13]

Here (A) prepares the ground for (B), by showing that the notion of identity (for individuals in different possible worlds) cannot be taken as an unproblematic, given notion.

As to (B), I have proposed to call the two kinds of methods of cross-identification *descriptive* methods and methods relying on *acquaintance*.[14] (Occasionally the latter may also be called *demonstrative, perspectival,* or *contextual* methods.) The former can be described briefly by saying that they are just the kinds

of methods we use in trying to cross-identify between
real life and a *roman à clef*. (This example illustrates
not only the general nature of these methods but also
the difficulty of spelling them out.) To describe these
methods a little bit more fully, one can say that they
often rely on the continuity of individuals in space
and time. This frequently enables one to trace them
back (or forth) all the way to the "inner story" consisting of those facts about our individuals which are
common to all the possible worlds considered. In our
example, these worlds are the actual world and the
world as described by the hypothetical *roman*. In more
realistic cases, the common parts of these worlds typically consist of all the facts whose negations are incompatible with the propositional attitude in question.
Once we come to this "common ground" in following
the world lives of two individuals in their respective
worlds, it suffices to see whether they coincide or not.

If continuity conventions of this sort fail, we have
to fall back on similarities and dissimilarities between
the members of the different possible worlds to decide
whether or not they are identical.

In contrast to these impersonal comparisons, cross-
identification by acquaintance relies on the role of the
person whose attitudes we are discussing. Let us suppose that that individual is myself and that the propositional attitude in question is memory. Then my own
firsthand memories of persons, times, places, and objects create a framework which serves to cross-identify
people, places, objects, etc. As long as they play the
same role in my personally remembered past, I can
treat them as identical (say in two autobiographical
novels, both compatible with everything I remember)
even though I do not remember enough of them to
say (truly) that I remember who, where, or what they
are, and although they therefore are not well-defined
individuals by the descriptive criteria.

Even more strikingly, my visual space (at some

given time) creates a similar framework. Even if I do not see who *that* man over *there* is, in all states of affairs compatible with what I see (seem to see), there is a man there, whom I can treat as one and the same man.

A moment's thought also shows that b's having such a location in my visual space is just what my seeing b means. (Direct object construction!) We are tempted to say that a has a place in my visual space if and only if a is one of my *visual objects*, and that being one of my visual objects is precisely what "my seeing a" means. There is no harm in yielding to this temptation as long as we remember that the distinctions between "visual objects" and "physical" or "public" or "descriptive objects" is entirely a matter of interworld comparisons and that no possible world therefore contains a special class of individuals called "visual objects." Likewise, I remember b (direct object construction again!) if and only if I can place him in the context of my personally remembered past.

This establishes an interesting connection between cross-identification by acquaintance and the direct object construction. This connection can be made even more striking by recalling the dependence of quantification (quantification *into* a context governed by a propositional-attitude verb) on cross-identification. Without cross-identification, we have not defined the entities our variables range over. No entity without cross-identity, we might say. By way of an alternative slogan, we might also say that in speaking of propositional attitudes the "real" ("unique," "well-defined") individuals are in the last analysis the "world lines" that connect the manifestations or embodiments of the same individual in different possible worlds. Now that we have uncovered two different sets of such world lines, there must likewise be two different kinds of quantifiers in the offing.

Let us use (Ex), (y), etc., as quantifiers relying on

descriptive cross-identification, and $(\exists x)$, $(\forall y)$, etc. as quantifiers relying on acquaintance.

Then

(8) $(\exists x)$ a remembers that $(b = x)$

will say that as far as cross-identification by acquaintance is concerned, the term "b" picks out a unique individual. This individual b is accordingly one whom a can place in the frame of reference of personal reminiscences, i.e., he is an individual of whom it is true to say

(9) a remembers b.

The same goes for other attitudes. For instance, a sees b if and only if a can find a room for b among those individuals whose place in his visual geometry is definite, i.e., if and only if the following is true:

(10) $(\exists x)$ a sees that $(b = x)$.

By the same token, (2) and (3) can (omitting minor qualifications) be said to be expressible as

(11) $(\exists x)$ a knows that $(b = x)$.

A terminological point may be in order here. The values of quantified variables are intended to be individuals in the fullest sense possible. Since it is seen that quantification is nevertheless relative to the principles of cross-identification, these principles could equally well be called principles of *individuation*. The notion of a (well-defined) individual is in a perfectly good sense relative to a cross-world comparison method as soon as one starts quantifying into propositional attitudes.

This may seem misleading, for a distinction is often made between individuation (roughly, the splitting up of one world or one state of affairs into individuals) and identification (roughly, tracing the "world-line" of an individual from one temporary state to another or from one possible world to another). This terminology seems to me highly unfortunate, for it hides the fact that in many important circumstances (e.g., in all contexts involving quantification into a propositional-attitude context) we simply do not have well-defined individuals before cross-identification. Cross-identification is thus almost as much part and parcel of an individual as so-called "individuation." From now on, I shall accordingly use "cross-identification" and "individuation" more or less interchangeably.

Here we perhaps begin to see in what sense "the understanding of meanings comes through acquaintance," as it, according to David Pears, comes on Russell's theory. (See Pears, *Bertrand Russell and the British Tradition in Philosophy*, London: Collins, 1967, p. 182; New York: Random House.) Acquaintance gives us a method of individuation (cross-identification). Without such a method, no singular term could be said (or denied) to specify a unique individual in different "possible worlds." In other words, without such a method, there would not be any telling what the individuals are that are picked out by our singular terms.

We also begin to see the great interest of individuation by acquaintance for philosophy. We have already reached a logical analysis of the direct object construction in terms of the that-construction for several propositional-attitude verbs. The *prima facie* reasons mentioned above for thinking of propositional attitudes as possibly involving a relation of a person to an object are thus eliminated—or at least considerably weakened.[15] Propositional attitudes *are* indeed inextricably propositional. The fact that the reduction of the direct object construction to the that-construction

involves a special sense of quantification does not
weaken this point at all.

More specifically, in (11) we have discovered the
logical form of the relation we express by "acquaintance." This gives us a useful starting point for further
observations.

For one thing, if what I have said is right, then we
have here a disproof of Russell's claim that "our knowledge of *things,* which we may call acquaintance" is
"logically independent of knowledge of truths" (*The
Problems of Philosophy,* p. 46). For an inspection of
(11) shows that the only context in which the concept
of knowledge is used there is in the that-construction,
which presumably must be thought of as expressing
"knowledge of truths." Yet (11) was found to express
a paradigmatic instance of our "knowledge of things"
(including of course here also persons).

It is important to realize, however, that in a sense
different from the one I just presupposed Russell may
be quite right. In the kind of logical semantics envisaged here, the truth-value of statements of the form
(8), (10), or (11) is not determined by the truth-
values of simpler statements involving no quantifiers.
Our friend a's knowledge of any number *de facto*
identities of the form "$b = d$" does not by itself determine whether he knows b or not, and the same goes
for a's knowledge of *de facto* truths about b. In this
important sense, our knowledge of things is indeed
logically independent of our knowledge of any particular facts about them.

This is not a peculiarity of the direct object construction, however, for the same things can in principle be said about the who-construction (4) as about
the direct object construction (11) in this respect.

One class of objects of acquaintance that we find
in Russell and in a number of other philosophers are
the so-called sense-data. Their status is an intricate
problem in its own rights. However, I have argued in
an earlier paper that the job which sense-data were

essentially intended to do by the most careful and perceptive sense-datum theorists is done by quantifiers relying on perceptual individuation (individuation by acquaintance for perceptual contexts).[16] If the "values" of variables bound to such quantifiers could be hypostatized into separate entities, they would be indistinguishable from sense-data (apart from certain psychological and phenomenological assumptions), I have ventured to suggest. However, this hypostatization is illicit, for perceptual quantifiers are not distinguished from the descriptive ones by the individuals they range over in any particular world, but rather by a special method of cross-world comparisons.

In order to see the connection between sense-data and quantifiers relying on perceptual cross-identification, one may recall what sense-data were supposed to be in the first place: objects of immediate perception, i.e., the individuals which our judgments of immediate perception are about. The role of the immediacy requirement here is to rule out all consideration of the actual physical situation. Thus sense-data are supposed to be those individuals we judge about perceptually when we do not perceive (or otherwise know) what descriptive (physical) individuals they are. This is precisely the service which individuation by acquaintance (perceptual individuation) renders us here: it provides us with individuals which we can speak of (judge about) even when we abstract completely from the actual physical objects involved. What quantifiers "ranging over" such individuals take as values are precisely "objects of immediate perception" or "perceptual objects," one is tempted to say. Sense-data are thus part and parcel of the same group of ideas as acquaintance for us no less than for Russell.[17] They are the objects of "perceptual acquaintance."

The main reason why traditional sense-data do not look like the values of my acquaintance-quantifiers is an assumption or, rather, a prejudice as to what we can immediately (spontaneously, noninferentially) perceive. For Russell or Moore, sense-data are typically like patches of color and shade and not three-dimensional occupants of one's perceptual space because they did not think that our sense-perceptions—especially visual ones—are spontaneously articulated into (apparent) three-dimensional objects, such as tables, bridges, and people. For this reason, sense-data are traditionally made much more ephemeral than my perceptually cross-identified individuals. However, the underlying reason for this immaterialization of sense-data is simply a mistake about the phenomenology of perception, a mistake which is easily disproved by a closer phenomenological and psychological analysis of the situation.

We can also see why some propositional attitudes are more prone to the direct object construction than others. It was seen that this construction involves individuation by acquaintance. This in turn presupposes a certain point of view or perspective, i.e., it presupposes that the person whose propositional attitudes are being discussed is interacting or has interacted with the objects of his attitude in such a way as to create a conceptual "perspective" on them. For otherwise there is not the kind of framework present in the different possible worlds involved here which would enable us to cross-identify perspectivally.

Now we always perceive from a certain vantage point, and remember people and events because we were personally there. Furthermore, our firsthand knowledge of persons and places is based on our actual cognitive interaction with them. In contrast, we can believe what we choose of sundry entities without having had much to do with them. No wonder, therefore, that we do not have a direct object construction with "believes" parallel to the direct object constructions we have studied.

Not too much deep significance should be read into

this fact, however, for it may very well be merely a matter of degree.

Notice, finally, the neat parallelism of the respective logical structures of the constructions (4) (i.e., (5)) and (11) (i.e., (2)). The only thing that distinguishes them is the kind of quantifier involved. This logical observation suggests a commonplace moral. It would be surprising if things so similar were always sharply distinguished in ordinary usage. In fact, the sharp distinction I have made above between the interrogative constructions and the direct object construction in terms of "knows" has to be taken with a grain of salt. It is easily seen that in ordinary language one construction is frequently used to denote what would be expressed perhaps slightly more appropriately by the other.[18] Language is at best a partial and incomplete guide to logic here. Acquaintance *may* be what "knowing who" naturally expresses in suitable circumstances.

An important example of this will be found in the opening lines of Russell's essay on "Knowledge by Acquaintance and Knowledge by Description."[19]

Our distinction between the two kinds of individuation methods appears to be new in the literature. However, it seems to me that individuation by acquaintance has in effect been discussed by philosophers more or less openly in several interesting contexts, of which Russell's theory of knowledge by acquaintance is the best known example.

As was already indicated, Russell opens his paper, "Knowledge by Acquaintance and Knowledge by Description," by saying that its object "is to consider what it is that we know in cases where we know propositions about 'the so-and-so' *without knowing who or what the so-and-so is*" (my italics). Taken literally, this is simply false, for Russell's favorite examples concern our knowledge of Bismarck and of Julius Caesar. (Surely we know, in the most straightforward sense of the expression, who these gentlemen are.) Hence some slightly unusual sense of knowing who (or what)

must be presupposed. Russell's explanations show
amply that what is involved is just a switch to individuation by acquaintance, at least insofar as particulars are concerned. (I shall here in this essay leave
alone Russell's remarks on universals.) One can
scarcely come closer than Russell to our symbolic treatment of individuation by acquaintance, as exemplified
by

$$(\exists a) \text{ we know that } (a = \text{the so-and-so}),$$

when he says that ". . . we have 'merely descriptive
knowledge' of the so-and-so when . . . we do not
know any proposition 'a is the so-and-so,' where a is
something with which we are acquainted."[20]

Many of the details of Russell's discussion are also
reminiscent of what has already been said in this
paper. For instance, my remarks on the perspectival
nature of contextual individuation (one's own personal role in the situation creates a frame of reference) are matched by Russell's emphasis on the relational character of acquaintance, i.e., on "the need
of a subject which is acquainted."[21] Russell's prime
example of the objects of acquaintance is the same
as the first example given above of contextual individuation, viz., sense-data (except for my disclaimer
that they do not exist as a separate class of entities
in any particular world).[22] Russell's sometime claim
that "there are only two words which are strictly
proper names of particulars, namely, 'I' and 'this'"
neither true nor even plausible unless individuation
by acquaintance is presupposed.[23] (In saying this, I
am of course presupposing the connection between
the notion of a logically proper name and uniqueness
of reference mentioned earlier.)

More than one aspect of Russell's theory of knowledge by acquaintance can be discussed from the vantage point we have reached. For instance, we can now

see why it was possible for Russell to maintain—as David Pears has argued that he did[24]—without any logical difficulties that one can have acquaintance with individuals which are not actually present, provided that one has come across them in the past. As was pointed out, personal memories normally give one enough reference-points to individuate persons and things by their means. In a sense, there is but a difference in degree between individuation by perceptual criteria and individuation by means of personal memory. Both can be classified as cases of individuation by acquaintance.[25]

More important is the possibility of partly reconstruing within our approach and evaluating Russell's famous thesis of the reducibility to acquaintance: "Every proposition which we can understand must be composed wholly of constituents with which we are acquainted."[26]

The first main point to be noted here is that Russell's thesis is primarily semantical and ontological and not only epistemological. That is, he is not only discussing the interrelation of different types of knowledge, but also the different types of entities involved in our propositions. As far as singulars are concerned, such questions of ontology lead us immediately to questions of individuation and cross-identification. It is in fact clear that at least a large part of what Russell is claiming can be expressed within our framework as a thesis to the effect that the only irreducible individuals are those created by contextual methods of cross-identification. In contrast to some secondhand expositions, Russell's own formulation of the reducibility thesis is in terms of understanding a proposition rather than coming to know it.

It seems clear to me that the gist of Russell's reducibility thesis can be recaptured in this way as a thesis to the effect that only demonstrative methods of cross-identification (individuation by acquaintance), not

physical (descriptive) ones, are indispensable. Even
apart from Russell, this thesis is important enough to
be discussed in some detail.

Is it true? I believe it is not. However, I do not have
any single knock-down argument to this effect. What
can be done is to indicate some of the great difficulties that face any serious attempt to dispense with individuals descriptively individuated, and also to give
partial and conditional arguments for the indispensa-
bility of individuals descriptively individuated. It
seems to me that the cumulative force of all these arguments is strong enough to justify us in considering
Russell's thesis as false.

For this purpose, it may be noted that merely interpreting singular terms as definite descriptions fails
to accomplish the elimination of "public" individuals,
contrary to what Russell in effect assumed earlier in
the penultimate paragraph of "On Denoting" (1905).
One reason for this is almost acknowledged by Russell.[27] It is based on the fact that, given a singular
term, say "Bismarck," we can make two different kinds
of statements in terms of it. We can make a statement
about whoever may be picked out by that term, i.e.,
whoever may meet the correlated description. One
may also make a statement about that individual who
in fact is (or was) Bismarck.[28] For instance, someone
(say a) may believe that whoever Bismarck was, he
was an astute diplomat. This can be formulated as

(12) a believes that Bismarck was an astute diplo-
       mat.

If he had instead had the same belief concerning Bismarck the man, we would have to say something different. Recalling that it is bound variables that range
over individuals ("individuals themselves," not individuals characterized in a certain way), we can see
that this can be expressed as follows:

(13) (*Ex*) ((*x* = Bismarck) & (*a* believes that *x* is
an astute diplomat)).

Suppose someone proposes to replace the proper
name "Bismarck" in (13) by a definite description
which in the last analysis is in terms of what can be
experienced. This does not bring us any closer to a
reduction to acquaintance, for in (13) the quantifier
may very well rely on public (descriptive) methods
of cross-identification. If so, it is the bound variable
and not the name "Bismarck" that forces us to consider
public individuals and not merely acquaintances. Then
no juggling with the free singular term "Bismarck"
will help the reduction.

It seems to me that Russell betrays awareness of
the distinction (12)–(13) when he discusses propositions which outsiders can only "describe" but cannot
"affirm." These, it appears from Russell's discussion,
are intended to be precisely propositions about the
man (the individual) himself, not as described in
this or that way.

Russell describes the situation in terms of judging
rather than believing, but this is an insignificant discrepancy. He writes: "It would seem that, when we
make a statement about something only known by
description, we often intend to make our statement,
not in the form of involving the description, but about
the *actual thing described*. That is to say, when we
say anything about Bismarck, we should like, if we
could, to make the judgment . . . of which he himself
is a constitutent. In this we are necessarily defeated,
since the actual Bismarck is unknown to us. But we
know that there is an object *B* called Bismarck, and
that *B* was an astute diplomatist. We can thus describe
the proposition we should like to affirm, namely, '*B*
was an astute diplomatist' where *B* is the object which
was Bismarck" (*Mysticism and Logic*, p. 218, my
italics).

Notice how close Russell comes to my formulation

(13). In fact, the judgment he is describing might almost be expressed as follows:

(Eb) (b = Bismarck & we judge that b was an astute diplomatist)

with a "B" taking actual objects as its values.

A minor discrepancy is nevertheless created by the fact that Russell is, in the quoted passage, apparently thinking of knowledge (individuation) by acquaintance in saying that Bismarck is "unknown to us." Hence '∃' rather than 'E' may best catch his intentions here. However, the logical point he is making is independent of the style of quantifiers (mode of individuation) employed.

The mistake Russell makes here is that he assumes that the reason why someone cannot assert a describable but unassertable proposition about Bismarck must be that he is not acquainted with Bismarck or with whomever we are talking about.[29] This is of course circular. It is true only if our quantifier in (13) presupposes individuation by acquaintance. If it relies on individuation by descriptive methods, the impossibility of using the name "Bismarck" to express one's beliefs about the person in question will be due to one's failure to *know who* Bismarck is, not to one's failure to *know* (to be acquainted with) him. It is difficult to suppress the suspicion that Russell is tacitly assimilating the notion of "knowing who" (or "knowing what") to the notion expressed by the (irreducible) direct object construction with "knows," i.e., to the notion of acquaintance. On a number of occasions (see, e.g., *The Problems of Philosophy*, pp. 44–45) Russell contrasts being acquainted with someone (knowledge by acquaintance) with merely knowing (truly judging) that he exists (knowledge by description). This is a false dichotomy, however, because there also is a third type of a proposition here, *viz.*, knowing who that someone is.

In any case, the main official reason Russell himself gives for the reducibility thesis is circular in that it in effect assimilates the two methods of individuation to each other. "The chief reason for supposing the principle true is that it seems scarcely possible to believe that we can make a judgment or entertain a supposition without knowing what it is that we are judging or supposing about."[30] From this it does not follow that we must be acquainted with what we are judging about, but rather that we must know what it is in the straightforward sense which does not seem to reduce to acquaintance.

Behind Russell's explicit arguments there nevertheless seems to lurk a deeper reason for concentrating on individuation by acquaintance. As was already mentioned, Russell tried to interpret judgment as some sort of relation between a mind and the objects proper to the judgment.[31] Anything like a normal concrete relation can be found between them only in the case of judgments (statements) about individuals cross-identified by acquaintance, as I have indicated, not in the case of descriptively individuated particulars, for only in the case of acquaintance does the position of the knower, perceiver, or rememberer make any difference. Hence Russell's theory of judgment predisposes him to concentrate on individuation by acquaintance.

A full-dress criticism of Russell's theory of judgment is impossible here. The best criticism is in the long range likely to be a superior alternative theory, which I cannot attempt to sketch here. It may nevertheless be pointed out that the principle Russell is appealing to is much less plausible than it might first seem. What is needed for us to understand a judgment, it seems to me, is not that we are acquainted with the objects of this judgment, or that we know who or what they are, but rather that we know what possibilities (one may think of them as possible experiences) it excludes. For this purpose, it is not required that we know in advance what objects give rise to these experiences. Suppose I form a judgment as to what I might find in an unknown environment, e.g., on Mars. Surely in some obvious sense I can do that without having any inkling as to what the individual objects are that I might encounter there.[32] Thus Russell's theory of judgment is not obviously superior to its alternatives. In my view, it overlooks an important aspect of the essentially propositional character of judgment.

I am thus criticizing Russell at two essentially different levels. First, I am suggesting that there is no need for us to know the individuals which we are judging about—or, rather, no need that our judgments always be *about* any particular individuals at all. Secondly, I have pointed out that even when a judgment is about a definite individual, this definiteness may be of the nature of our *knowing who* (or what) we are judging about, not of the nature of our *knowing him* (or it).

Moreover, one of the main reasons—at least plausible reasons—for thinking of any propositional attitudes as involving (logically speaking) relations between a person or a mind and the objects of these attitudes has already been disposed of. This reason was the prevalence of the (non-elliptical) direct object construction with many of the verbs expressing propositional attitudes, which suggests that the proper analysis of these attitudes involves some kind of a direct relation. This construction was seen to be reducible to the that-construction, however.

What about topical reasons for or against the reducibility? One thing is in any case clear. Although our discussion has mostly been in informal terms, it goes together with an explicit semantical theory of propositional attitudes. Although I cannot discuss any details here, this semantics makes it clear that, in the simple languages consisting of quantification theory plus verbs for propositional attitudes, there is no hope whatsoever of reducing one kind of quantification to the other. If our semantics is correct on the whole, any reduction would thus have to turn on some concepts not represented in these languages. What these further concepts could be seems impossible to gather from the literature or to excogitate on theoretical grounds. Hence there appear to be good grounds for thinking that Russell's acquaintance thesis is wrong. In any case, the onus of proof is very much on the upholders (if any) of Russell's thesis.

NOTES

1. The main sources are Russell's essay "Knowledge by Acquaintance and Knowledge by Description," *Mysticism and Logic,* London: Longmans, Green and Co., 1918, pp. 209–32; New York: Barnes & Noble, Inc., parts of which had appeared previously in the *Proceedings of the Aristotelian Society,* Vol. 11 (1910–11), pp. 108–28, and Chapter 5 of *The Problems of Philosophy,* which follows the Aristotelian Society paper and to which I shall refer in the Galaxy Book (Oxford Paperback) edition (1959). Much of Russell's other early work is also relevant here, particularly some of the other essays in *Mysticism and Logic* and the essays reprinted in R. C. Marsh, ed., *Logic and Knowledge,* London: Allen & Unwin, 1956; New York: Macmillan.

2. The main thesis of the early parts of the present paper, *viz.,* the existence of a duality between two kinds of individuation methods, was put forward and explained in my paper "Objects of Knowledge and Belief: Acquaintances and Public Figures," *Journal of Philosophy,* Vol. 67 (1970), pp. 869–83. For background and for special cases, cf. also the following papers of mine: "The Semantics of Modal Notions and the Indeterminacy of Ontology," *Synthese,* Vol. 21 (1970), pp. 159–75; "On the Logic of Perception," in N. S. Care and R. H. Grimm, eds., *Percep-*

tion and Personal Identity, Cleveland: Press of Case Western Reserve University, 1969, pp. 140–73 (reprinted in Jaakko Hintikka, *Models for Modalities,* Dordrecht: D. Reidel Publishing Co., 1969, pp. 151–83); "On the Different Constructions in Terms of the Basic Epistemological Concepts," in R. E. Olson and A. M. Paul, eds., *Contemporary Philosophy in Scandinavia,* Baltimore: Johns Hopkins Press, 1971; "On Attributions of 'Self-Knowledge,'" *Journal of Philosophy,* Vol. 67 (1970), pp. 73–87. Cf. further my *Models for Modalities* (mentioned above) and *Knowledge and Belief,* Ithaca, N.Y.: Cornell University Press, 1962.

3. The term "propositional attitude" nevertheless belongs to a much later period of Russell's philosophical activity. See *An Inquiry into Meaning and Truth,* London: Allen & Unwin, 1940; New York: Macmillan.

4. Thus Russell writes in *An Inquiry into Meaning and Truth:* "Memory, when veridical, is causally dependent upon previous perception."

5. This seems to be Russell's position in *An Inquiry into Meaning and Truth,* for he says there of words involving what he calls "propositional attitudes" that all of them, "when they occur in a sentence, must be followed by a subordinate sentence telling what it is that is believed or desired or doubted."

6. See the works mentioned in note 2 above. It seems to me that the point is also fairly clear without much elaborate argument. It is to be admitted, however, that in the colloquial interrogative constructions there may be sundry presuppositions of uniqueness present which are not necessarily captured by our paraphrases. This is not a very important point, however.

7. *Mysticism and Logic,* p. 219.

8. For my own work in this area, see note 2 above. The papers mentioned there contain references to the work of others.

9. The fact that we do not always know (believe, remember, etc.) the logical consequences of what we know (believe, remember, etc.) shows that often we have to consider here "worlds" that only appear possible to our logically unperspicacious mind's eye, over and above worlds that are "really" possible. This complication does not matter to our present purposes, however.

10. See the further explanations of the meaning of this term in Russell and of its role in Russell's thinking given by David Pears, *Bertrand Russell and the British Tradition in Philosophy*, London: Collins, 1967; New York: Random House.

11. This is one of the main theses of my paper "The Semantics of Modal Notions and the Indeterminacy of Ontology" (note 2 above).

12. See my paper "The Semantics of Modal Notions and the Indeterminacy of Ontology" (note 2 above).

13. See my paper "Objects of Knowledge and Belief: Acquaintances and Public Figures" (note 2 above).

14. See "Objects of Knowledge and Belief" and "On the Logic of Perception" (note 2 above).

15. They are not completely eliminated because I have not yet dealt with two further questions which may seem to encourage the simple-minded relational analysis of perception. These questions are the possibility of a *de re* interpretation of perceptual statements and the causal element in our perceptual concepts. Both problems can be dealt with without weakening

my point, although I cannot do so here for reasons of space.

16. See "On the Logic of Perception" (note 2 above).

17. "When we ask what are the kinds of objects with which we are acquainted, the first and most obvious example are *sense-data*" (Russell, *Mysticism and Logic*, p. 210).

18. For examples, see my paper "Objects of Knowledge and Belief" (note 2 above).

19. *Mysticism and Logic,* p. 209 (note 1 above).

20. *Op. cit.*, p. 215.

21. *Op. cit.*, p. 210.

22. *Loc. cit.*

23. *Mysticism and Logic*, p. 224.

24. *Op. cit.*, pp. 71, 181–82.

25. On p. 133 of *Logic and Knowledge*, Russell seems to restrict the range of things experienced in the past much more narrowly than this. It may appear from his formulation that an acquaintance with a past object is possible only "in immediate memory of something which has just happened." This has also provoked some criticism against Pears. (See J. O. Urmson's discussion of Pears's book in *Philosophical Review*, Vol. 78 [1969], pp. 510–15.) However, all we have in the case of acquaintance by memory is strictly parallel with acquaintance by perception *apud* Russell. There, too, the range of entities that we can be acquainted with is narrowed very much by Russell for largely psychological reasons, in fact narrowed to rather ephemeral sense-data and to ourselves, these allegedly being the only entities we can "immediately" (noninferentially) perceive. Likewise, Russell seems

to have thought that the things we can immediately remember are few and fleeting. In fact, Russell refers here to the "psychology of memory" as a source of his opinions. I do not see anything here to belie the logical point made in the text.

26. *Mysticism and Logic*, p. 219; *The Problems of Philosophy*, p. 58.

27. With the following, compare pp. 216–18 of *Mysticism and Logic*.

28. This is to all intents and purposes the old *de dicto–de re* distinction. For a brief discussion of it, see my paper "Semantics for Propositional Attitudes" in *Models for Modalities* (note 2 above).

29. The reason why Russell says that "the actual Bismarck is unknown to us" obviously cannot be that we do not know who Bismarck is, but rather the earlier (p. 217) announced fact that we do not know Bismarck, i.e., are "not . . . acquainted with the entity in question."

30. *Mysticism and Logic*, p. 219.

31. See, e.g., *Mysticism and Logic*, pp. 219–21.

32. Of course Russell does not claim that we must *know*, sight unseen, what these objects are. However, in order to reconcile such situations with his reducibility to acquaintance, he was forced to resort to such more or less desperate remedies as acquaintance with universals, propositions that can be described but not asserted, and the replacement of virtually all names (and other singular terms) by definite descriptions. I cannot here criticize these attempted ways adequately. However, the very need to resort to them is perhaps enough to suggest the difficulties with Russell's theory judgment.

RUSSELL'S PHILOSOPHY OF MIND

Anthony Quinton

1

Although Russell devoted a good deal of attention to it, including a whole book, the *Analysis of Mind*, the philosophy of mind was always one of his more peripheral interests. In his mature philosophy it is part of the general theory of neutral monism, a Humean correlate to the more or less Berkeleyan account of the nature of material objects first propounded in *Our Knowledge of the External World* in 1914. This supplementation of Berkeleyan objects with Humean minds took some time. Four years after defining a material thing as the class of its appearances he was still insisting on the irreducibly mental character of the relation of acquaintance and, rather less firmly, on the ineliminability of the subject of consciousness. Not until 1921, with the *Analysis of Mind*, was he finally converted to a version of James's thesis that "consciousness does not exist" or, more properly, that minds are not part of the ultimate constituents of the world.

In this essay I shall first consider the kind of qualified Cartesian dualism which Russell set forth in *The Problems of Philosophy* in 1912, largely it would appear under the influence of Moore. I shall go on to examine his neglected essay on "The Nature of Acquaintance" of 1918, first with regard to its muddled and precipitate rejection of idealism and then with regard to its more interesting critique of the neutral monism of James and Mach. A discussion of the *Analysis of Mind* will follow (abbreviated to *AM*), the work in which Russell adopts neutral monism, works out its consequences in detail, and seeks to rem-

This paper is published for the first time in this volume.

edy its deficiencies with judicious infusions of behaviorism. The amendments to this position that he made in his later career are minor and involve no substantial change of view.

2

I described Russell's account of mind in *The Problems of Philosophy* (abbreviated to *PP*) as qualified Cartesian dualism. There are two main qualifications. First, Russell is led by Hume's point about the empirical elusiveness of the substantial self to hold that the self with which we are acquainted in introspection is at most momentary. He is tempted to deny that any substantial self, even a momentary one, is an object of acquaintance at all but resists the temptation. Secondly, Russell gives reiterated expression to his loyalty to Moore's distinction between acts of consciousness, which are unquestionably mental, and their objects, which need not be. An implication of this, together with the principle that material things are not objects of direct acquaintance, though he does not draw it explicitly, is that the sense-data we are acquainted with in perception are neither mental nor physical.

Russell begins by evincing some discomfort with the received Cartesian account of the distinction between mind and matter. "We commonly mean by 'matter' something which is opposed to 'mind,' something which we think of as occupying space and as radically incapable of any sort of thought or consciousness" (*PP*, p. 13). The tentative, provisional air of this suggests a doubt inspired by the complexity, of which traditional dualism takes no account, of the concept of space. Russell distinguishes logical, physical or public and private or sensory space. He does not pursue the point, but its relevant feature would seem to be that sense-data, although not physical, are nevertheless spatial. No doubt at least some sense-data are, although not all if Strawson is right about sounds, but

the Cartesian distinction can survive this if the criterion of physicality is reformulated in terms of occu-
pancy of the single, public, physical space.

Matter is not an object of acquaintance, it is not
directly known in perception. It is a theoretical inference from the sense-data we do directly perceive,
the simplest theory, in Russell's view, consistent with
our perceptual experience. The mental, however, is
the object of acquaintance, in particular of that species of acquaintance we may call either introspection
or self-consciousness. Each person has some acquaintance with mental entities, with those that constitute
or are otherwise involved in his own mental life, certainly with his own mental states and probably with
the substantial self that is the subject of these states,
provided that it is not conceived as a persisting thing.
But we have only indirect knowledge of the mental
states, and *a fortiori* minds, of others, which we acquire by analogical inference from what we perceive
them to do or say.

Russell expresses his doubts about the self in very
much Hume's words. "When we try to look into ourselves we always seem to come upon some particular
thought or feeling, and not upon the 'I' which has the
thought or feeling" (*PP*, p. 50). But he does not go all
the way with Hume. The mental entities with which
I am introspectively acquainted are awarenesses, and
as such seem inescapably relational and to entail a
subject of the awareness at one end and an object at
the other. Secondly, it is hard to see how we could understand, let alone know the truth of, an introspective
report, such as "I am acquainted with this sense-
datum," unless we were acquainted with something to
which the word "I" refers. The point is made in Russell's criticism of the way in which Descartes expresses
the indubitable residue of his systematic doubts. "When
I look at my table and see a certain brown colour,
what is quite certain at once is not 'I am seeing a
brown colour,' but rather, 'a brown colour is being

seen.' But experience is not subjectless. 'This of course involves something (or somebody) which (or who) sees the brown colour.' But the subject cannot be known to be more than momentary. That a brown colour is being seen 'does not of itself involve that more or less permanent person whom we call "I"'" (*PP*, p. 19).

Russell does not raise the question of how a momentary self existing at one time is known to be part of the same person as a momentary self existing at another. Nor does he consider the possibility of identifying the persisting person with a related collection or sequence of mental states. The fact that of all words "I" most closely answers to his specifications for a logically proper name may have dissuaded him from the thought that the person is a logical construction and thus an object of knowledge by description and never of acquaintance. For provided that the physical vehicle of the word "I" is being used to utter it and is not just a natural phenomenon, a trick of the wind or a stain on a piece of paper, it logically cannot fail to refer.

A more substantial departure from Cartesianism is Russell's view that sense-data are not mental even if the acts of sensation that are directed on to them are. But the argument from illusion seems to show that the immediate objects of perception are not material either. At this point Russell should have provided some account of the intermediate status, neither mental nor material, accorded to sense-data by the joint operation of Moore's act-object distinction and the refutation of direct or "naïve" realism. But he does not. Moore's original account of the act-object distinction did not countenance a third realm of objects of consciousness that are neither mental nor material. He allowed that the objects of acts of consciousness could be mental but he insisted that they could just as well be material. "The existence of a table in space is related to my experience of *it* in precisely the same

way as the existence of my own experience is related
to my experience of *that*. . . . I am as directly aware
of the existence of material things in space as of my
own sensations" (*Philosophical Studies,* pp. 29–30).

Moore's more considered reflections on the nature
of the mental are to be found in a paper on "The
Subject-Matter of Psychology" he delivered to a meet-
ing of the Aristotelian Society in December 1909
which Russell attended and took part in. It may well
be the main source of Russell's initial views about the
mind. Moore contends in it that acts of consciousness
are the only indubitably mental entities. Although he
thinks every such act belongs, together with others,
to a mind, he suggests that unowned acts are possible.
Against the criterion of mentality, which he finds attractive, as being directly knowable by one mind only,
he argues, or rather asserts, that some mental entities
may not be logically private and that not all private
entities need be mental.

He goes on to consider two kinds of things whose
mental status he regards as doubtful: minds and sense-
data. For the odd conclusion that the mind is not mental he offers the odd argument that it would be mental if it were an "entity," but it may be a Humean
collection. But why should a Humean collection all of
whose parts are mental not be an entity and a mental
one at that? An aggregate of material parts like a stone
is a perfectly good material entity. As for sense-data,
Moore attributes the prevalent idea that they are
mental to the fact that they have been confused with
the acts of which they are objects. But the confused-
ness of this idea does not show that they are *not* mental and Moore reaches no definite conclusion about
their status.

But Russell, by firmly denying that sense-data are
mental, goes further than this, in effect to the position
that they are neutral entities, neither mental nor
material nor, for that matter, abstract. At one point,
indeed, he seems to deny that *any* objects of acquaint-

ance are mental when he says "acquaintance with objects essentially consists in a relation between the mind and something other than the mind" (*PP*, p. 42). But this is presumably an inadvertence in view of his acknowledgment of introspective acquaintance with one's own mental states and, probably, with one's momentary self.

Berkeley's idealism or, more specifically, the idea that all the direct objects of the mind are mental comes to grief, in his view, through an equivocation about the word "idea." It can mean either "thought of a thing" or "thing thought of," act of apprehension *in* the mind or thing apprehended *before* the mind. He rightly maintains that it does not follow from the fact that thought and knowledge are mental, that everything thought of or known is mental. But this is irrelevant; the point at issue is the status of the objects of *direct* knowledge or acquaintance. And even if, as he holds, the direct object of memory is a past event, not a present image, it could still be a past mental event.

Furthermore he soon qualifies the thesis that the objects of perceptual acquaintance are nonmental almost out of recognition. "Berkeley was right in treating the sense-data which constitute our perception of the tree as more or less subjective, in the sense that they depend on us as much as upon the tree, and would not exist if the tree were not being perceived" (*PP*, p. 41). If sense-data, although objects rather than acts of consciousness, are nevertheless subjective and mind-dependent, they would seem to be mental enough.

Russell does not, then, succeed in showing that sense-data are not mental. Although he does not explicitly develop the conception of them as neutral entities, that his position implies its submerged presence in his theory may have prepared the way for his eventual acceptance of neutral monism.

3

Two years later, in 1914, Russell published "The Nature of Acquaintance," the first of his writings to be concerned exclusively with the philosophy of mind. It is in some ways a rather typically Russellian piece of work: ingenious, fertile, offhand, helter-skelter, a desultory sequence of nimble impromptus. Its markedly inchoate character may explain why critics and commentators have so consistently steered clear of it. The main point at issue is clear enough, namely the defense of dualism against the neutral monism of James and Mach, but a great deal of other matter clusters around this in a confused and confusing way. At one stage he suggests that his main aim is to adjudicate between idealism, neutral monism, and dualism. But it is not so much that he is engaged in the defense of dualism against two distinct opponents as that he is engaged in defending one aspect of dualism against the idealists, namely the ontologically realistic thesis that more exists and can be known to exist than what is present to my mind now or my mind in general or any mind, and another aspect of dualism against the neutral monists who are not in general and certainly should not be antirealistic, namely the epistemological thesis that the relation of acquaintance is irreducible to more or less causal relations between the objects of acquaintance, being a unique relation with a unique and irreducible kind of first term, a conscious subject. The precipitate form in which the argument is presented is distinctly bewildering. In due course Russell overcame his own bewilderment by becoming converted to neutral monism.

The kinds of idealist ontology that Russell seeks to refute derive in part from the principle that all objects of direct knowledge or acquaintance are mental. But this principle is a consistent part of such realistic philosophies as Descartes' and Meinong's. To yield idealism it must be conjoined with some principle that rules out transcendental inference to entities of a kind that are not objects of acquaintance. Curiously, in view of his repeated denials of it in *The Problems of Philosophy*, Russell does not criticize idealism here by way of objections to the principle that all objects of acquaintance are mental. Nor does he make a direct assault on the idealists' exclusion of transcendental inference. His main tactic is to cite items that are known to exist but are not mental.

Thus, against the instantaneous solipsism which holds that nothing can be known to exist but what is in my experience now, he argues that in memory I know past events and not just present images. This, of course, might be true even if the past events in question were themselves mental, namely previous experiences of mind. It also assumes that not all memory is spurious, which is reasonable enough but a little odd for Russell, in view of the kind of lavish skepticism about memory he has often said to be incapable of disproof. As a possible ground for this kind of solipsism he mentions the principle that "every word that we now understand must have a meaning which falls within our present experience" (*Logic and Knowledge*, R. C. Marsh, ed., abbreviated to *LK*, p. 134). If "meaning" here means reference, the principle is ludicrous; if it does not, it is a truism and not to the point.

Against ordinary solipsism (or "subjective idealism") he invokes the possibility of knowledge by description and the fact that we have such knowledge of the existence of an infinity of arithmetical facts with which we are not directly acquainted. This consideration is also used to rebut solipsism's more sociable counterpart: objective idealism, the theory that everything that exists or can be known to exist falls within somebody's experience. It does not matter if my life, or the life of the species, is infinitely long since "the number of functions of a real variable is infinitely greater than the number of moments of time" (*LK*,

p. 137). Russell would seem to have forgotten Berkeley's God (and, for that matter, St. Augustine's, one
reason for believing in whom are the eternal truths
which require an infinite mind to think them).

Russell goes on to argue that it is a reasonable working hypothesis against solipsism, that there are other
minds than one's own and, against objective idealism,
that there are unperceived material things. But the
main weight of his anti-idealist argument is carried by
mathematical facts. Such facts, in his view, are complexes of mathematical objects of a kind with which
we are acquainted, but these objects are universals
and, in the terminology of *The Problems of Philosophy,*
do not exist but rather subsist. So our knowledge that,
in the appropriate sense, there "are" such things outside any (finite) experience establishes only a very
attenuated sort of realism.

In general the theory that we have knowledge by
description of unexperienced things, knowledge expressed by means of "incomplete symbols," amounts
to something like an endorsement of transcendental
inference. It ought not to do so since incomplete symbols must be definable in terms of expressions with
whose references, or, in the case of predicates, senses,
we are acquainted. Although Russell invokes his earlier doctrine that the objects of acquaintance are not
ipso facto mental only in the course of a fairly per-
functory criticism of Meinong's content theory, it is
really presupposed in his conclusion that, since we
know that there are mathematical objects, we know
that there is something which can be independent of
any mind.

A further conclusion that Russell draws from the
"description of experience" which is inextricably
bound up with his refutation of idealism is that in
one's experiencing of a thing more than the mere thing
is involved. This is important for the ensuing debate
with the neutral monists for it seems to imply that, in
contrast to their view, for a thing to be experienced

it is not enough for it to be related to other experienced things of the same kind. Russell's direct argument for this conclusion is that there is a difference between remembering an event and remembering one's experiencing the event, as when we hear a striking clock and "become aware that it has already struck several times before we noticed it" (*LK*, p. 136). Even if this awareness shows that we really did experience the unnoticed strokes we do not remember doing so.

However, some support for Russell's conclusion can be derived from the falsity of idealism. My experience, present or total, or everyone's experience, includes only a selection of all that there is. It is thus a further fact about the objects of experience that they constitute such an experienced selection over and above the fact that they exist. Russell's dualist view is that what links the elements of an experienced selection together is, in the case of my present experience, the fact that they are all related to a momentary subject outside the set and, in the case of my total experience, the fact that they are related to a connected sequence of such momentary subjects, the last member of which at least is outside the set.

But in fact, neutral monism is not carried away in the collapse of idealism. A neutral monist can be a realist in the sense that he can admit that there are neutral elements which are not, although they could be, actually experienced. For an element to be experienced is for it to stand in certain relations to other such elements, and not in a special relation to a special, nonelemental, kind of thing, namely a subject. And he need not require every element to be related to some others in this way.

4

The main topic of "The Nature of Acquaintance" is the neutral monism of James and Mach, according to which mental and physical things, minds and material

objects, are not utterly different in character but are
differently arranged complexes of neutral elements:
items of "pure experience" for James, "sensations" for
Mach. In all forms of neutral monism there are some
elements which enter into the constitution both of a
mind and a material thing, those, as we should ordinarily say, which are veridical perceptions. It is less
clear whether every element is part of some mind or,
on the other hand, part of some material thing. Images and what may be called misperceptions (the content of radical perceptual errors as contrasted with
the merely perspectivally distorted aspects of things
which, according to neutral monism, are part of the
constitution of those things) are parts of minds but
not of material things. On the other hand there are,
if idealism is false, unperceived aspects of things, each
of which is part of the constitution of some material
thing but not of any mind.

The type of neutral monism with which Russell is
concerned does not regard unperceived aspects as
merely potential, in the manner of phenomenalism.
For James, some of "pure experience" as a whole, the
sum of what there ultimately is, is perceived, and thus
part of some mind or other, but much is not. Russell's
term for unperceived aspects—"sensibilia"—at least refers to them substantively. But its termination suggests that they are the possessors of possible rather
than actual existence, as does another phrase—"ideal
percepts"—that he uses for them. On the other hand,
images and misperceptions would seem to be as actual
as the sort of perceived aspects of things which enter
into their constitution and they are not part of any
material thing. On this view the sorting-out of the neutral elements into minds and material objects is not
exclusive, for perceived aspects are included in both,
although unperceived aspects figure only in material
objects and images and misperceptions only in minds.
The sorting-out does seem to be exhaustive, however,
for there is no provision made for unperceived images

and misperceptions (as, indeed, this way of describing them would seem logically to require). But any element could be a perceived aspect.

It is clear from the start that the neutral monist's conception of the mind is a very impoverished one. The mind for him is a dispassionate perceiver without emotions or will. It is, no doubt, with a view to giving neutral monism a fair run for its money that Russell chooses to ignore the account James gives of the non-cognitive features of mental life. His aim here is to refute James's theory on the ground where it is strongest.

The obvious objection to neutral monism that first occurs to mind is that there is a radical difference of kind between the elements that enter into the constitution of a mind and those that enter into the constitution of a material thing. In the spirit of Moore's act-object distinction, the latter will be the objects of immediate perception, patches or surfaces, let us say, in the fields of sight and touch, while the former will be awarenesses, whether veridical or not, of such objects. Russell reaches this conclusion in the end but not by way of a dogmatic affirmation of Moore's distinction. For it is an essential feature of James's position that awareness or consciousness is not a "stuff" or quality (or, one might say, a special relation between elements and a subject that is not an element) but is, rather, a relation of a particular kind between the elements that go to constitute a given mind, on all fours with, although, of course, different from, the relation between a set of elements constituting a given material thing.

James's account of this relation is characteristically nebulous and sweeping. Two elements are part of the same mind if one "leads" to the other; they are the knower and the known if they are "two pieces of *actual* experience . . . with definite tracts of conjunctive transitional experience between them" and the known can be "a *possible* experience . . . to which the said conjunctive transitions *would* lead, if sufficiently prolonged." This notion of elements "leading" to other elements may be the outline of a solution to the problem of what it is for the occurrence of an element to amount to a knowledge of some material thing, though the outline is very sketchy. A percept of a dog-shaped patch of color in a given consciousness, if it is associated with expectant images of hairy texture, barking, etc., would amount to knowledge that a dog is present provided that the associated images are, or would be, followed by corresponding perceptions of touch and hearing. If no such consequences do, or would, ensue then it is not a case of knowledge but of error. James's talk of "leading" is not a very good solution to this problem, perhaps, but at least it is relevant to the problem. But it casts no light whatever on the ostensible topic with which James is concerned which is what it is for an element to be part of a mind, of the history of a consciousness. One can only suppose that he thought this psychologistic account of the difference between perceptual knowledge and error has something to do with consciousness because of his assumption that consciousness is, as he puts it, a "faculty of knowing." But it is also a "faculty of erring."

Russell treats this worthless theory of leading with a respect it does not deserve. The fact is that it provides no answer at all to the question of what relation between elements makes a mind out of them. Russell makes the point against James that his doctrine makes a momentary mind logically impossible; he argues that neutral monism cannot satisfactorily explain false belief; he maintains that an "extraneous mental particular" is required to explain how abstract, nontemporal facts are sometimes actually believed or thought of and sometimes not. But apart from insisting that there is an immediate, nonrelational difference between a seen patch of red and an unseen one he does not really get to the heart of the matter, the fact that no relevant and intelligible account of the relation be-

tween a set of elements that makes them into a mind
has been produced.

The situation would be different if the elements
were conceived, not as perceptible or imageable
patches and surfaces, but as incidents of experience,
individual consciousnesses of such patches and surfaces. Elements so understood are at least logically
fitted to be parts of minds. Each of them is, indeed, a
momentary mind of the sort Russell holds to be logically possible. But such an interpretation of the elements would be faced with serious difficulties in accounting for material things in the required, aggrega-
tive way. The material world would have to be
conceived with a fragmentariness appropriate to the
highly selective perceptiveness of finite minds or
Berkeley's God would have to be brought out of re-
tirement or absolutely unperceived material things
would have to be countenanced and catered for in a
phenomenalistic way, not as wholes whose parts are
elements, but by some altogether more complex form
of analysis. But whichever option were taken up the
neutrality of neutral monism would be forfeited. For
on this interpretation every element is part of some
mind, but by no means all elements are parts (or phenomenalistic ingredients) of material things. In general, neutral monism is faced with a dilemma. If the
elements are just data, that is to say patches and surfaces, no related complex of elements will amount to
a mind. If they are consciousnesses of such data, on
the other hand, then every element is a mind or a part
of one while material things are not collections of elements but constructions out of elements of a kind of
complexity which puts them on a different logical level
from that on which both elements and the minds they
compose are. Neutral monism, in short, becomes idealism or phenomenalism.

The faint and deliberate nature of Russell's objections to neutral monism testify to its attractions for
him. He praises it for its splendid simplification. But

they are sufficient to leave him convinced that acquaintance is a "brute fact," a relation between an element and a temporal particular, a subject, which is not itself an object of acquaintance. There is a difference between a red patch and the experiencing of a red patch. We know this empirically because there is an empirical difference between the sensory awareness of the patch and the introspective experiencing of that awareness. One has form sAp, the other the form s'A((∃s)sAp). The introspective subject is distinguished from the sensory one since they will be identical only as parts of a construction, a persisting mind of which they are momentary phases. The introspected subject of the sensory awareness is referred to indefinitely to mark Russell's conviction that it is not an object of acquaintance. What was allowed as probable in *The Problems of Philosophy* has now, under the pressure of Hume's argument, been finally rejected. This leaves behind it a difficulty which Russell did not acknowledge. How can the fact that I am aware of a red patch be itself an object of acquaintance unless the items of which it is composed are too? Only, perhaps, if acquaintance is interpreted, initially at any rate, as a quality of its objects. Ap would still be different from A(Ap) on this interpretation. The ascription of acquaintances with which one is acquainted to oneself as subject would come about only with the development or construction of the concept of other minds in the manner of Carnap's *Aufbau* in which "das Gegebene ist subjektlos."

Russell is, then, still a dualist in "The Nature of Acquaintance," but an even more qualified one than he was in *The Problems of Philosophy:* the act-object distinction is no longer put forward as obvious but is elaborately argued for, the subject, even when momentary, is no longer directly knowable and his sense of the attractions of neutral monism, soon to be overwhelming, is clearly expressed.

5

Russell's conversion to neutral monism (or to something approximating to it) is first suggested in the closing pages of his "The Philosophy of Logical Atomism" (1918), in which he says, "I feel more and more inclined to think that it may be true" (*LK*, p. 279). The chief obstacles to his acceptance of it at this stage are its difficulties in accounting for belief, although a behavioristic theory may allow this difficulty to be circumvented, and for "emphatic particulars" which seem to require a distinction between experiencing a particular and the experience itself.

The main lines of the form of neutral monism (if that is what it is) that Russell is able to accept are drawn in his article "On Propositions" of 1919 (in *LK*). There is not, as in James, just one kind of ultimate neutral stuff but three, mutually irreducible, kinds, which are, nevertheless, fairly closely analogous to each other: "there are some particulars which obey only physical laws (namely, unperceived material things), some which obey only psychological laws (namely, images, at least), and some which obey both (namely, sensations)" (*LK*, p. 299).

The full exposition of Russell's considered doctrine about the mind is contained in *The Analysis of Mind* (1921). He begins by drawing attention to the way in which physics and psychology have been converging (indeed, as he represents the situation, the two sciences have passed by each other and are as far apart as ever since they have pretty well changed places). In physics, matter has been dematerialized; in behavioristic psychology, mind has been dementalized. So the time is ripe, in his view, for a nondualistic account of their subject-matters which, if not exactly identical, at least exhibit a good deal of overlap and a good deal of community of character.

The overall strategy of the book from this unificatory point of view is never very clearly set out, but essentially it is a two-stage operation. Much, but not all, of mental life is internal, accessible to introspection. All of this is interpreted in terms of sensations and images. Secondly, much, but not all, of mental life is susceptible to a behavioristic interpretation; it amounts to laws, habits or dispositions of behavior, and behavior consists of the activities of certain pieces of matter, namely, human bodies. At this point the other side of Russell's neutral monism is brought into play: the account of material things as complexes of sensations and sensibilia. Mentality, therefore, whether introspective or behavioral, all reduces to the three kinds of neutral element. The introspectable is just sensations and images; the behavioral is reducible to sensations and sensibilia. I shall first consider this project in rather general terms before going on to examine some of the more detailed analyses with which Russell tries to carry it out. The latter will inevitably lose some of their interest if, as I believe, the project itself is misconceived.

The fundamental point is that Russell never abandoned the basic objection he had raised against the strict neutral monism of James and Mach. He cannot allow that the constituents of material objects and of minds do more than overlap; in particular, he never endorses the practice of using a single expression, be it James's "pure experience" or Mach's "sensation," to cover both the aspects of material things which, though they could be, are not in actual fact, perceived and the actual perceivings which make up an important part of the content of all minds.

At times he comes very near to James's position. (Cf. *AM*, pp. 141–42.) But a material object, he says at one point, "is a system of particulars analogous in their nature to sensations, and in fact often including actual sensations among their number" (*AM*, p. 108). There is a touching eagerness about that final clause. If only material things were always and entirely made of sensations. But Russell sees very clearly that they are not and is too honest to conceal what he thinks.

The material world is ultimately an array of sensibilia, which, in effect, are all the possible views there are of all the material things that there are. One way of grouping them is in virtue of relations of similarity, juxtaposition, and increasing size, in which case the resulting groups are material things, perspectivally orderly systems of possible appearances. Another is to group together all the sensibilia or aspects of things, obtainable at one moment from one place; the result is a "perspective," a possible, but not yet actual, momentary perceiver. A series of perspectives that are temporally closely successive and each of which is at or near the place of its neighbors in the temporal series is a "biography." But a biography is not a life, any more than a perspective is a perceiver. A world of sensibilia could exist without any actual perceiving taking place at all and, in fact, to a great extent does so exist. Most perspectives are not perceivers and most biographies are not lives since most of what materially is is not perceived by anyone.

There is, then, more to minds than sensibilia, namely whatever it is that turns a sensibile into a sensation. And there is also more to minds than sensations, though Russell believes that somehow or other, with the aid of those trusty instruments, hook and crook, it can all be analyzed into images. If this analysis is possible, then the admission that there is more to minds than sensations does not amount to all that much. For there is no intrinsic difference between sensations and images (Hume's "vivacity" is insufficient to distinguish them). Both are data (while sensibilia are inferred entities) and are distinguished from each other by their respective relations to further data and, one had better add, sensibilia. A datum is a sensation if it is part of a system of sensibilia constitutive of a material thing, an image if it is not. Its status as a sensation can be assured only if the associated sensibilia are actually sensed, but it will have the status provided they are there to be sensed.

In contrast the difference between data, whether sensations or images, and sensibilia does seem to be intrinsic. At times, leaning over toward James, Russell seems to be trying to account for the sensedness of sensations in a relational way. A sensibile is actually sensed, he says, when (a) there is a brain or nervous system at the place *from* which it is and (b) if it is subject to mnemic causation. But the presence of a brain cannot be what the sensing of a sensibile actually consists in; at most it can be a causal condition of a sensibile's being sensed. As for mnemic causation, which is the influence exercised over a time gap on present experience by past experience, this applies only to images; it is invoked to explain association, the nonsensational element in perception and event-memory, but not sensations themselves.

In the light of Russell's recognition of a radical and intrinsic difference between sensa and sensibilia, between actual and possible sensations, his somewhat labored rehearsal of more or less Jamesian objections to the dualism of Brentano and Meinong, which takes consciousness or intentionality to be the essence of the mental, is out of place. For, at least as far as the introspectable aspect of the mental, namely sensations and images, is concerned, it is consciousness which distinguishes them from the sensibilia which are the indispensable majority constituent of the physical world. All the same there are substantial points of difference between him and the school of Brentano. Where they allow for a variety of irreducibly different mental acts, he seeks to reduce all inner mental life to sensations and images. Where they take all mental life to involve consciousness, he is prepared to give a behavioristic account of much of it from which consciousness is dispensable.

He begins by drawing attention to the continuity between animal and human psychology. But this, of course, cuts both ways. If we attribute desires to animals because they go through routines of disturbance, purposive activity, and quiescence, we may just as well attribute consciousness to animals on this basis as deny it to humans because they go through analogous routines of behavior. More to the point is the evidence of psychoanalysis that we have desires of which we are not conscious. This is backed up by common knowledge, as is the possibility of unconscious belief to which the phenomenon of surprise testifies. We are often wrong about our own motives. There is an anticipation of Ryle in Russell's remark that "the discovery of our own motives can only be made by the same process by which we discover other people's, namely, the process of observing our actions and inferring the desire which could prompt them" (*AM*, p. 31).

The detailed program of *The Analysis of Mind* is to show that all the generally recognized forms of mental life can either be reduced to sensations and images or else be interpreted behavioristically. I have argued that even if successful this program would not achieve its general purpose of analyzing both mind and matter in terms of strictly neutral elements. The sensations and images in which the nonbehavioral aspect of mind consists are states of consciousness; the unsensed sensibilia of which matter is predominantly composed are not. Consciousness has not been analyzed away. However Russell's analysis of mind into data and behavior could still have a point as reducing the number of ultimate kinds of entity that have to be countenanced. Furthermore, it is not very remote from the theory of mind characteristic of logical positivism in the 1930s. I am referring here to the semi-behaviorism of Carnap's *Aufbau* and Ayer's *Language, Truth and Logic*. On this view the basic entities are my own experiences, sensory and other. My own mind is largely a construction out of these experiences. My sensory experiences form the basis of a phenomenalistic construction of material things, including human bodies. The minds of others, as well as those aspects of my own of which I am not introspectively aware, are then constructed out of the behavior of their bodies.

This is a much more coherent theory than Russell's, although there are numerous objections to it. Its chief weakness as a theory of mind is the asymmetry it implies in the ascription of mental states to oneself and to others. For this has the consequence that "I am angry" said *by* me is logically independent of "you are angry" said *to* me, so that one could be true and the other false. But whatever its merits or defects it is not a form of neutral monism (although Carnap and Ayer seem to think it is, cf. Carnap *Aufbau,* section 162 and Ayer, *Language, Truth and Logic,* 1st ed., pp. 189–92). It is, rather, idealistic, for although minds, like material things, are constructions, the elements are mental, because literal parts of minds, but not physical.

6

We may now turn to consider some of the detailed theses of Russell's *Analysis of Mind,* in particular his attempts to interpret introspectable states of consciousness as complexes of sensations and images. The starting point of his investigations into the nature of desire, emotion, belief, thought, perception, and memory is that, although these may often be understood in purely behavioristic terms, they are also often conscious states and thus involve more than habits or laws of behavior. His project is to analyze these conscious, trans-behavioral states as wholly made up of sensations and images and the unsatisfactory method he generally adopts is to supply an appropriate "feeling" to eke out the sort of sensations and images that typically occur in the conscious states in question and then to state or imply that these indispensable differentiating "feelings" are really sensations.

Conscious desire, for example, consists in a feeling

of discomfort and a belief (which may well be mistaken) about what would relieve the discomfort. The analysis of belief is remitted for further consideration and the feeling of discomfort is accommodated within the range of permitted ultimates by being called a quality of sensation. Now a quality of sensation is not the same as a sensation and sensations conceived as constituents of the material world do not have qualities of this kind. If anything, discomfort, and its intenser cognates, should perhaps be considered as a relation between a sensation and a sentient being. But this is one of Russell's less extreme stretchings of the term "sensation" to cover an irreducible element of mental life so as to bring it within the scope of his theory. He dallies for a while with the notion that discomfort is a causal quality of a sensation, the propensity of sensation to produce behavior of a purposive sort. But this would be hard to square with the immediacy of one's knowledge of one's discomforts and the very large differences of purposive activity to which a given sensation, of a sugary taste for example, can give rise.

In his discussion of emotion, Russell considers adopting the theory that it is a perception of bodily change but in the end settles for the conclusion, altogether less useful for his purposes, that it is caused by such perceptions of bodily change. But what is involved in emotion beyond such perceptions is, he holds, desires, pleasures, and pains, which have already been disposed of.

Belief he regards as the "central problem," the mental state whose reduction to sensations and images would make the largest contribution to his program. Much belief is unconscious, as revealed by the surprise that brings to our notice expectations we did not know we had. When conscious it is a matter of images or words or both, and, where the belief is perceptual, a case of recognition, sensations as well. But there is more to belief than that, for these mental contents have a meaning, a reference beyond themselves. This, he suggests, can be explained in terms of the causes and effects of the belief's contents: the sensations that occasion them, the expectations and behavior to which they give rise. But this still fails to distinguish belief from mere considering, which also has a meaning, a propositional object, and one kind of belief from another, bare assent from memory and expectation.

He argues that belief and mere considering (the bare "entertainment" of a proposition) must differ intrinsically because otherwise they would have the same content but quite different behavioral effects. So he is constrained to invoke something called a belief-feeling, which he describes as a complex of sensations at one point and as a feeling of assent at another. This, like his comparable treatment of discomfort, is a barefaced exploitation of the somewhat permissive regulations in force in discussions of this kind with regard to the use of the words "sensation" and "feeling." A feeling of assent is grist to his theoretical mill only to the extent that it is assumed that the feeling involved is, as some feelings no doubt are, a sensation. But assent is not a sensation, or a complex of sensations, at least in the sense of the word in which sensations are constituents of the physical world, dependent for their occurrence on the sense organs and so forth.

The same unconvincing manipulation of the word "feeling" occurs in his well-known account of memory as a combination of imagery with "feelings" of familiarity and pastness, the latter of which is equated with the belief: "this has existed before." In this case one forcible "sensationalization" is superimposed on another. To endow some imagery with a retrospective reference it is associated with a feeling of pastness. This is then said to be or involve a belief about the past, which must take the form of another image of the past event in question, together with the dubiously sensational "belief-feeling."

In the last section I argued that Russell's project of reducing all states of consciousness to sensations and images would not, even if successful, have served its stated purpose of showing both the mental and the material to be wholly constituted out of neutral ultimate stuff. In this I have gone on to argue that the reduction is only apparent since Russell's crucial analyses contain indispensable elements which are only nominally reduced to his selected basis by playing fast and loose with the words "sensation" and "feeling." This is not to say that *The Analysis of Mind* is not an important book. It is courageously comprehensive in its scope, is based on wide knowledge and understanding of the relevant scientific disciplines, and it set an altogether new standard of thoroughness and seriousness in the discussion of its subject. Although neither its general theory nor its specific analyses are defensible, it succeeded in raising most of the problems that have preoccupied subsequent philosophers of mind, with the odd exception of the most influential of all, that of our knowledge of other minds. In its partial endorsement of behaviorism, furthermore, it began the process of undermining naïve Cartesian introspectionism, which has been the most significant negative accomplishment of modern philosophical reflection in this field. Finally, Russell's nose for philosophically crucial issues is shown in his view that belief is the central problem for any philosophy of mind. If his "belief-feeling" is not a very appetizing alternative to a strictly behaviorist account of belief, nothing very much better has been found to replace it.

One or two other matters, less intimately related to his main theme, should be mentioned. One is the quiet abandonment of the theory that universals are objects of acquaintance which had been an emphatic part of *The Problems of Philosophy* and was still maintained in subsequent writings. "I *think*," he says, "a logical argument could be produced to show that universals are part of the structure of the world, but they are an inferred part, not a part of our data" (*AM*, p. 228). This change probably reflects the influence on Russell of Wittgenstein's ideas about necessary truth. If necessary truths are tautologies, universals are no longer needed as a subject matter for them to be about; their only remaining task is to serve as a theoretical explanation of our ability to classify things under general terms.

The idea of mnemic causation plays a large part in Russell's mature philosophy of mind. Although in the end he does not accept it as the criterion of the mental, he uses it to distinguish sensations (as the data that are caused by a current stimulus) from images (as the data whose proximate cause is some past event) and, secondly, together with the brain, to distinguish perspectives (points of observation where a mind could be) from actual percipients. His ground for rejecting mnemic causation as the criterion of mentality is that it is "too wide" (*AM*, p. 295). This is presumably an acknowledgment of the fact that temporally remote causes, which are not linked to any hitherto discoverable present state of affairs, have to be invoked to explain the responses of living organisms generally, and not just those that have minds. He even admits that "this characteristic is not wholly confined to living organisms. For example, magnetized steel looks just like steel which has not been magnetized, but its behavior is in some ways different" (*AM*, p. 78).

But, as it turns out, he is in some doubt as to whether there really is such a thing as mnemic causation, that is to say, causal connections between temporally separated events where there actually is no intervening causal chain, no trace or persisting structural modification due to the remote cause, as against connections where we do not know what the intervening linkage is. It is not "difficult to invent satisfactory hypotheses as to the microscopic changes of structure which mediate between the past occurrence and the present changed response" (*ibid.*). But analogous hypotheses can be formed about the structure of the brain so that what appears to be mnemic causation may really be physiological causation of a less mysterious kind. In that case the presence of a brain alone would be enough to distinguish a perspective from an actual percipient. At the very end of the book he inclines to the view that mnemic causation does not really exist, or is not, as he puts it, "ultimate." "I think the bulk of the evidence points to the materialistic answer as the more probable" (*AM*, p. 303).

The suggestion with which the book closes confirms the assessment at the end of the previous section that Russell is more of an idealist than a neutral monist. "An ultimate scientific account of what goes on in the world," he says, "if it were ascertainable, would resemble psychology rather than physics. . . . This fundamental science would cause physics to become derivative" (*AM*, pp. 305, 307). The reason is that minds, as made up of sensations and images, are wholly composed of data, of actual existences, whereas matter is a logical fiction, a piece of matter being a fictitious system of regular appearances. All data or actual existences fall within psychology; only a few of them fall within physics; most of what falls within physics is fictitious or hypothetical.

7

The only extended discussion by Russell of the philosophy of mind after 1921 is to be found in Parts 1 and 3 of his *Outline of Philosophy* of 1927. In this and subsequent works down to *My Philosophical Development* of 1959 (cf. Chapter 12: Consciousness and Experience), he proclaims his continued adherence to neutral monism but there are certain modifications to the position of that book: most notably the notorious doctrine that percepts are in the brain. In a brief explanation of his views about the mind contributed to C. W. Morris's *Six Theories of Mind* (1932) Russell

says, "There are things in *The Analysis of Mind* which
I no longer care to defend," though he does not say
precisely what they are, and he closes by according
canonical status to the views expressed in *The Outline
of Philosophy*. Two chapters of *Human Knowledge*
(1948), which may be taken as the final authoritative
statement of his position, are devoted to the subject
(Part 1, Chapter 6: The Science of Mind, and Part 3,
Chapter 7: Mind and Matter) and these are very close,
respectively, to Parts 1 and 3 of *The Outline of
Philosophy*.

In Part 1 of the *Outline* ("Man from without") he
provides a thorough, coherent, and factually well-
supported account, on strictly behaviorist lines, of a
wide range of mental phenomena. Learning is presented as the acquisition of behavior habits; the use
of language, both heard and uttered, is interpreted
in terms of its causation *of* behavior and *by* the objects to which it refers; perception is defined in terms
of discriminative behavior; memory, inference, and
desire are treated along similar lines.

But Russell insists that, for all its merits, behaviorist
psychology covers only part of the field. There are
two main reasons for this: one empirical, the other
theoretical or epistemological. The empirical reason
is that there irreducibly is such a thing as inner experience, there are entities such as sensations and
images which are known only by self-observation. The
theoretical reason is that physics (within the scope
of which, very broadly conceived, behaviorist psychology falls) necessarily rests on the kind of subjective
data revealed to self-observation. The examination of
these events within ourselves on which physics rests
and which (or many of which, Russell is none too clear
about this) "would not be included in an absolutely
complete knowledge of physics" are sense qualities
as perceived, pleasure and pain, images and dreams.

There is a tension, amounting to something like in-
coherence, between Russell's continued adhesion to

neutral monism, to the idea that there is no ultimate difference between mind and matter because they are both wholly made up of neutral "events," and his revived insistence on the radical difference between material objects, as they "really are," according to physics, and our sensations, a conviction central to *The Problems of Philosophy* and reanimated, no doubt, by the rapid and startling developments of the mid-1920s in quantum physics. On the one hand, material things are made of just the same sort of stuff as percipient minds; on the other, the two are utterly different.

This tension could be overcome if a distinction were drawn between the possible sensations or sensibilia which are the *logically* ultimate ingredients of material things and the unobservable events which are their *physically* ultimate ingredients. But Russell never develops a difference between the way in which material things are made of sensibilia and the way in which they are made of elementary particles. He continues to assert, with James, that for an event to be known, to be part of an experience, is simply a matter of its relations to other events: an experienced event is one that would be remembered, that modifies habits, that has mnemic effects. On this view material things are literally composed of sensations, to the extent that they are observed, and of things just like them, except relationally, to the extent that they are not. In that case the real, logical constitution of material things is not significantly different from the real constitution of minds. What the surprising deliverances of modern physics show is that the causal laws of sensations and of the sensibilia we inductively extrapolate from them are much more complicated than common sense supposes. But Russell combines the view that matter is made of sensations (or percepts) and things just like them with the conviction that "not a single one of the occurrences that we are told take place in the physical world is a sensation" (*Human Knowledge,* p. 62).

The chief novelty of Russell's later philosophy of mind is his thesis that percepts or sensations are in the brain of the perceiver, expressed with maximum provocativeness in the contention that when a physiologist is examining what he takes to be the brain of another what he is really doing is inspecting his own. What Russell has done is to superimpose on the sense-datum theory of perception the conclusion that since the proximate causes and effects of the immediate objects of perception are in the brain those objects must be there too. This is an extension of the earlier view that events are mental if they are mnemically related to other events, for mnemically related events occur as far as we know only where there is a brain. Thus the mentality of an event comes to be defined as its forming part of the history of a living brain. With this Russell comes fairly close to the identity theory of mind and brain propounded in recent years by Smart (*Philosophy and Scientific Realism,* Chapter 5) and Armstrong (*A Materialist Theory of the Mind*). In an article on "Mind and Matter," in *Portraits from Memory* (1956), Russell says, "what I suggest is that the events that make a living brain are actually identical with those that make the corresponding mind" (p. 153).

But this addition implicitly reinstates the act-object distinction of Moore from which Russell had so laboriously tried to shake himself free. Consider the sensation or percept of a red patch. On his final view this is a constituent both of an "external" object, a pillar box let us say, and of the perceiver's brain. But the pillar box and the brain are different things existing at different places. To achieve consistency the percept must be divided: into a perceiving which is located, if anywhere, in the brain of the perceiver and a red patch perceived which is either, as with the early Moore, literally part of the pillar box, and so in a different place from the perceiving of it, or, as with the phenomenalists, an element in the analysis of the proposition that a pillar box is there but is a literal part neither of the pillar box nor of the perceiver's mind.

With his insistence on the radical difference between the physical world as it really is in itself and the physical world as we perceive it, which are quite distinct and only causally related, and with the return to the act-object distinction implied by his conception of percepts being events in the brain, Russell, despite his lingering Jamesian protestations, returned in the end to something very little different from the qualified dualism of *The Problems of Philosophy*.

RUSSELL ON PERCEPTION: A STUDY
IN PHILOSOPHICAL METHOD

Grover Maxwell

Some of Russell's views on perception held during the last forty-five years of his life will be considered in this essay. I shall not be concerned, except in a kind of negative way, with his earlier work on the subject such as his brief but notorious flirtation with phenomenalism, *circa* 1914.[1] This theory of perception was first given in detail by him in *The Analysis of Matter,* published in 1927 (London: Allen & Unwin; New York: Dover Publications, Inc.; hereafter *AM*). Although he subsequently modified it somewhat and considerably augmented it in *Human Knowledge: Its Scope and Limits* (New York: Simon and Schuster, 1948; hereafter *HK*), it remained remarkably constant for the rest of his life. Russell felt that his theory was "almost universally misunderstood" (*MPD*, p. 16). My experience confirms his feeling—either misunderstood or totally neglected, I should say; and I fear he is almost, but not quite, correct when he says that nobody has accepted it, adding that he believes and hopes that this is only because it has not been understood (*MPD*, p. 15). The misunderstanding and neglect are, I believe, extremely unfortunate, for it seems to me that these later views of Russell on perception and related matters are crucially important and, moreover, that

Some of the research that provided material for this essay was supported by the National Science Foundation, The Carnegie Foundation, and the Minnesota Center for Philosophy of Science of the University of Minnesota. This paper is here published for the first time.

[1] See, e.g., B. Russell, *My Philosophical Development* (hereafter abbreviated *MPD*), New York: Simon and Schuster, 1959, pp. 104–5.

they are the nearest thing to the truth about these issues that have been proposed to date. For these reasons, this essay will be mainly expository, interpretative, and apologetic rather than critical, although I shall not hesitate to call attention to what appear to be deficiencies when they occur, either in the substance of the theory or in the clarity of Russell's presentation of it.

The task that I have set is a broad one, for in order to understand Russell's views on perception it is necessary, I believe, to be acquainted with his general epistemological and metaphysical outlook, including his "event ontology" and the theory of space-time that he develops from it, his interpretations of physics, physiology, and psychophysiology, and, of especial importance, his later views on the foundations of nondemonstrative inference (i.e., on the so-called "problem of induction," or, in general, the problems of confirmation theory). This will lead us immediately into a consideration of what Russell takes the goals and methods of philosophical inquiry to be, and misunderstandings about this matter may well turn out to have been the greatest obstacles to a sympathetic understanding of Russell's views. It is only by considering his views on all of these matters and by reflection on his attempts to synthesize them into a comprehensive world view that one is able to understand and appreciate his theory of perception.[2] And until this is done, I should maintain, any critique of these views is premature. Surely this is one among several reasons why Russell's later views have been, as he says, "almost universally misunderstood." World views are given short shrift these days, even when they consist, as Russell's do, mainly of attempts to give a systematic, consistent, and coherent summary of certain related parts of our scientific and common-sense knowledge. At any rate, this paper will contain at least a

[2] These attempts appear in detail in *HK*.

brief exposition of Russell's views on each of these topics and of how they fit together, as he sees it, into a comprehensive account of the nature of knowledge and its subject matter such as the physical world, mental events, the self, etc. In other words, I shall try to give a reasonably brief, but comprehensible, synoptic account of Russell's theories on these matters; and I shall not be concerned with extensive documentation and other such scholarly details, for such a project would require one if not several volumes the size of this collection. For similar reasons I shall omit almost altogether considerations of certain aspects of Russell's theory of perception, such as, for example, his attempt to "eliminate the subject," which amounts to an attempt to dispense with any *act-object* distinction in perception as well as questions about whether his event ontology provides him with a viable theory of space-time or whether his new "substances" such as *redness* (see, e.g., *MPD*, p. 171) can be coherently so viewed, etc. Finally, in the interest of better comprehension, I shall, from time to time, make explicit what seem to me to be some of Russell's unstated, perhaps unconscious, assumptions that play an important role in understanding his philosophical motivation.

The crucial basic assumption made by Russell has been stated by him on numerous occasions: it is that our most reliable knowledge in certain appropriate domains is provided by physics and other natural sciences, including, I would judge, psychophysiology or neuropsychology. (See, e.g., *MPD*, p. 17, and also numerous places in *AM* and *HK*, and, for an *especially* good statement and defense of this assumption, P. A. Schilpp, ed., *The Philosophy of Bertrand Russell*, Carbondale, Ill.: The Library of Living Philosophers, 1944, pp. 700–1; hereafter, *PBR*.) He begins by saying in the last-mentioned reference that he wishes "to distinguish sharply between ontology and epistemology. In ontology I start by accepting the truth of physics;[3] in epistemology I ask myself: Given the truth of physics, what can be meant by an organism having 'knowledge,' and what knowledge can it have?"

He goes on to explain that he has "merely a common-sense basis . . . for accepting the truth of physics" —that almost any nonphilosopher, nonphysicist would agree that physics has a much better chance of being true than any philosophical system, and that attempts "to set up [philosophies] against physics . . . have always ended in disaster." Essentially the same (brief) "justification" is given in the other references mentioned above. Now I believe that Russell has much more extensive grounds for "accepting the truth of physics" than he ever gives in these passages. He does make most of these grounds explicit in other places but perhaps does not make sufficiently clear their relevance to his starting "ontological assumption." This is unfortunate, for it contributes to the misunderstanding of his views, and, for many philosophers, it certainly raises insurmountable obstacles to their acceptance. For example, it seems reasonable to hold against Russell that the philosopher, certainly the philosopher of physics, far from merely accepting the pronouncements of physics, should subject them to severe critical scrutiny. He should ask himself what, *if any,* good reasons can be adduced that will furnish a foundation for such knowledge as physics purports to provide. Russell's answer to such an objection, or the one he would have given had he set out explicitly to give one, would be provided by his theory of "nondemonstrative inference." Using Russell's views as obtained from various of his works, I shall try to provide such a reply as well as replies to other objections to his apparently almost cavalier "acceptance" of physics, but all of this in due course.

In fairness, it should be noted that, even at this

[3] He, presumably, means to include other natural sciences, as mentioned above.

point, Russell does go on to give a (partial) explanation of what he *means* by the phrase "accepting the
truth of physics" (*loc. cit.,* pp. 700–1). First, he says,
". . . although progressive changes are to be expected
in physics, the present doctrines are likely to be nearer
to the truth than any rival doctrines now before the
world. . . . It is, therefore, rational to accept . . .
[them] hypothetically" (*MPD,* p. 17). The other,
much more difficult dimension of the meaning of "accepting the truth of physics" involves the question:
What do we take physics to assert? In the passage
mainly under consideration now (*PBR,* p. 701), he
gives a partial answer, one, moreover, not argued for
there. He merely expresses his adherence to a *realist*
interpretation of physics, saying, ". . . an honest acceptance of physics demands recognition of unob-
served occurrences." Thus he emphatically rejects not
only phenomenalism but *any* kind of instrumentalist
interpretation, whatever. Regarding his early flirtation
with phenomenalism, he says (*loc. cit.*), "There are
some who deny that physics need say anything about
what *cannot* be observed [my italics]; at times I have
been one of them. But I have become persuaded that
such an interpretation of physics is at best an intellectual game. . . ." In view of such clear and unequivo-
cal passages as this, as well as numerous other ones
to the same effect,[4] it is remarkable that many philosophers of my acquaintance seem to believe that
Russell remained a phenomenalist throughout his philosophical career.[5]

[4] See, e.g., *MPD,* p. 205, and numerous places in *HK* and
AM.

[5] It is true that Russell does stoutly maintain, throughout
his career, his "principle of acquaintance," which may be put
as: If we can understand what a sentence means, all of its nonlogical (i.e., descriptive) terms must either directly denote
items with which we are acquainted or be definable in
terms that denote only such items. But it is a grave mis-
reading of the principle to take it to be incompatible with a

"Accepting the truth of physics," then, means, for Russell, accepting physical theory, *interpreted* in a realist manner, which in turn, means interpreting physical theory as referring to unobservable things and events. Elsewhere at various places (*AM, HK, Inquiry into Meaning and Truth* [hereafter *IMT*], *MPD*, and others), he gives, it seems to me, two kinds of (mutually complementary) grounds for this view of physical theory: (1) Those who propose and use the theories interpret them realistically and (2) (more importantly), given Russell's theory of nondemonstrative inference (which I shall discuss later), this is the only reasonable way to interpret them.

Russell then goes on to say that the main business of physics involves *causal laws* (*PBR*, pp. 701–2). The notion of causality used here is a broad one; for example, the gas laws such as Boyle's law would be considered to express causal relations holding between changes of pressure and changes of volume, etc. Taking the concern of physics (including, as almost always for Russell, physiology and psychophysiology) to be causal relations among events (some of which are unobservable) makes acceptance of "the causal theory

strong realism or to suppose that it gives any support to phenomenalism, instrumentalism, or related views. For, Russell's own theory of descriptions, *definite and indefinite* descriptions, provides a method of *denoting* and, thus, making assertions about, holding beliefs about, having knowledge about, etc., items with which we are *not* acquainted (including items that are unobservable). Such denotation is accomplished *indirectly* by means of logical terms (usually existential quantifiers or their natural language equivalents) plus descriptive terms that do denote items of acquaintance. For a detailed discussion of these matters, including a discussion of how Russell's theory of descriptions may be extended to unobservable properties using the *Ramsey Sentence*, see my "Structural Realism and the Meaning of Theoretical Terms," in M. Radner and S. Winokur, *Minnesota Studies in the Philosophy of Science*, Vol. IV, Minneapolis: University of Minnesota Press, 1971.

of perception" virtually inescapable, or so Russell contends. The "ontological assumption," thus, provides at least a partial answer to the "epistemological question." For, our best-grounded theories of physics, physiology, and psychophysiology tell us, at least in broad outline, how our perceptual experiences are related to the appropriate, physical events that are causally connected with them. These theories, thus, tell us what kind of knowledge that perception, properly interpreted, can provide the organism. It is this component of Russell's theory of perception with which the major portion of this essay will be concerned. This is because my main purposes are to facilitate understanding of and increase the credibility of Russell's work on the matter, and I believe that it is just this part of his theory that comprises the most serious obstacles to this.

But before examining the fascinating and, to many philosophers, shocking and outrageous inferences that Russell draws at this point, it is advisable to discuss his grounds for accepting the causal theory of perception in a little more detail. This, in turn, will lead us into a study of his general methods of inquiry and his views about the nature and function of philosophical activity.

Russell expresses surprise at finding "the causal theory of perception treated as something that could be questioned." He can "understand Hume's questioning of causality in general, but if causality in general is admitted," he says, "I do not see on what grounds perception should be excepted from its scope" (*PBR*, p. 702). It is interesting and important to note that at another place (and an earlier time), he anticipates and elegantly blocks the "'perception'-is-a-*success-word*" maneuver[6]: "I do not like the word 'perception' for the complete experience consisting of a sensory

[6] See, e.g., Gilbert Ryle, *Dilemmas*, Cambridge: Cambridge University Press, 1954.

core supplemented by expectations, *because the word 'perception' suggests too strongly that the beliefs involved are true* [italics added]. I will therefore use the phrase 'perceptive experience.' Thus whenever I think I see a cat, I have the perceptive experience of 'seeing a cat,'[7] even if, on this occasion, no physical cat is present." (From *IMT*.) Thus a *perceptive experience* is properly labeled as a *perception* only if it is veridical ("successful"). It follows that all *perceptions* are *perceptive experiences* but not all *perceptive experiences* are *perceptions*. So that, if all perceptive experiences are in the causal network (that they are is argued below), then all *perceptions* must be there also.

Consider Russell's favorite example—a case in which I see the sun (*PBR*, pp. 702–3). If science is right, he says, I will see the sun only when radiation of suitable frequency has traveled to me from the sun and has produced certain physiological effects (in the eye, the optic nerve, and the brain). "The waves can be stopped by a screen, [and] the [necessary] physiological effects [can be stopped] by destroying the optic nerve or excising the visual centers in the brain. If this is not to be accepted as evidence of the causal ancestry of seeing the sun, all scientific reasoning will have to be remodeled." Such arguments as well as even simpler ones from common sense (e.g., *PBR*, p. 702) are so compelling that I would share Russell's surprise if I ever encountered someone who flatly rejected the causal theory of perception. Philosophers that I know or read, however, are more cagey (and more obscure). Ryle, for example (*loc. cit.*), does not deny, as I understand him, that light waves, the eye, the optic nerve, and the brain are somehow involved

---

[7] The inverted commas here are crucial, for there is the same difficulty with the word "see" as there is with the word "perception." (See, e.g., *PBR*, pp. 704–5.) I may "see a cat" without seeing a cat. I will accomplish the latter only if the perceptual experience of "seeing a cat" is veridical.

in vision. He argues, however, that perception is not
a process, from which it obviously follows that it cannot be a physiological process but also, and more importantly for the point at issue, since it is not a process
or an event it follows that it cannot be in the causal
network. But as regards the latter inference, even if
one grants the premise (which I do not[8]), the conclusion by no means follows. For Russell's arguments,
just cited, for the causal theory of perception as well
as numerous others, similar arguments from science and
even from prescientific common sense hold with just
as much force if perception is *not* process-like or event-
like as if it *is* so regarded. That is, even if "see" is *just*
a "success word" (*whatever* this may mean) and even
if there is no such thing as a *process* or an *event* of
seeing, the arguments still show—if they ever showed
anything—that certain physical and physiological
events, processes, or states of affairs are *causally necessary* in order for us ("successfully") to *see the sun*.

Other arguments have been offered, of course,
against casting the causal theory of perception in any
kind of crucial epistemic (or epistemological) role—
and, indeed, against allowing it *any* essential "philosophical" significance. An understanding of the philosophical motivations behind such arguments is not
hard to come by, but it is well worth considering in
any effort to assess their force. The main motivation
seems to be the desire to maintain a strongly empiricist
epistemology. This, in turn, seems to have led a very
large portion of contemporary philosophers to defend,
or at the very least to hold tacitly, certain rather definite positions on the nature of logic, the nature of

[8] For more detailed arguments against Ryle's position, see
my "Theories, Perception, and Structural Realism," in R.
Colodny, ed., *The Nature and Function of Scientific Theories:
Essays in Contemporary Science and Philosophy*, Vol. 4 in
the University of Pittsburgh Series in the Philosophy of Science, Pittsburgh: University of Pittsburgh Press, 1970, pp.
25–26.

induction (and confirmation, in general), and the nature of philosophical inquiry itself. With one exception, these currently popular positions were rejected by Russell, and it is for this reason that our attention turns toward them now.

The basic, almost exclusive epistemic priority that empiricism accords sense perception has been responsible for notorious and grave epistemological difficulties. These were clearly recognized and delineated by Hume, who quite straightforwardly acknowledged that he found them insurmountable. Since he was unwilling to abandon empiricism, he proclaimed skepticism to be the only rational remaining option. Of course he found skepticism to be psychologically impossible to maintain (as Russell puts it), so, again with his characteristic honesty, he admitted that all of his (and our) beliefs about matters beyond sense impressions of the moment are irrational. Empiricists, since the time of Hume, have generally not been so forthright.

Hume's dilemma arises for the empiricist in a quite simple way. According to empiricism, all of our (factual) knowledge is either direct, in which case it is *known directly* through sense perception, or it is indirect, in which case it must be confirmed by *direct* knowledge. Direct knowledge is usually considered to be relatively unproblematic, but the question then arises as to the nature of the confirmation relationship whereby the claims of indirect knowledge must be supported by direct knowledge. Hume argued lengthily and decisively that no such relationship can hold *necessarily*. But if it does not hold necessarily, the relation must always be a contingent (factual) one. That is, if it is ever true that a set of propositions (expressing direct knowledge) are evidence for some other proposition(s) (expressing indirect knowledge) it is only *contingently* true; and, moreover, it is not a contingent truth that can be known directly (by perception). Therefore, if empiricist principles are maintained, *any claim that one set of propositions is evidence for (confirms) another is a claim that stands in need of confirmation itself,* so that any attempt at confirmation leads either to vicious infinite regress or to vicious circularity, as was so clearly shown again by Hume.

Although empiricists have quite generally acknowledged the acuteness of Hume's insights and the poignancy of the "problem of induction" that he posed, they have seemed, almost to a man (and woman), to have assumed that he was wrong. Thus the literature still abounds in attempts to "justify induction," "vindicate" it, "pragmatically justify" it, show that it really needs no justification (e.g., because of [part of] the very meaning of the word, "justification"), etc., etc.; and whether an empiricist would judge any of such attempts successful or not, he would assume, typically, that there must *exist* some solution and that the nondeductive reasoning necessary to extend our knowledge beyond perceptions of the moment is not only legitimate but consistent with empiricism. For many years, Russell was no exception, but he slowly and gradually became convinced that Hume's dilemma is, indeed, inescapable. Unlike Hume, he rejected skepticism and embraced the other horn, recognizing the limitations of empiricism, the rather drastic modifications it must suffer, and the exceptions it must admit in order to be justifiably maintained at all. I maintain that, even before he made these views explicit, they began to have an important effect on the development of his thought, including his views about the nature of philosophical inquiry. By way of contrast, it will be useful first to consider the development of the *main* strands of contemporary empiricism.

Lulled by the comfortable belief (faith?) that there must be some way of getting around Hume's dilemma —that nondeductive ("inductive") reasoning is somehow consistent with a thoroughgoing empiricism—empiricists, when they have thought about it at all, have usually gone on to the even more comforting belief in the existence of "inductive logic." Of course, inductive inferences were admittedly "risky" and were not necessarily truth-preserving, but the word "logic" nevertheless was intended in a fairly strong and definite sense: (1) it was the *logical form* of the nondeductive inference or argument that was supposed to bestow upon it its legitimacy and (2) reasoning by means of these legitimate, nondeductive forms was thought to be the "rational" way to reason in all possible worlds. This belief that the relationship between evidence and what is *evidenced* is a *logical* relationship, is comfortable (or comforting), of course, because it allows the empiricist to maintain his empiricism—to hold that our selections of the best supported claims to indirect knowledge are based on direct knowledge and logic (in the fairly tough sense of "logic" just explained) and nothing else.[9] (The empiricist philosophy of logic, whereby its principles are "factually empty," is assumed, of course, and it is not my purpose to call it into question.) With these simple views of confirmation, in particular, and of theory of knowledge, in general, being held, it is easy to understand why the temptation to take the next step and adopt a "confirmability meaning criterion" is virtually irresistible. Any knowledge claim that is neither direct knowledge nor capable of being "confirmed" in the manner just discussed is quite naturally viewed as being beyond the pale, not worthy of serious consideration, and, indeed, "meaningless."

Empiricists, then, have found themselves left with two kinds of "meaningful" statements: those expressing direct knowledge or confirmable by direct knowledge on the one hand, and those that can be certified

[9] For a more detailed discussion of these matters, see my "Theories, Perception, and Structural Realism," *op. cit.*, and "Corroboration without Demarcation," in P. A. Schilpp, ed., *The Philosophy of Karl Popper*, La Salle, Ill.: Open Court, forthcoming.

(or rejected) solely on the basis of the meaning of the language used, i.e., logical truths, analytic statements, etc. Statements of the former kind say something contingent about the world, while those of the latter are necessarily true (or false) but factually empty. This line of thought immediately raised crucial questions about the nature of philosophy. Statements of the first kind express *empirical* knowledge and thus, it was thought, belong to either simple, contingent, common-sense knowledge, or, to the "empirical sciences." In neither case were they allowed to be considered properly *philosophical.* Philosophy, then, in order to avoid meaninglessness would have to restrict its realm to statements of the second kind; it would have to deal only with matters that can be settled on the basis of logical, conceptual, or linguistic grounds.

The reason that philosophers who hold such views deny so vehemently the relevance of the causal theory of perception for philosophical problems about perception in particular and theory of knowledge in general should now be obvious. For, they would hold, the causal theory is ("merely") a contingent, ("merely") a scientific theory, and (thus!) cannot be used in answering philosophical questions. But someone who holds a radically different view about the nature of the confirmation relationship (about the "problem of induction"), as did Russell, may very well feel very differently about the relevance of the causal theory in particular and about the nature of philosophy in general. Unfortunately, when one looks at his explicit pronouncements on the matter, it is not easy to decide what view on the nature of philosophy Russell considered himself to hold.[10] But, I shall hold, if one examines his philosophical activity and its results, especially since *circa* 1925, along with a

[10] See, e.g., Alan Wood, "Russell's Philosophy" in *MPD,* p. 276.

few select statements he made in its defense, a fairly clear picture emerges. It is true that he emphasizes again and again that his method is "the method of analyzing" and unfortunately this is doubly misleading. First, "analysis" for him does not mean the currently fashionable "philosophical analysis," nor does it mean merely logical analysis, "conceptual analysis," or linguistic analysis. Second, he, himself, seems to use the word ambiguously. Sometimes he seems to intend it in its original sense of *analyzing* a *whole* into its parts (see, e.g., *IMT*, Chap. 24) and sometimes he uses it in a sense which he explains: "Every truly philosophical problem is a problem of analysis; and in problems of analysis the best method is that which sets out from results and arrives at the premises.[11] This may be an odd use of the word "analysis," but this latter kind of method is surely the one used by Russell in his later philosophical work. For example, he explicitly endorses it and adopts it in *IMT* (see Chap. 9). The striking thing to note is that this is also the method used in physics and other advanced sciences; the scientist "starts" with "results," i.e., experimental results, or observations, or other "facts," and he "arrives" at "premises," i.e., theories and/or hypotheses that *explain* the results. Again, Russell recognizes this explicitly: "I do not pretend that the above theory [about perception, the relation of mind and matter, etc.] can be proved. What I contend is that like the theories of physics, it cannot be disproved, and gives an answer to many problems which older theorists have found puzzling. I do not think that any prudent person will claim more than this for any theory" (*MPD*, p. 27).[12]

[11] "Philosophical Importance of Mathematical Logic," *Monist*, October 1913; quoted by Alan Wood, *op. cit.*, p. 264.

[12] Russell says earlier (*MPD*, p. 15) that he arrived at the part of the theory that "[solves] the problem of the relation of mind and matter by analyzing physics and perception." Surely "analyzing" here must mean something like "proposing

It is at this point that Russell's position concerning nondeductive reasoning sheds light on his views about the methods of philosophical (and scientific) inquiry. We have seen that here (and elsewhere, e.g., *AM*, pp. 194–96) he endorses *hypothetico-deductive* reasoning, as it is called. ("Hypothetico-inferential" would be a better term, since sometimes the inferences from theories or hypotheses to evidence may be statistical.) That is, theories and/or hypotheses are proposed that *explain* the evidence, i.e., yield the evidence as consequences. The pattern of reasoning may be outlined as follows. Suppose we have some evidence expressed by a conjunction of statements— call the conjunction *E*—and suppose a theory is proposed that, when conjoined with appropriate "background" theories and auxiliary theories and with appropriate hypotheses about initial conditions, *explains* the evidence—call this latter conjunction *T*. We then proceed: (1) *T* implies *E*, (2) *E*, therefore . . . Therefore what? It seems incontrovertible that the temptation to say, "Therefore *T*," is one to which we yield repeatedly, both in scientific and in common-sense reasoning. It might be more prudent to say, rather, that since *T* implies *E* and *E* is true, we have *some* evidence, or *some* reason for *tentatively* accepting *T*. However, this does not appreciably diminish the problematic character of the "inference." This backwards "inference" in the opposite direction from deductive validity—this blatant "affirmation of the consequent" turns out to be the cornerstone of most of our important, nontrivial reasoning, reasoning by means of which most of our knowledge claims that go beyond sense experience of the moment are confirmed. It is this kind of *inference* that Russell should be interpreted as talking about when he discusses, for example, "inferences" from private "percepts" to

a theory that *explains* the relevant portions of physics and perception."

the existence of physical objects and to the ("structural") properties of them that play an important causal role in the production of the percepts. (Of course we do not normally perform *any* conscious inference. The sense experience, under appropriate conditions, produces in us the belief that here is an *object with such-and-such properties.* But the "inference" refers to the kind of reasoning in which we should engage if we were called upon to justify the belief.) In such a case T would be the causal theory of perception conjoined with appropriate propositions about initial conditions, etc., e.g., the "hypothesis" that *here is a chair[13] with such-and-such (structural) properties, etc.*, while E might be a conjunction of statements asserting that *I am visually aware of certain colored shapes, tactilely aware of certain degrees of roughness, smoothness, etc., etc.* Evidence such as E, thus, hypothetico-inferentially confirms not only the causal theory of perception *and* auxiliary and background theories from physics, physiology, etc., but specific singular hypotheses ("initial conditions") such as "A chair is now near," as well.

But can Russell, or anyone, seriously contend that our only legitimate reasons for accepting our nontrivial knowledge claims—our only means of confirmation—arise from repeatedly committing an elementary logic textbook fallacy? Surely, it might be objected, our old-fashioned "inductive methods" such as induction by simple enumeration, Mills Methods, etc., suspect though they may be, cannot be as logically indefensible as *affirming the consequent!* But Russell (and Hume) have a ready reply: logically, they are all on a par; hypothetico-inferential reason-

[13] More accurately: *there is a certain collection of electrons, protons, etc., having certain (structural) properties and certain relations to each other and to certain other collections such as the one commonly called "my body," etc.*—still more accurately: *there is a certain family of events, having certain structural properties and relations, etc., etc.*

ing is no worse off (and no better off) logically than,
for example, induction by simple enumeration. Just
how badly off are they? Pretty bad; as Russell has
put it (*MPD*, p. 14), "Unfortunately, it can be proved
that induction by simple enumeration, if conducted
without regard to common sense, leads more often to
error than to truth. And if a principle needs common
sense before it can be safely used, it is not the sort of
principle that can satisfy a logician." (It should be
noted that what Russell has in mind as needed from
common sense here is contingent and, thus, extralogical.) The proof of Russell's contention can be accomplished by proving that for any argument by induction by simple enumeration that has true premises
and a true conclusion there can be constructed an indefinitely large number of arguments with the same
logical form as the argument in question, each argument having true premises but, in each case, a conclusion that is inconsistent with the (true) original
conclusion. This can be done in many ways.[14]

We have seen that hypothetico-inferential reasoning, although no worse off logically than other, more
traditionally recognized "inductive" reasoning, is no
better off either. Indeed, it is again easy to prove that,
given any amount of evidence (say, any amount of
direct knowledge), there will exist an indefinitely
large number of mutually incompatible theories all
of which *explain* the evidence and all of which, thus,
are logically on a par with each other with respect to
the evidence. Thus, even if theories could be falsified
(say, by new evidence), which I maintain with Russell they cannot be if they are of much interest or importance,[15] there would always still remain a poten-
tially infinite number of mutually incompatible

[14] See, e.g., my "Theories, Perception, and Structural Realism," *op. cit.*

[15] See the quotation from Russell above, p. 95, and my *ibid.*
and "Corroboration without Demarcation," *op. cit.*

theories that would explain the new (falsifying) evidence and the old as well.

What reasons, then, can we have for having any confidence in any of our nondeductive modes of reasoning and, thus, for having any confidence in any knowledge claim that goes beyond the trivialities of momentary perception? Unlike Hume, Russell does not answer, "None!" However, he insists, entirely correctly I believe, that any such reasons must be extralogical (and extraconceptual), and therefore they must be contingent. The assumption that we have nontrivial knowledge can be defended only by further assumptions about the structure of our world—the actual world as opposed to the infinite number of other possible worlds. He says, for example (*HK*, p. 496), "Owing to the world being such as it is, certain occurrences are sometimes, in fact, evidence for certain others; and owing to animals being adapted to their environment, occurrences which are, in fact, evidence of others tend to arouse expectation of those others."

How, then, do we, or should we go about discovering and choosing among the bewildering *embarras de richesses* of claims to indirect knowledge (theories, hypotheses, etc.), all of which, as far as logic is concerned, are equally well (or equally badly) supported by the evidence we may happen to have? In spite of the considerable amount of effort that Russell devoted to this matter, it does not seem to me that he ever got quite clear about it. His "postulates of scientific inference" (*HK*, Part Six), while perhaps true and perhaps employed by us at times, do not seem to be, as he had hoped, sufficient to allow the rest of common sense and scientific reasoning to proceed on the basis of direct knowledge and logic alone.[16] I

---

[16] For an alternative account of nondeductive reasoning see my "Corroboration without Demarcation," *op. cit.*, and "Theories, Perception, and Structural Realism," *op. cit.*

mention this here not to argue it but to contrast it
with another view that is, again, implicit in his philosophical activity, if not in his explicit pronouncements, the view that in each problem situation we
must make a (risky) choice of the theory that seems
to us best to solve the problems at hand (i.e., to *explain* the evidence in, say, e.g., an elegant, parsimo-
nious, intuitively satisfactory manner, etc., etc.); to
quote again from *MPD*, p. 27, "I do not pretend that
the above theory [about perception, mind, matter,
etc.] can be proved. What I contend is that, *like the
theories of physics,* it cannot be disproved, and gives
an answer to many problems which older theorists
have found puzzling. *I do not think that any prudent
person will claim more than this for any theory*" [all
italics added to the original].

None of this provides an escape from Hume's dilemma, and, we have noted, Russell does not believe
that there is any escape. He has said on numerous occasions (e.g., *HK*, xi) that skepticism (or solipsism
of the moment, etc.) is logically impeccable (although psychologically impossible). However, he has
no patience with any "partial skepticism" (*loc. cit.*)
such as phenomenalism, subjective idealism, or even,
say, a direct realism that, however, interprets statements about (putative) unobservables instrumentally. For any such partial skepticism must admit
principles of inference that are no better off *logically*
than those required for, say, the most rampant and
speculative realism. Moreover, if logic can provide
no arguments against skepticism, neither can it provide any in its favor, and it cannot provide any reasons for not adopting what we hope are contingently
legitimate principles of reasoning in science and enlightened common sense. We cannot prove that
(nontrivial) knowledge is possible, but there is nothing irrational about seeking for it, and hoping or even
believing (e.g., on the basis of hunches, or intuition,
etc.) that our quest will be partially successful. There

are no *a priori* reasons against believing that we have the capacity to make, fairly often, good proposals (that we can, on occasion make fairly good guesses) and the capacity to make correct choices from among the indefinitely large number of possible theories that can explain any evidence we may happen to have (that we are able to order our guesses in a manner not hopelessly out of line with their true *prior* probabilities);[17] in fact, it is difficult, though of course by no means impossible, to explain our survival or to explain our ability to make bigger and better hydrogen bombs unless we do suppose that we have such capacities. Of course we do not *know* whether or not we shall continue to survive; but if we do not, we shall no longer be bothered with the problem of induction nor will there be any more need for hydrogen bombs.

Empiricists (and others) have seen correctly that experience (direct knowledge) plus logic is not sufficient to conclusively decide between, say, phenomenalism and realism, or between mind-body monism, interactionism, and psychophysical parallelism or epiphenomenalism. Because they failed to see that exactly the same difficulty exists in deciding between two or more competing theories in physics and any other reasonably advanced science they felt that they were forced to the strange conclusion that traditional philosophical issues like those just mentioned were pseudo-controversies and that, e.g., both the assertion of the existence of external world (realism) and its denial (say, by subjective idealism) were meaningless "pseudo-assertions"[18] or to the even more mystifying (to me at least) conclusion that, contrary to all appearances, they were really just controversies about the meaning of certain parts of our language or

[17] For details see my "Corroboration without Demarcation," *op. cit.*

[18] See, e.g., R. Carnap, in "Replies to Criticisms," in P. A. Schilpp, ed., *The Philosophy of Rudolf Carnap*, La Salle, Ill.: Open Court, 1963, p. 868.

differences of opinion about which "language system"
one should adopt (see, e.g., Carnap, *loc. cit.*). Russell, however, clearly believes that such "philosophical" positions are *contingent* assertions about the
world, and, since experience plus logical (or conceptual, or linguistic) analysis is not sufficient to conclusively decide among them, we must proceed exactly
as we do when the same situation arises in science
and select the position that seems to us to most satisfactorily explain the evidence. For example, he opts
for realism (of a certain variety) as best explaining
the "evidence," the evidence in this case including
not only our direct knowledge gained by perception
but much of our other common-sense and scientific
knowledge as well. It goes without saying that almost
any other position, say phenomenalism, can be elaborated so that it too explains the evidence (provided
we interpret scientific theories instrumentally, etc.),
just as we can always patch up any scientific theory
no matter what the evidence in its domain may be.
But Russell would say that phenomenalism does not
explain it *as well* as realism. Realism affords a more
elegant, more coherent, and, perhaps just as importantly, a more intuitively plausible explanation; as I
would put it, I would estimate the prior probability
of realism to be much higher than the prior probability of its competitors. Are phenomenalism and realism, since they are contingent theories, to be classified as *philosophical* or *scientific?* The easy answer is
that one is free to use the words "philosophical" and
"scientific" in any way one chooses. For my part, I
feel that the word "science" has been overworked and
to an even greater extent misused, and I had just as
soon give it a complete rest. However, we should note
once more that if the theories of, say, physics are
scientific, then, for reasons just given, theories such
as realism, mind-body monism, epiphenomenalism,
etc., seem to have almost as good a claim to the word.
On the other hand, such theories have occupied a

great portion of the attention of the thinkers that we traditionally classify as philosophers, and if contemporary philosophers are to concern themselves with matters other than the trivialities that can be gleaned from logical, conceptual, and linguistic "analysis," it would seem that these problems must continue to be so treated; at any rate, this is Russell's view of the matter.

With the abandonment of the empiricists' forlorn hope that inductivism (or what I have called elsewhere *strict confirmationism*[19]) can somehow be salvaged and the resulting realization that the empiricist confirmability meaning criterion is not only without justification but untenable and impossible,[20] the way becomes completely open for the philosopher to treat his problems—or at least a significant subset of them—in the open, speculative manner of the best theoretical scientists—in the manner, also, of the best detectives; for a striking illustration of how hypothetico-inferential reasoning provides most of our significant common-sense knowledge, reread any Sherlock Holmes or other *good* detective story. It is by this method of open theorizing that most of Russell's later philosophy has been produced.

We have finally come around full circle. Russell accepts physics (in the broad sense explained earlier to include physiology, psychophysiology, all of the causal theory of perception, etc.), and he accepts it because it explains the relevant facts from everyday life and from the laboratory in the *most satisfactory manner*—in the sense of "explain," "satisfactory manner," etc., that we have been discussing. Moreover, a realist interpretation of physics provides a *more satisfactory explanation* than does any "partial skepticism" such as instrumentalism. For example, instrumentalism leaves the fact that our theories make the

[19] "Theories, Perception, and Structural Realism," *op. cit.*
[20] See my *ibid.*

(sometimes startling) true predictions that they do completely unexplained or explained in a contrived and intuitively unsatisfactory manner, while realism explains this very simply by saying that, since the theories make genuine assertions and are, we hope, true (or reasonably close to the truth), their consequences including their predictions, must be true also.

Russell's next step is to try to come up with a theory that is consistent with physics (and with as much of common sense as is possible) and that will *explain,* in the most satisfactory way, the "facts" of perception, in particular, and of our acquisition of (contingent) knowledge, in general. Such a theory is needed for a number of reasons; one of these is the *prima facie* inconsistency of physics and that part of common sense that philosophers call *naïve realism.* The argument for the existence of such an inconsistency is a venerable one—germinal no later than Democritus and the Skeptics and given in one form or another by Galileo, Descartes, Locke, the American Critical Realists, and many others, including a disappointingly small number of contemporary thinkers.[21] One can do no better than read Russell himself on the matter (for example, in HK, MPD, PBR, AM), so I shall just summarize the argument briefly here with two quotations, the first from my "Theories, Perception, and Structural Realism" (*op. cit.,* p. 19) and

[21] For a fuller discussion (and more references) see my "Scientific Methodology and the Causal Theory of Perception," and "Reply [to Professors Quine, Ayer, Popper, and Kneale]," both in I. Lakatos and Alan Musgrave, eds., *Problems in the Philosophy of Science,* Amsterdam: North Holland Publishing Co., 1968, pp. 148–77; "Structural Realism and the Meaning of Theoretical Terms," in S. Winokur and M. Radner, *Minnesota Studies in the Philosophy of Science,* Minneapolis: University of Minnesota Press; and "Theories, Perception, and Structural Realism," *op. cit.*

the second from my "Scientific Methodology and the Causal Theory of Perception" (*op. cit.,* p. 170):

> If our current theories in physics, neurophysiology, and psychophysiology are at all close to the truth or even if they are at all headed in the right direction, then a complete description, including a complete causal account, of everything that is involved in perception except the private experience itself would mention only such entities and events as submicroscopic particles, electromagnetic quanta, etc., and their relations and interactions with one another and with, for example, neural termini in the retina, afferent neural impulses, and patterns of neuronal activity in the brain. At no point in the entire, complete description and causal explanation is there mention of any first order property such as colors *until* we come to the private experience that results from the pattern of neuron firings in the brain. It seems to me that we must conclude that colors are exemplified *only* in our private experiences and there is no reason to believe that they are ever properties of the material objects of the external environment. *What holds for colors must also be true for all of the first order properties that we perceive directly.*

Here, something of crucial importance must be emphasized: the decisive point is *not,* as is sometimes held, that it is meaningless or self-contradictory to think of electrons, light quanta, etc., or atoms, molecules, or even aggregates thereof as being colored; rather, it is that *even if such things were colored it would make no difference.* Even if it made sense to talk of a collection of blue-colored molecules or atoms which emitted blue-colored light photons, such a "blue" aggregate could cause us to see the surface in question as a *red* one just as effectively as a collection of red-colored ones emitting red-colored quanta; the only relevant fact concerning the color we see is the

amount of energy per quantum, or, what amounts to
the same thing, the frequency of the radiation. So
even if there are colored entities—even colored surfaces
as we ordinarily conceive them—in the physical environment, we never see them and their being colored
plays no role in *any* process whereby we acquire or
confirm knowledge. We thus have no more (perhaps
less) reason for believing that there are instances of
color in the external world than we do for believing
in the existence of disembodied spirits.

As Russell acknowledges, the argument does not
show that physics and naïve realism are inconsistent
with each other; it shows that if physics is true there
can be no reason to believe naïve realism. He says, for
example, in a letter to A. J. Ayer,[22] "You say that
from the fact that the perceived qualities of perception are causally dependent upon the state of the percipient, it does not follow that the object does not
really have them. This, of course, is true. What does
follow is that there is no reason to suppose that it has
them. From the fact that when I wear blue specta-
cles, things look blue, it does not follow that they are
not blue, but it does follow that I have no reason to
suppose they are blue."

What I have called "first order properties" in the
passages above correspond to Russell's "intrinsic
properties," while second and higher order properties
(properties of properties, properties of properties of
properties, etc.) of a certain kind correspond to his
"structural properties." The first tenet of the theory
that Russell proposes, then, is that our only well-
confirmed knowledge claims about the external,
physical world must be about its second order or
structural properties and that we must remain ignorant about its first order or intrinsic properties. How-

[22] B. Russell, *Autobiography,* Vol. III, New York: Simon
and Schuster, 1969, p. 179.

ever, this manner of putting his thesis, which is unfortunately the manner he employs, is misleading and not, I believe, exactly what he intended. For, if physics and certain reformulated parts of common sense are true, we *do* know *something* about the first order (or intrinsic) properties of the physical world; we know that there are such things and we know something about them—we know *what* some of *their* properties are; in fact, the latter assertion is exactly equivalent to the assertion that we know *what* (some of) the *structural properties* of the physical world *are*, for structural properties *are* properties of *intrinsic* properties (and properties of other structural properties). The difference is that, while we have this kind of knowledge about some of the intrinsic properties of the external world, we do not know *what* they are, while we do know *what* some of its structural properties are.[23] We *do* know what the intrinsic (first order) properties exemplified in our sense experience are; they are properties such as *redness, warmth* (as felt), *being warmer* than, etc. and, of course, we know some of the structural properties as well; we know, for example, that the property of *being to the left of* in the (experienced) visual field has the structural properties of *transitivity* and *asymmetry*. Since we know *what* structural properties such as transitivity and asymmetry *are* (or in Russell's terms *we are acquainted* with structural properties such as transitivity and asymmetry) and since transitivity, asymmetry, etc., are also exemplified in the external world, we *do* know *what* (some of) the structural properties of the external world *are*. But of the first order (intrinsic) properties of the external world we can only know *that* they are and that they have the higher order (structural) properties that our well-confirmed theories assert that they have.

[23] For a fuller discussion, see my "Structural Realism and the Meaning of Theoretical Terms," *op. cit.*

The preceding considerations provide the means of understanding how Russell can maintain his "principle of acquaintance" and also defend a strong realism regarding the external world and all of the unobservables referred to by our theories. The principle forbids direct reference by any descriptive (nonlogical) term to any individual or property with which we are not acquainted. The question thus arises: How can we even talk about, much less have knowledge of, anything that is not exemplified in our direct experience? The answers are that our knowledge of such things is *knowledge by* description, and (indirect) reference to such items is accomplished by means of indefinite or definite *descriptions,* i.e., by means of variables (usually existentially quantified ones) together with terms whose *direct* referents *are* items in our experience. Suppose that I assert (truly let us suppose and on the basis of appropriate evidence) that someone stood near my window last night, someone who was tall and large. Suppose, further, that I did not see the person and do not know *who* it was, i.e., I did not and do not have knowledge by acquaintance of him. Nevertheless by means of terms whose direct referents are items of my acquaintance (my window, the properties of *tallness, standing near,* etc.) plus an implicit variable, existentially quantified (indicated by the word "someone"), I am able to refer indirectly to whomever it was and to attribute properties such as tallness, etc., to him, even though there is no descriptive term—no name—that refers directly to the suspected voyeur. Similarly we can refer to the unobservable individuals and (first order) properties of the physical world by means of quantified individual *and* predicate variables plus terms whose direct referents are observables. (Observables for Russell are, of course, strictly speaking, always ingredients of our private experience.) This removes one of the two main traditional objections that have been offered to representative realism, a variety of which can be quite fairly

attributed to Russell. (I have called it, not too felici-
tously I now fear, "structural realism.")

Once again we may ask: How do we know what the
structural properties of the world are, indeed, how do
we know that such a world exists? Russell's immediate answer is that we "infer" such knowledge from
our "percepts" (sense experience). But we should remember the special sense that must be given "infer"
here if we are to give him a sympathetic reading; "to
infer *p* from our percepts" must mean something like
"to propose *p* as the theory (and/or hypothesis) that
best explains our percepts." Once verificationism and
inductivism are seen to be untenable and hypothetico-
inferential confirmation in the manner outlined herein
is adopted, the other main traditional objection to a
realism of this kind is removed.

There still may linger an uneasiness about the existence of an apparent miracle. If our direct knowledge
is limited to knowledge about our private experience
and, given the existence of an infinite number of possible explanations of it, it is just too much to swallow,
it might be objected, to suppose that we can fairly
often conjure up just those *guesses* that are not too
far off the mark in giving us an accurate description
of the nonexperiential (external) world. And why, it
might be asked, does the fact that we *feel* that a certain guess, a certain "theory," provides a satisfactory
explanation of the evidence—why does this provide
any reason for supposing that this guess is any closer
to the truth than any of the others that we or someone
else may be bright enough to dream up? But to raise
such objections is to fail to appreciate the force of the
earlier critique of *inductivism* and *strict confirmationism*, in particular, and of traditional and contemporary
empiricism in general—the critique initiated by Hume
and elaborated by Russell and others. Experience, direct knowledge, observation knowledge—call it what
you may—plus logic (even when logic is taken in a
broad sense to include conceptual analysis, linguistic

analysis, etc.)—all of these together are not sufficient to avoid skepticism. So if we are to reject the *logically unassailable* position of skepticism, the question is: What *contingent* theory best *explains* the (hoped for) existence of (nontrivial) knowledge? I should be interested in hearing a large number of such theories proposed. But until these proposals are forthcoming, the one that I have proposed and that I have claimed was held by Russell, partly explicitly, partly implicitly, seems to me to do the job better than any other of which I am aware. As Russell says, "I do not think that any prudent person will claim any more than this for any theory."

The questions raised in the preceding paragraph can be given further answers, although they will do nothing to improve the situation from a purely logical standpoint nor will they in any way assuage the misgivings of an unregenerate empiricist. We could answer, for example, that we are able to make fairly good guesses in response to our sense experiences because our brains are "wired" in an appropriate manner, and that our brains are the way they are because we are adapted (not *too* hopelessly, we pray) to our environment, and that we are adapted to our environment because of *natural selection,* or because God made us that way, etc., etc. I am not concerned to argue for such answers here; however, I would contend that whatever the answers may be, they must be contingent ones.

The questions just discussed also call attention to the epistemic priority that is accorded sense experience or "percepts" by empiricism. It might appear that Russell uncritically incorporates this into his own views. But such an appearance, if it exists, is misleading. He explicitly gives *arguments* on the matter in his reply to Chisholm (*PBR,* pp. 710–14). He concludes that (private) sense experience does have a kind of priority, but that it does is contingent, not necessary. It is true that he accords logic a role in determining some epistemic priorities but, as to the matter at hand, the essential considerations are from common sense and from physics. Here as in so many cases, Russell begins with common-sense knowledge (or common-sense putative knowledge). Then he subjects it to critical scrutiny and, by a boots-strap operation, he endeavors to improve and expand it into something that is self-consistent, that is more comprehensive, that, as he puts it, makes fewer mistakes, etc. And when he says that he accomplishes this by "analysis," we have seen that this must mean that he proposes *theories* that solve the problems—remove the inconsistencies, satisfactorily *explain* the results, imply that certain new results should be obtained under appropriate conditions, etc. It is, then, no accident that he holds that this is precisely the way science comes into being. It evolves in this manner from common sense and differs from common sense, mainly, in that it makes fewer mistakes.[24] Nor is there any wonder that he has no qualms about admitting that his reason for accepting the truth of physics (again in the broad sense of "physics" already explained) as his starting point in ontology and epistemology is "merely" a common-sense reason.

Much the same arguments from common sense and especially from physics for the epistemic priority of perception are given by Russell for the *privacy* of percepts. If what science tells us about perception is correct, then the same sense experience can be produced in many ways. For example, we can be caused to see a red chair in the usual way, but the same visual experience could be produced, if neurophysiological and psychophysiological techniques were sufficiently advanced, by appropriately stimulating the optic nerve or the visual centers of the brain by, say, electrodes; or

[24] I clearly remember this assertion of his about fewer mistakes, but I have not been able to relocate the reference.

such an experience may occur in a dream. The same pattern of neuronal activity in the appropriate region of the brain is both sufficient and necessary for us to have exactly the same sense experience. Unless we were aware of the "artificial" stimulation and its effects, or, in the case of a dream, that we were dreaming, we would judge, in each case that we saw the same red chair. Now all of this does not *prove* in the sense of *"logically entail"* either the epistemic priority of percepts or their privacy. What it does do, according to Russell, is to make *unsatisfactory*, in the sense we have discussed, any account or explanation of perception and of the knowledge, direct and indirect, obtained thereby that does not assume this priority and privacy.

I have discussed other objections to Russell's approach to the problems of perception elsewhere in some detail,[25] for example, the argument against the possibility of a "private language," and arguments against the existence of sense-data. As regards the latter, sense-data are by no means necessary for the theory. In fact, Russell tells us that he "emphatically abandoned them in 1921" (*MPD*, p. 245). When he speaks of *data* in places like *HK*, he is referring to "percepts" or direct knowledge of them, and percepts for him are some of the events or the ingredients of events that comprise sense experience. I have argued at length against the former argument ("no private language") in the first of the two references just cited. I have contended that it is based on a naïve verificationism, that it commits the *fallacy of epistemologism* (i.e., it confuses "we cannot know [for certain] whether or not a case of so-and-so is a case of such-and-such" with "there *is* no difference between a case of so-and-so and a case of such-and-such"), and it

[25] E.g., in "Theories, Perception, and Structural Realism," *op. cit.*, and "Scientific Methodology and the Causal Theory of Perception," *op. cit.*

takes as a premise that we cannot know anything unless we can know it with absolute certainty.

I have sometimes been told in informal discussions
that theories like Russell's are crucially dependent
upon a "reference theory of meaning," and that when
a *correct,* i.e., a *use* theory of meaning is operative,
such a theory cannot get off the ground. No doubt
my failure to understand this objection is partially due
to my not understanding the "use" theory of meaning
very well. I cheerfully grant that, if one knows the use
of an expression, one knows its meaning. However,
it seems to me that the main *use* of most descriptive
terms is to *refer* to things, qualities, relations, etc. Be
that as it may, since Russell's theory can be stated entirely in the object language without talking about
meanings at all—though perhaps with some incon-
venience—this objection does not seem to have much
sting.

One of the "many problems which older theorists
have found puzzling" to which Russell thinks his theory "gives an answer" (*MPD,* p. 27) is the "problem
of the relation of mind and matter" (*ibid.,* p. 15), the
traditional mind-body problem. This involves his
event ontology and his theory of space-time, and I
shall summarize these in a manner which is sketchy
and inaccurate but which, I trust, will not do violence
to his views. He rejects *substance* metaphysics altogether and replaces *things*—clumps of matter (physical objects), etc., with classes or families of *events.*
Examples of events are: a twinge of pain, the occurrence of a patch of red in the visual field, etc. These
examples are events such that we know *what* they
are. This is *not* true of the events that comprise the
vast bulk of the physical (external) world. We do
not know *what* these events are; we do not know their
intrinsic nature; we do not know *what* the first order
properties are that are exemplified in them. What we
do know, if our theories from physics, etc., and refined
common sense are true or close to the truth, are some

of the structural properties (mostly relational) of these
events. The most prominent of such properties are the
causal relations that hold among the events. Russell's
theory of space-time amounts to "constructing" space-
time out of events and their causal relationships to
each other—a truly *relational* theory of space-time.
Thus, as he puts it, "when the causal relations of an
event are known, its position in space-time follows
tautologically" (*PBR*, p. 705). Since we have already
located mental events (the occurrence of perceptive
experiences, etc.) in the causal network, they thereby
acquire a spatio-temporal location, and a kind of mind-
body "identity theory" automatically follows as a consequence of the theory. I believe that the matter can
be made more clear if we adopt definitions of "mental"
and "physical" slightly different from Russell's. Let us
call anything "a physical event" that is in the causal
(and, thus, in the spatio-temporal) network, and
something will be called "a mental event" if and only
if it is an event in our direct experience (as Russell
puts it, if it [or its ingredients] can be known otherwise than by inference—in Russell's special sense of
"inference" already discussed).[26] Now, since mental
events are in space-time—i.e., they play a causal role
—it follows that all mental events are physical events.
Since there *are* such things as mental events, it also
follows that some physical events are mental events;
of what other physical events are like, or what their
intrinsic nature is we are ignorant, so ignorant, Russell
says, that we do not know whether they are similar
to (in their first order or intrinsic properties) or totally
different from the events in our experience (whose
first order or intrinsic properties we do know by acquaintance). What we do know about physical events
(including those that are mental, although about these

[26] Russell first defines "mental event" in this manner and
then defines "a physical event" as one not known (or not
known to be known) except by inference.

we know more besides) are (some of) their structural or higher order properties, the more important of which give their spatio-temporal (or causal) structure.

At the risk of repetition, I must stress a point of crucial importance. The mental events that comprise our experience, that we live through and know in all of their qualitative richness *really are physical events* (they *really are* mental events too, of course). As with other physical events, each has its own position in the spatio-temporal—causal—network and is *not* an epi-phenomenal or parallelistic correlate of some other "truly physical" event that is supposed to play the "real" spatio-temporal or causal role. There *is* no such *other* physical event at the spatio-temporal locus in question. Every "truly mental" event is also "truly physical" (though not conversely so far as we know). We regard them differently than we do other physical events because they comprise our experience and, thus, we know their intrinsic properties as well as their structural ones.

Since the brain, like all portions of matter, consists of a family—or families—of events, causally related in appropriate ways, and since neurophysiology and psychophysiology give us the causal locus that they do for the events that comprise our experience (our thoughts, feelings, etc.), it follows that our thoughts and feelings are, quite literally, among the constituents of our brains.

As Russell says, this theory may seem fantastic, but he clearly believes it is true or close to the truth and, at any rate, that it is the theory best supported by the evidence from science and enlightened common sense. Not the least component of its support comes from the fact that contemporary physics seems much better formulable using an event ontology than with using a *substance* one. In physics today, the "dematerialization of matter" is virtually complete. Be that as it may, I do not believe that there are any insurmountable obstacles to *understanding* the theory, especially if we remember the commonplace from the history of science that, when novel theories are proposed, old words take on meanings that, while they are quite similar to the old meanings in many respects, are sometimes bewilderingly different from them in others. And Russell's famous statement which, he says, profoundly shocked Ernest Nagel—and others as well (*PBR*, p. 705)—is seen to be an unexceptionable consequence of the theory. The statement is to the effect that when a physiologist examines another man's brain what he sees is a portion of his own brain. Of course, the word "see" here has a somewhat different meaning from its ordinary one. For the ordinary one is a naïve realist one (with possibly some of its uses excepted)—to say that we see something ordinarily implies that we perceive something external. But according to Russell we never see *anything* in this ordinary sense of "see." All that we ever perceive visually are ingredients of the events that comprise our experience and are, thus, literally in (or are constituents of) our own brains. Russell provides for avoidance of misunderstanding here by his distinction between physical space and perceptual space, e.g., visual space. Physical space, we recall, is constructed out of events and their causal interrelationships, but my visual space, in which I am aware of qualitative extension, shapes, locations of color patches, and other visual "percepts," is an ingredient of events in my experience. Thus all of my visual space, no matter how many miles common sense may indicate that it spreads over, is located at a point or within a small volume in physical space, in, as a matter of fact, my (physical) brain. Let us call the physiologist's percept that common sense mistakenly identifies with the other man's brain, which is really located in the physiologist's (private) visual space, and which the other man's brain does play a crucial causal role in producing—let us refer to this percept as the physiologist's percept of the other man's brain. Then it is quite clear that the physiologist's percept of the other man's brain is external to the physiologist's percept of his own body (in the physiologist's visual space), while both percepts are in the physiologist's brain in physical space.

The difference between this kind of mind-body monism and traditional materialistic mind-body theories is extreme. Traditional materialism took our conception and knowledge of matter, of the physical, to be straightforward and unproblematic. The mental, on the other hand, was held to be not only problematic but metaphysically and epistemologically undesirable, what with its alleged privacy or subjectivity, ineffability, etc., and therefore it was something best got shut of, or, at any rate, swept under a rug such as epiphenomenalism or psychophysical parallelism. Traditional materialism's conception of matter was one that resulted from naïve realism or from a not too pervasive modification thereof. Matter was something good and solid. One could *see* and *feel* that it was good and solid; as Russell says, it was bumpable into. Modern science, however, according to Russell, makes necessary the drastic revision of our conception of matter that has been discussed in this paper. It turns out that we cannot see or feel matter at all, except for those events in our visual and tactile experience that comprise a small portion of our brains. Our traditional notions of matter, rather than those of mind, turn out to be the problematic ones. Traditional materialism, by accepting common-sense naïve realism, fell into the error of identifying visual and tactile percepts with the physical objects that are merely (one crucial part of) their causes. Thus, contrary to what traditional materialism seemed to want, the mental remains every bit as mental as anyone could hope for, in spite of the fact that it is also physical. However, the portion of physical events that are mental, as far as we know today, is subject to the same principles and laws of nature as the rest of the physical world. Russell's mind-body monism retains this much in common with materialism. Whether or not further investigation will reveal that additional laws are required remains an open question.

I have discussed some of the aspects of Russell's theory of perception and of his philosophical method, theory of knowledge, and world view that evolved while he was developing the theory. I have selected those aspects that seemed to me to have the greatest importance or the greatest difficulties or both. Of necessity, I have had to omit even mention of large portions of his theory. By far the best source on Russell is still Russell himself, and probably the best single source on these matters is *HK*. However, *AM* (a sort of early version of *HK*, although he develops his theory of space-time in much more detail in it than is done in *HK*), *PBR*—especially Russell's replies to Nagel, Stace, and Chisholm—*IMT*, and portions of *MPD* are highly recommended.

I believe that Russell's later philosophy has provided solutions, in the sense that science provides solutions—tentative ones, for which many contemporary philosophers (and scientists, e.g., psychologists, neurophysiologists, and, especially, psychophysiologists) are still groping. But whether I am right about this or not, I have absolutely no doubt that his later philosophy deserves immeasurably more study than it has received and that our knowledge will be extensively enriched when this is forthcoming.

RUSSELL'S PHILOSOPHY OF SCIENCE

Charles A. Fritz, Jr.

The philosophy of science, as Russell understands it, should reconcile our ordinary knowledge from experience with the truths of science. We have seen water, we have tasted it, we have seen it freeze; but the scientific analysis of water and the scientific account of freezing are not in terms of "transparent," "tasting of chlorine," or "cold" or other common-sense descriptions. Are the scientist and the ordinary observer talking about the same thing? If so, can both descriptions be in some sense true? The resolution of these problems requires an investigation of the nature of knowledge from experience, the types of entities entering into scientific principles, and the relation—if any—between the two. A philosophy of science so oriented differs in approach from many current works on the subject, but there is an overlap in problems. Both the current philosopher of science and Russell are concerned with an analysis of observation terms, an analysis of scientific concepts, and the nature of scientific reasoning. Although Russell's analyses are often not as detailed or precise as those of more recent writers, the latter have in many cases been inspired by his work and there can be no doubt that his thought is an important milestone in the reconciliation of science and common sense.

As I see it, Russell's philosophy of science includes two different views, an earlier one, which I shall call the "logical atomism" view, found primarily in *Our Knowledge of the External World, Mysticism and Logic* (in part), and his "Philosophy of Logical Atomism," all written between 1914–19, and his later view

This paper is here published for the first time.

which is developed in the *Analysis of Matter* (1927) and found in *Human Knowledge* (1948). I propose in part 1 to discuss the bases of these views within the framework of Russell's general philosophical position. In part 2 I shall undertake a summary of the role of logical constructions in the logical atomism period with emphasis on the relation between definite descriptions and logical constructions. A review of Russell's later view in part 3 will be followed by a brief evaluation of Russell's philosophy of science as a whole. A condensation of this sort does not do justice to the subtlety of Russell's work; I can only hope that in summarizing I have not distorted.

1

To uncover the foundation upon which our knowledge rests, Russell turns to our beliefs based on experience, our "knowledge" of things in the world, of other people, of actions and of events, and asks whether or not this knowledge is as trustworthy as we usually assume it to be. Russell is looking for knowledge that is "basic" in the sense of being "certain" (or almost certain) which can serve as premises for the remainder of our beliefs. Not only does he hope to determine what is actually, certainly, known in experience, but using this as a foundation, to reorder our knowledge, to "reconstruct" it, so that its basis is clear at every stage, and any assumptions or inferences can be clearly seen. However, our ordinary "knowledge" of people, animals, buildings, and the like proves not to be the "basic" knowledge he seeks. Familiar epistemological arguments, such as those concerning the scientific causes and the relativity of perception, lead Russell to believe that we immediately experience sense-data, percepts, not public material objects. On this point Russell follows the classical British empirical tradition. That which we perceive or immediately experience he called in his earlier writings "sense-data" or "sensations"; in his later writings he prefers the term "percepts." Sense-data or percepts are subjective, fragmentary, momentary, shapes, colors, noises, smells, tastes, bodily feelings; they are known "indubitably," "immediately," and are "certain," known "without inference." Such sense-data (including some facts of memory and of introspection) Russell accepts as our basic data, the foundation upon which the rest of our knowledge should be shown to rest.

The most important characteristic of sense-data is what Russell saw to be their "certainty." Although Russell speaks of sense-data themselves as "certain," I believe this is merely to be brief; the matter, as Russell recognizes, is more complex than this. It is beliefs about sense-data that are certain, and the sense-data themselves provide the complete evidence for making those beliefs certain. For Russell, "certainty" points primarily to the fact that sense-data are "immediately" known, known without inference, or at least involve minimal inference. However, Russell's interpretation of the certainty of sense-data does exhibit some variations; in his later writings he finds it conceivable that sense-data may not be entirely certain, although they are at least as nearly certain as any of our beliefs.

To say that sense-data are immediately known is to say that their being present to a perceiver is complete evidence for beliefs concerning them. Any belief which extends beyond the evidence would be an inference and not immediate knowledge. Consciously inferred beliefs clearly constitute examples of inference, but so also are those beliefs which in Russell's terms are "spontaneous," "physiological," or "animal" inferences, e.g., interpretations of given sensations. Thus we have a noise sense-datum, on the basis of which we believe there is a car passing outside. We have "unconsciously" interpreted our heard sense-datum as a car, thus "inferred" that there was a car passing outside. At what point inference, physiological or otherwise, begins and sense-data end cannot be clearly defined. The vagueness of the borderline does not for Russell invalidate the distinction between sense-data and inference, since in most cases he sees the inferred element to be fairly obvious. In contrast to beliefs which are inferred, sense-data can then be the hardest core of beliefs.

There are two general classes of inferred beliefs with which Russell is especially concerned; those referring to the existence of common-sense material objects, and those about scientific entities. His aim is to identify the basis of knowledge for each kind, and then to make clear the inferences involved and their justification at every stage. During the logical atomism period Russell tried to reduce the number of inferred entities, and corresponding inferences, to a minimum; he later found that this could be done only at the cost of presenting a philosophical view which is implausible, and his task then became one of merely exhibiting the inferences involved in statements about scientific or common-sense entities and proposing a justification for them. Actually, he never carried this program out in great detail, but was content to outline how such a justification might proceed.

Besides the sense-data, or percepts, which provide us with the secure base, there are two other important sources of empirical knowledge, universals and the *a priori* truths of logic. The kind of knowledge we have in "knowing" or being aware of sense-data, Russell (at least in his earlier writings) called "acquaintance." In some sense of "acquaintance" we are also acquainted with universals, though in precisely what sense I am not clear. As for logical truths, these are tautologies, analytic, and not derived from experience.

In Russell's philosophy of science there is no problem concerning the justification of mathematics. In his logical work, Russell was devoted to the construction of a logical system within which mathematics could be derived, hence making mathematics derivative from logic, or a "part" of it. Since basic logical truths were accepted as *a priori,* mathematics rested for Russell on an *a priori* base. Thus for Russell, mathematics becomes a purely formal science posing no questions concerning an origin in experience. Parts of mathematics, e.g., geometry, insofar as they have an application to the world, are seen as resembling empirical sciences and are treated as such.

In summary, for Russell it is neither common-sense knowledge nor scientific knowledge which gives us "certain" knowledge, but rather sense-data, and universals, together with logical truths. Russell has little doubt that much of our common-sense and scientific knowledge is true, but he sees it as needing to be "justified" in the sense of making clear its derivation from the "certain" base. Science is held to be in large part true in the everyday sense that one can have confidence in the statements in science texts. One can distinguish between the highly confirmed parts of the science and those that are to some extent controversial. Controversy usually concerns more recently proposed theories, or the most inclusive higher-level theories. Thus generalizations such as "copper conducts electricity" and "water freezes at 32° F" (assuming appropriate conditions) are firmly established, while theories as to the origin of the universe are highly controversial. Justifying the truth of scientific statements would show how they are based on sense-data, our "certain" knowledge, and exhibit the patterns of inference involved in moving beyond sense-data. This task requires an analysis of the scientific terms employed to determine their meaning and relation to sense-data and to identify the kinds of entities (if any) to which they refer.

It may be argued with some justice that Russell's assumption that science is in large part "true" is prejudging one of the basic points in the philosophic analysis of science. It is debatable in the philosophy of science whether scientific laws and theories can be said to be "true" in any sense; rather, they may just be useful instruments. According to an instrumentalist view, laws and theories are symbolic devices, useful tools in predicting future experience, useful in dealing with our environment. A similar view is that laws and theories are "rules of inference," by which, given various antecedent states of affairs, we can infer future objects or events. During the logical atomism period, Russell seems to approach this latter view. At this period scientific statements are interpreted in terms of sense-data, and are "true" only of constructions out of sense-data. In his later view, however, scientific statements are true when interpreted as holding for certain structures of external, independent events. Russell took neither common-sense statements nor scientific ones as true in the literal sense that objects exist in the real world with just the properties predicated of them in the corresponding statements. "True" for Russell involves the relation of an interpretation of scientific entities to sense-data or (in his later theory) to events.

Russell's assertion of the "truth" of science is most revealing as a reflection of two of his basic philosophical convictions: (1) Throughout his philosophic career Russell maintained some form of the correspondence theory of truth, and consistently opposed pragmatic or instrumentalist notions of truth. He had little sympathy or understanding for the instrumentalist or pragmatist. (2) Especially in his later period the assertion that science is "true" signified the existence of objects of some kind in the "external" world. The basic importance in Russell's assertion that science is "true" is thus its indication of his commitment to a realist view which holds that there are real external objects and events which causally interact and affect each other and that science is true in that it in some manner "corresponds" to these objects and events.

2

Possibly the most significant feature of Russell's philosophy of science is his theory of descriptions and the adaptation he made of it in the "logical constructions" he applied to the analysis of scientific statements. Early in the century after Russell became converted from idealism to realism, his answer to problems of ontology was relatively simple. "Whatever may be an object of thought, or may occur in any true or false proposition, or can be counted as *one*, I call a *term*. . . . A man, a moment, a number, a class, a relation, a chimaera, or anything else that can be mentioned, is sure to be a term . . ." (*Principles of Mathematics*, 1903, p. 43). This principle makes the task of analysis relatively straightforward; the nonlogical terms of common-sense and scientific statements are seen as referring to existent entities of one kind or another, whether numbers, things, or chimaeras. Actually, I find it rather odd that this principle should be in such sweeping terms in the *Principles of Mathematics*, since one of the principal accomplishments of that book was to define cardinal numbers in terms of classes of classes. "Number" so "reduced" to class was no longer an entity with Being.

Russell's philosophy for the next dozen or so years represents an important stage in the development of logical analysis. At first it had seemed clear to Russell that every nonlogical term in a proposition corresponds to a real entity, but the definition of number showed that there might be exceptions. His theory of definite descriptions, which achieved its final formulation in *Principia Mathematica*, led him to believe that in many cases it could not be assumed that the components of statements or propositions invariably corresponded to metaphysically real entities. It then became clear that he must "analyze" statements to determine the real entities referred to by them and the nature of the reality to which they correspond. "Analysis" more recently has seemed to many to be a more strictly linguistic enterprise, with some philosophers associating no ontological implications whatever with it; but, though analysis as Russell practiced it clearly had linguistic effects, as in the theory of descriptions, its metaphysical aspect was always important to him. Analysis had the result of reducing the number of kinds of entities he believed it necessary to assume, e.g., he found there need be no "object described," no "number," no "class," and no material objects of the common-sense variety. It is conceivable that analysis might have shown that there are actually more kinds of things than one had at first supposed, but this was not Russell's conclusion. One might also argue that the logical analysis of statements is not in itself sufficient ground for assuming, or denying, the existence of various kinds of entities without the support of other metaphysical or epistemological considerations, but Russell maintains that if analysis shows the assumption of a kind of entity unnecessary, then lacking any grounds in favor of its assumption, we do not need to assume it exists.

The theory of definite descriptions provides an analysis of statements whose superficial subject is a descriptive phrase. Thus, in "the house across the street is made of red brick" it is "the house across the street" which is the apparent subject. If "the house across the street" is symbolized $(\imath x)(Gx)$ then, letting "B" be "made of red brick," the entire statement would become $B_{(\imath x)(Gx)}$. In Russell's view, if a term can be an argument for a function, as values of x are for Fx, then these values or terms must in some sense exist. If these values are people, animals, or known objects of some other kind, there is no problem, since such objects exist in the ordinary sense of the word. Without analysis one might be tempted to extend his ontology to say that since numbers, or objects described, or scientific entities, seem to be values for variables, then these entities may be presumed to exist also. Thus in the description above, since $(\imath x)(Gx)$ is a value for Bx, $(\imath x)(Gx)$ would be assumed to be an existent entity. However, numbers and scientific entities clearly do not exist in the manner of houses and people, and descriptive phrases do not refer in the same way as do names or purely denotative phrases. The "object" (if any) referred to by a descriptive phrase is a different one from the object referred to by a name. Either ordinary existence must be granted some odd entities, or we must have a special indeterminate sort of existence for odd entities, or analysis must offer a third alternative.

Russell, of course, turned to analysis, as he had in the case of numbers. Statements in which $(\imath x)(Gx)$ occurs are analyzed by the theory of descriptions as equivalent to statements in which this term does not occur, but only concepts (functions) and their arguments occur. Thus on a preliminary level, "the house across the street is made of red brick" instead of being symbolized $B_{(\imath x)(Gx)}$, becomes $(\exists x)(H_x.A_x.B_x)$, or "there is an x such that it is a house, is across the street, and is made of red brick" (with additional restrictions ensuring that there is one and only one value of x satisfying the expression). Now the values satisfying x are material objects such as the object which is the house across the street, and we need admit no such ontologically queer things as "the x which is so-and-so." (If there is no value satisfying the x in the description, or in the example above, if there is no house across the street, or some of the other functions in the expression are not satisfied, the expression is simply false.)

I mentioned that this was only a "preliminary" analysis. When Russell discusses the theory of descriptions, either informally or in its most rigorous development in *Principia Mathematica*, he uses examples similar to mine. Yet when he is primarily concerned with epistemological and metaphysical questions, it is clear that he does not believe ordinary material objects exist as such, but that in their place we have classes of "particulars" or sense-data. Thus in the complete analysis of my example the values of x would be sense-data, arguments for functions which serve to make them members of a group of sense-data which we call the material object in question. It is a pity that Russell never worked out the formal details of this "deeper" analysis, but was content with a general, informal, exposition. The principle, however, seems clear; the values of variables must be entities which are or may be directly known by us, or, as he puts it, known by "acquaintance."

Thus Russell's view of empirical knowledge is that it is based upon sense-data. Like many other empiricists, he believed that what we know of material objects can be wholly expressed in terms of sense-data, e.g., this piece of paper upon which I write can be described in terms of the white sense-datum I am having, the visual datum of size, the tactile and visual data of smoothness; for other objects, cars, say, the visual sense-data are more varied, are associated with data from other senses such as sound when the car is moving, and possibly smell. The inference from such data to a permanent material object causing the sense-data, or to even more remote scientific objects is the problematic inference which Russell is concerned to examine and if necessary to "justify." The theory of descriptions is an example of a technique of "logical constructions" which gave him an analytical tool for resolving such problems of inference. In his earlier, logical atomism period, he found that logical constructions from sense-data could be used to replace common-sense material objects and scientific objects, thus making scientific laws "true" of groups of sense-data and obviating the need to justify inferences to "external" objects.

If material objects are by analysis found to be logical constructions then an accounting must be forthcoming for the belief in the permanence, objectivity, and publicity of these external objects. This common-sense belief offers an explanation of the relative continuity of our sense-data, and also of the fact that different observers have similar sense-data. Russell sees the belief in permanence to be accounted for entirely by means of sense-data if one realizes that what an observer means by "objective" or "public" is that other observers may have sense-data similar to his, or if they vary from his (as do sense-data of the perceived shape observed from different points of view), such variations could correlate with his in accord with the usual principles of perspective. "Permanence" is to mean simply that other observers and myself will receive sense-data at a later time very similar to those we can receive now. If we simply call these sets of sense-data "this piece of paper" we can say everything that we could if we had assumed a piece of paper which is "permanent," "objective," and "public" in the naïve sense.

However, the popular supposition of a permanent object serves one further purpose, that of enabling us to speak of objects when no one is experiencing them, or of speaking of them under conditions of observation where no one is observing them. To allow for this on the sense-data hypothesis, Russell adds to the previous set of sense-data all those sense-data which *would* be seen if some observer were present under appropriate conditions at some place or time where no observer in fact is situated. These are called "hypothetical" or "ideal" sense-data, projected or calculated on the basis of sense-data which in fact some observer has. The resultant inclusive set of sense-data will serve all the purposes of the supposed permanent, public, material object, and, if Russell's analysis is sound, the inference to the existence of the material object can be dispensed with as serving no useful purpose. The basic argument for the analysis can be put quite briefly: everything that can be said about a material object can be said wholly in terms of sense-data.

Material objects, like descriptions, thus become "logical constructions." If this view of material objects were developed formally, then statements referring to material objects and taking objects as values of variables, would be equivalent to statements in which the variables take only sense-data as values, and are arguments for functions or relations between sense-data. The sets of arguments for these functions or relations would be classes of sense-data and would serve all the purposes which the supposed material object served. Unfortunately Russell never gave anything more than a general account of how this construction might be carried out. Since the time he formulated this view, philosophers of a phenomenalist persuasion have given more thorough and detailed accounts of the replacement of material objects by sense-data. Many other philosophers have found the success of such accounts dubious. Rather than pursue general criticisms of phenomenalism, I shall consider several difficulties peculiar to Russell's version.

One of Russell's original problems was the possible justification of inferences from sense-data to material objects and scientific entities. In avoiding the assumption of common-sense material objects, he made the inference to their existence unnecessary, but several "risky" inferences still remain. The belief in the sense-data of others is essential for his analysis, but a belief in "other minds" is an inference that, in turn, needs justifying. Further, we must infer the existence of un-perceived or "ideal" sense-data. It might be argued that this latter inference seems little improvement over that to material objects. However, in reply, it could be maintained that the inference to material objects is an inference to a different kind of entity, one that cannot be directly perceived, while "ideal" sense-data at least are much the same kind of thing as known sense-data.

"Ideal" sense-data, however, raise other difficulties. Ordinary sense-data are existent entities with definite ontological status; "ideal" sense-data are held to share in this status to some extent, although it is never clear to me in exactly what way. It does seem clear, however, that they are held by Russell to be in some sense *real*. Thus at one time he calls them "sensibilia" that have the same "metaphysical and physical status as sense-data without necessarily being data to any mind" ("The Relation of Sense-Data to Physics," 1914, *Mysticism and Logic*, p. 148). Although material objects may be known only, if at all, by inference, it might seem a questionable advance to substitute for them entities of such a puzzling nature.

Other phenomenalists have avoided this difficulty by explicitly avoiding any metaphysical questions and talking in purely linguistic terms. To such phenomenalists Russell's analysis of material objects would be viewed as one which substitutes statements expressed in terms of sense-data for statements using material object terms. Russell's work has been very useful for philosophers of this persuasion, and his work can be easily adapted by ignoring his metaphysical discussions. The limitation of this interpretation is that it raises for those of a realist persuasion the embarrassing question of what we are talking about when we use material object terms and sense-data terms. Russell never accepted a purely linguistic approach to philosophy and believed that statements in terms of sense-data were really referring to some kind of thing called "sense-data" whose reality in some sense or other he never doubted.

Not only common-sense material objects but scientific entities can be "replaced" by logical constructions. Russell's best-known examples are of points and instants, which he "constructs" by several methods. The general procedure can be briefly explained as follows: consider a series of overlapping areas (or of durations of time). With more and more members added to the series, the area (or duration) common to the members becomes smaller and smaller. One might assume that this series has a limit and take that limit to be a point (or an instant), but this would then leave us with the problem of determining whether such a limit is an entity, and if so, what kind. Instead, if one simply takes the series itself as the point (or instant), then expressions apparently referring to points or instants can be replaced by expressions referring only to these series of areas or durations. Russell shows that such an analysis satisfies all the usual logical and mathematical uses of points and instants. This analysis is a "logical construction" since no "unknown" or "inferred" entity, point or instant, need be assumed to exist, but only known entities, visual areas, or durations.

This method of constructing points and instants can be divorced more easily from Russell's general philosophical aims than most other aspects of his philosophy of science. The method can be viewed as a way of giving an empirical interpretation to points and instants as they occur in mathematics or science. It would no longer on this interpretation be necessary to consider whether points and instants really exist as independent entities, nor would the constructions have to be restricted to sense-data for basic materials. Areas and durations can be given a wider meaning than Russell accepted, and the construction may be viewed as a procedure for correlating points and instants to empirical subject-matter.

3

In his earlier philosophy of science, Russell defined material objects and scientific entities in terms of sense-data. Common-sense objects and scientific entities were based on sense-data in the obvious sense of being nothing other than classes of sense-data. The "truth" of common sense and science became "truth" about sets of sense-data and their relationships, although the constructions themselves required inferences that were considerably less than certain. However, Russell did not maintain this view for long. He abandoned it for a view closer to the realism of common sense, a realism to which he had subscribed before his phenomenalist period. One factor causing this change was the difficulty with unperceived sense-data which I have already mentioned. Another and probably more important factor is the implausibility of accounts of physical causation under a phenomenalist account of the world. Objects seem to affect other objects and to produce changes in them. There seem to be causative agents involved in changes that cannot be accounted for by mere sequences of sense-data.

A causal theory of perception on the other hand is a natural and plausible explanation of our perceptions and the changes in them. A cat, for example, comes into the room and is noticed by several observers. The fact that the different observers have similar sense-data is not explained by the phenomenalist account, but their similar sense-data are merely collected. The causal theory assumes a real object, or series of events, that can affect all observers present. The cat is hungry, is fed, and washes itself. Again, there is a series of events, food before cat, cat eating, and all observers have similar sense-data. The change in the cat's behavior from discontent to satisfaction is brought about by a change in a real object, causing corresponding changes in the sense-data of the observers. This, to Russell, is a more convincing explanation than one in terms of various inexplicable changes in sequences of an individual's sense-data. Finally, a causal theory unlike a phenomenalistic description can account for mechanical perceiving devices, cameras, and recording devices.

In Russell's interpretation in this later period, however, the "external" causes of our perceptions are not large-scale "things" such as tables and rocks, or even subatomic particles. We are not to assume that be-

cause we have a group of percepts, e.g., "rock," that
its external correlate is like them, or even that our
percept "red" corresponds to some external "red" thing
in the same sense. What we can assume is that changes
in our percepts are correlated with changes in external
events; at least this seems to Russell a safe assumption, although there may very well be changes in external events which are not reflected by corresponding changes in our percepts (e.g., the movement of
bacteria in a glass of water). The similarity between
our percepts and their external causes is seen as a
similarity of structure.

The world, to Russell at this time, is constituted
by a multitude of events, many of them grouped
around "centers." These we can call "objects." They
have "lines" or "chains" of events radiating outwards
from them which can intersect, or react, with lines
from other events, or with observers. When they encounter an observer with appropriate sensory appa-
ratus, the last event in the chain is a percept. Changes
in the intervening medium, or in the physiological
state of the observer, effect modifications in the later
events of a chain; the group of events composed of
the percept, the preceding events in the chain including those near the "center," are now the "object." The
causal laws of science are interpreted as based on the
interrelations between various chains of events. Material objects and scientific entities are still "constructions," because they are not *one* thing, but are the set
of events that compose various chains of events radiating outward from a center. The observer's percepts
are included as a subclass of these events. The mind
consists of still different chains of events, connected
by "mental" relations, among them memory. The difference between mental and physical is one of ar-
rangement, some chains of events are "mental," different chains are "physical"; this is not an intrinsic
difference between kinds of events.

Some readers may believe that constructions have

lost some of their significance in this later period. In the logical atomism period, constructions made it possible to substitute classes of sense-data for external objects. Now, since Russell has admitted external events, constructions can serve no such radical purpose. They still, however, enable us to substitute statements referring to classes of entities in place of statements referring to *an* entity of a particular kind—material object or scientific entity. The constructions have a further interest in that objects are not only classes of physical events, but include percepts (sense-data) as well. Thus percepts become literally parts of material objects or of scientific entities; we do not have events constituting physical objects on the one hand and the observer's percepts *of* that object on the other, but rather the object is constituted by a group of events which includes percepts. It might be argued that this is no great advantage. Whereas on some views one has to explain how physical objects can affect a completely different type of thing, namely, a mind, and produce sense-data in it, Russell has the problem of explaining how some events (nonpercepts) can be so unlike other events (percepts) in the chain and yet affect them causally. However, it is, I think, some improvement that the problem is no longer stated in the old metaphysical terms of matter versus mind, but in more straightforward terms of causal relationships between different events.

There is an obvious difference between this later view of the philosophy of science and that of the logical atomism period, but to my mind the difference is not as great as might at first sight appear. In both periods he was attempting to reconcile perception and science, with the further goal of basing both science and common-sense knowledge as far as possible on the "certain" (or nearly certain) knowledge gained from perception. In both periods he sought to reveal, or if possible eliminate, the "risky" inferences from perceptual knowledge. In the earlier period he placed greater stress on the "certainty" aspect, interpreting science in terms of sense-data, even at the expense of plausibility; in his later writings he placed more stress on the plausibility of ordinary common-sense views of science and less stress on certainty. A great difference in theory is thus brought about by a relatively small shift in emphasis.

In the earlier period, the reconciliation between perception and science is brought about by accepting sense-data as ultimately real, and interpreting common-sense and scientific objects wholly in terms of sense-data; the reconciliation in the later view takes place by accepting external events as real and maintaining (1) that although there is no need to doubt percepts, their role is not that of presenting an accurate picture of external physical reality; (2) that the common-sense belief in permanent, relatively large, external objects cannot be accepted without modification; and finally (3) that science is true if interpreted according to Russell's picture of the world as composed of events. In consequence, percepts are seen to correspond at least in basic structural characteristics with the external events which have caused them, common sense is found to be correct in proposing that there are external causes for our percepts (although these are to be interpreted as series of events, rather than as one single, permanent object), and the series of events now provides an interpretation of science which preserves its truth.

However, the inferences from percepts to these chains of events are not by themselves "certain." To remedy this Russell developed, in *Human Knowledge* (1948) and later in *My Philosophical Development* (1959), several postulates whose acceptance would justify the inference to events. Among these is one postulate that asserts the existence of causal lines (i.e., causal sequences of events), one that maintains spatio-temporal continuity, and one that maintains that structurally similar complexes of events close to each other have a common series of causal lines as origin, and one of analogy. The postulates appear to be a re-statement, now as rules of inference, of the principal points of Russell's view of the world, and the word "postulate" itself may very well suggest a claim weaker than Russell wishes to make or feels is justi-fied. If I understand Russell, the purpose of these pos-tulates is to show that in a particular inference from percepts to some definite causal chain, the particular inference is justified by the postulate that in general such causal lines exist. With the aid of the postulates we are to infer from our percepts to the chains of events in the external world, and conversely, from those events to our percepts. An analogous situation would be the naïve realist who maintained that we perceive objects with exactly the qualities they in fact possess. The naïve realist, paralleling Russell, could adopt a postulate of "directly perceivable objects." Then if he had percepts of a green rug, with the aid of his postulate, "in perception I directly perceive real objects with just the qualities I perceive them to have," he could justify his inference to "I see a real rug which is in fact green like my perception."

The justification of the postulates themselves, and of Russell's view of the world (which comes to the same thing), rests on the fact that his interpretation of science and common sense reconciles perception with science and common-sense beliefs. In Russell's estimation his theory performs this reconciliation more successfully than alternative views.

4

To a contemporary philosopher, is Russell's phi-losophy of science anything more than a historical curi-osity, a milestone passed? I have in the course of dis-cussion indicated a number of reservations to specific points in Russell's theory, but I do not believe these justify an outright dismissal of it. In spite of the reser-vations indicated and other criticisms, I believe Russell's theory has more than historical interest for the present.

It might be argued that Russell's sense-data epistemology, or in fact any sense-data epistemology, is outdated and untenable. Since Russell's work is based upon such an epistemology, it too might be judged untenable. It is not my purpose to debate the usefulness of sense-data theories of knowledge, though we may note that they still have their advocates. However, even if it were granted that a sense-data epistemology is unsound, and in spite of the reasons Russell himself advanced for rejecting his logical atomism view, I believe Russell's work could be reinterpreted in such a way as still to be of value. As I mentioned in discussing Russell's logical atomism view, if one does not accept his interpretation of sense-data, it is possible to reinterpret his constructions in linguistic terms so that they become procedures for substituting statements referring to the individual's sense experience for statements purporting to refer to material objects. So reinterpreted, the theory might seem plausible and familiar to many phenomenalist writers. We can, in short, neglecting epistemological and metaphysical issues, look upon Russell's view as a means of talking entirely in observational or experiential terms rather than in material object or scientific terms. In addition, the view has its appeal, if for no other reason, at least for the remarkable skill and ingenuity it displays.

When we come to Russell's later philosophy of science, we can, I think, again minimize specific epistemological doctrines. Objects are here held to be causal chains of events; Russell's epistemological view is that the percept is the last event in the chain, and that we "infer" the other events from it. The interpretation of objects as chains of events is of interest independently of a specific theory of perception and is compatible with either Russell's view of perception or some modification of it. There seem, for example, to be good reasons for holding that, though the last event in the causal chain is a percept which constitutes the observer's "seeing," yet *what* he sees may be some earlier event in the chain. However, the chain of events theory of objects may be evaluated and be of interest without commitment to a definite theory of perception.

It is unfortunate that Russell's later theories are stated only in very general terms, with little indication of how they could actually be applied. In his earlier and his later view he carried out the construction of points and instants and in the *Analysis of Matter* of other entities as well. They are not, however, formalized in symbolic terms, as is the theory of descriptions, and it would be interesting to see this done. Russell believed, perhaps overoptimistically, that the direction in which one should proceed is clear and that the details can be worked out by anyone who wishes to do so.

Not only are Russell's later views stated in a general way, but a certain speculative cast to his writing may put off a contemporary reader. It is a type of philosophy which may very well not appeal to those who favor precise, detailed arguments of carefully formulated issues (such readers would prefer Russell's theory of descriptions), nor by those who are primarily interested in problems of language. The grand plan for his philosophy of science is to resolve the problem of the relation of observation, common-sense truths, and scientific laws. To offer a compelling argument against his theory one must show that it fails in its purpose or one must present a more successful alternative theory. Until we find such an alternative, and even then, Russell's theory will command respect as a skillful and persuasive reconciliation of common sense and science.

BERTRAND RUSSELL'S LOGIC

G. Kreisel

Those who are interested in Russell's logic at all will surely have looked at his own lucid expositions, for instance his charming *Introduction to Mathematical Philosophy*. And those interested in the circumstances in which the work was done will have read the first volume of his autobiography and his earlier essays on his intellectual development. I, for one, certainly cannot improve on Russell's own accounts.

What can perhaps be done is to try and supplement these accounts from a different point of view.

As far as his logic is concerned, the obvious question to ask is how it looks to us, or at least some of us, sixty years later. Russell himself did not write about this matter at all, and as far as I know did not speculate about it. But to judge both from G. H. Hardy's "A Mathematician's Apology" and from my own conversations with Russell, he was concerned about it.

As far as atmosphere is concerned, the atmosphere in which his logical work was done, I have of course no direct information. But I can draw attention to some accounts which complement Russell's own writings.

I do not think that the facts or overt actions of the period are in doubt. All this is found in Russell's writings. But, attractive as they are, with their robust Victorian style, there is something missing for our present way of thinking. Somehow there isn't much awareness of an unconscious, least of all in himself.

I think much more of it is found in the accounts of the period by Russell's contemporaries or near con-

This paper was read on 5th March 1970 to the Hume Society, Stanford University, at a symposium on the life and works of Bertrand Russell. It is published for the first time in this volume.

temporaries, such as the economist Lord Keynes, the philosopher C. D. Broad, the mathematician G. H. Hardy, and to some extent the historian Trevelyan. These accounts are more highly charged, more Edwardian. The English Edwardians seem to have discovered a bit of an unconscious, different no doubt from Freud's version, which fits middle-aged Viennese housewives so well.

I can add one thing that may be useful. It so happens that in my student days at Trinity (Cambridge), Russell's old college, I had personal contact with the contemporaries mentioned. Now, descriptions of atmosphere require sensitivity and other perfectly objective but simply rare talents. One will attach weight to such descriptions only if one trusts the author. God knows, personal contact doesn't always increase one's trust in people's judgment. But at least retrospectively I find that my personal contact with this group has definitely given me more confidence, and thus helped me to form a more vivid and, I believe, more complete picture of the period of Russell's work on logic. It is just possible that some of you who may have overlooked this material will share my impression.

Naturally, in these circumstances I couldn't help hearing of little-known events, for example those related to Russell's pacifism in the First World War. But it seems natural to reserve such anecdotes, or stories of my own meetings with Russell, for Question Time. It is always difficult to make a selection from isolated stories; why not wait till somebody expresses a specific interest?

Logic

Russell was a pioneer. So his work did not depend on a great deal of previous knowledge. Indeed, it is easy to say what it was about.

The question was: What is mathematics?

The proposed answer was to be given in *logical*

terms, involving such general concepts as *object* or *thing, proposition* or *property* and operations on these concepts, so-called *logical operations*. It could not reasonably be expected that familiar mathematical experience would become more certain in this way, but more understandable from a theoretical point of view. A hackneyed but good parallel is the *atomic theory* to answer the question: *What is matter?* Evidently, just as we don't have detailed knowledge of atoms when we start, so we do not expect to start with too detailed knowledge of general logical ideas. But equally obviously, it would be idle to start if one had nothing definite, no laws at all to build on.

What Russell had to build on were two great and by now well-known contributions of the nineteenth century, now almost a hundred years old, Frege's *logical language* and Cantor's *theory of classes*. The logical language—⊃, λ, v, ∃, ∀ —is an unexpected discovery: an extraordinarily simple vocabulary to express the logically significant aspects of our thoughts. Not *all* significant ones, because not all of them are *logically* significant. It's something to be compared to the discovery that physically significant quantities can be expressed in terms of *mass, length,* and *time.* As to Cantor's theory of classes, fortunately we live in the era of the New Maths; so Cantor's theory of classes or sets need not be explained. Whatever weaknesses the New Maths may have for learning mathematics, it's an excellent preparation for listening to a popular exposition of Russell's logic.

When we now look back at these two discoveries, no single application of them can compare in interest to the discoveries themselves. This was very different when Russell entered the scene. To seize the imagination, to get sense and direction, a *general scheme needs problems; either* problems from outside which are understandable without the notions of the theory and solved by means of the theory, *or* problems within the theory to pinpoint its weaknesses and to show where it needs attention. Russell provided both sorts of problems.

The first kind of problem concerned a quite modest but perfectly intelligible puzzle. Its solution, by Russell's theory of descriptions, gives a good idea of the kind of uses one could make of a logical language. The puzzle is this:

Is it true that the King of France is bald?

Obviously one can survive without giving a second thought to the puzzle. There is no King of France, so what are you talking about? One ignores the question, or, if one prefers current jargon, one dubs it as meaningless (and continues to ignore it). In short, in the ordinary sense of the word, it isn't necessary to consider the question. The philosophical question is different. Not whether it is necessary, but whether it is possible to make something of the question. This is a luxury, an intellectual luxury. (But then, at least in an Age of Affluence, men do not live by bread alone.) Russell gave an analysis by essential use of logical language. The King of France is bald if and only if

There is a unique object which has two properties: first, of being King of France, second, of being bald.

Evidently this assertion is plainly *false*, because there is no object which is King of France, let alone a unique object which is both King of France and also bald.

Naturally, if today we want to illustrate the use of logical language, we wouldn't quote a mere puzzle. One might recommend, say, Sacks's lecture at Berkeley tomorrow. But given some imagination, one could see in Russell's analysis a hint of something that works, so to speak, on its own steam.

As an example of the second kind of problem, of pinpointing a weakness in the general theory, we have Russell's famous paradox. (I mean a weakness in the theory, current at his time, of the logical concepts to be used for answering the question: What is mathematics?) Let me say a word about it, not only because of its intrinsic interest, but also because popular expositions are quite different from the way Russell himself looked at it, according to his autobiography.

I mentioned earlier on the logical vocabulary in terms of which the question: What is mathematics? was to be answered. One of these terms is the relation, usually called ϵ, where $a \in b$ means: the object a has the property b (if b is a property), or the object a belongs to the class b, or simply a is a b.

If you do logic, if you want to answer the grand question in logical terms, you are supposed to understand this relation. Frege's logical language tells you how to build up logically complicated expressions from it.

But before we have a theory, we must have *laws*, principles for forming new objects, in particular new classes from given ones. A very tempting principle was:

Given a property P defined in logical language, form the class of *all objects* which have the property P.

In the normal course of events the principle is certainly something quite simple, e.g., the class of people in this room under 5′5″. The empty class, I suppose, under 3″. But by no stretch of the imagination could one say that the principle above is very clear. We are not talking of concrete properties, but of *logical* ones. The hallmark of a logical property is its generality. So the objects which might satisfy such a property can be anything under the sun, objects of the past, present, future, etc.

It is one thing to be mildly uncomfortable about it. But this is very different from finding a clear-cut error. Russell considered the property of objects:

$$X \notin X$$

and derived a contradiction. Put slightly more positively, he showed: To any class C satisfying the condition: if $X \in C$ then $X \notin X$, there is a class bigger than C, namely C ∪ {C}, which also satisfies the condition.

The paradox is superficially similar to the puzzle solved by the theory of descriptions. In the latter, we had the odd phrase "The king of France"; here we have "The class of all classes that don't belong to themselves." There Russell could retranslate the odd phrase in a natural way. Here he needed more than a rephrasing (for his aim of setting up a genuine theory of classes).

A very obvious reason for being disturbed by the paradox was not slightly hysterical, but quite serious.

Having got accustomed to the principle, people had not considered the possibility of needing others; they were unprepared. They did not look for others (I called the principle tempting, and I suppose temptation often makes one forget alternatives. Sometimes of course it draws attention to new ones). Russell, in contrast to many, was not panicky, and did look for alternatives.

The result, the so-called *doctrine of types*, has dominated the subject for the last sixty years. The idea is quite simple. We don't mix cabbages and kings. More seriously, the idea was that objects present themselves in a hierarchy, objects which are not classes at all (say of type o); classes of such objects, say of type 1, and so on. There are refinements of this, concerning also the *definitions* of these classes. But the basic idea is that possible members of a class have a uniform type.

It is fair to say that Russell lost interest in the idea. I do not mean he rejected it, but that he lost interest. And I think it's intelligible. Surely a universe laid out in such types is more manageable. But as a philosopher he could not be satisfied because our actual mathematical experience does not present itself in this way. At this stage the mathematicians took over, in particular Zermelo, in a way typical of mathematics. Leaving aside the question of an analysis of actual objects, the mathematicians considered those objects, or rather some of those objects, which are built up in the way Russell postulated. The greater clarity of the structure makes it indeed manageable, satisfying remarkable formal laws. It is in fact nothing else but the current theory of sets, the foundation of the bulk of existing mathematical practice.

The reason just given for Russell's loss of interest is sheer speculation. But it seems more convincing than his own reason. He was, he said, exhausted and disgusted after the labor of writing *Principia*.[1] This would hardly explain his permanent loss of interest.

This has brought us to *Principia*, the work containing the evidence for Russell's answer to the question: What is mathematics? It does not make exciting reading; in fact, it is not read, and its details are never quoted. I believe its role is parallel to that of other massive studies behind the answers to grand questions such as: What is gravity? Remember the massive experimental work of Eötvös which showed that gravity is universal, independent of the color, shape, or chemical composition of the objects. Nobody looks at the details, but the existence of this work has shaped an important part of our whole view of the physical world.

Similarly, it may fairly be said that the existence of the *Principia* has shaped the modern mathematician's view of his own subject and, even more, his exposition, what he says about it. For better or for worse, every text begins with a chapter on set theory even if this chapter is not referred to again in the rest of the text. The chapter on sets is there essentially because the *Principia* says that this is what mathematics is about.

[1] *The Autobiography of Bertrand Russell*, Vol. I, London, Allen & Unwin, pp. 152–53, 156, 164.

THE LOGICIST FOUNDATIONS OF MATHEMATICS

Rudolf Carnap

The problem of the logical and epistemological foundations of mathematics has not yet been completely solved. This problem vitally concerns both mathematicians and philosophers, for any uncertainty in the foundations of the "most certain of all the sciences" is extremely disconcerting. Of the various attempts already made to solve the problem none can be said to have resolved every difficulty. These efforts, the leading ideas of which will be presented in these three papers, have taken essentially three directions: *Logicism,* the chief proponent of which is Russell; *Intuitionism,* advocated by Brouwer; and Hilbert's *Formalism.*

Since I wish to draw you a rough sketch of the salient features of the logicist construction of mathematics, I think I should not only point out those areas in which the logicist program has been completely or at least partly successful but also call attention to the difficulties peculiar to this approach. One of the most important questions for the foundations of mathematics is that of the relation between mathematics and logic. *Logicism* is the thesis that mathematics is reducible to logic, hence nothing but a part of logic. Frege was the first to espouse this view (1884). In their great work, *Principia Mathematica,* the English mathematicians A. N. Whitehead and B. Russell pro-

This essay first appeared in *Erkenntnis,* 1931, p. 91 ff. It was translated by Erna Putnam and Gerald J. Massey and reprinted in *Philosophy of Mathematics: Selected Readings,* ed. by Paul Benacerraf and Hilary Putnam, Engelwood Cliffs, N.J.: Prentice-Hall, © 1964. It is reprinted by permission of Mrs. Thost-Carnap and Prentice-Hall, Inc.

duced a systematization of logic from which they constructed mathematics.

We will split the logicist thesis into two parts for separate discussion:

1. The *concepts* of mathematics can be derived from logical concepts through explicit definitions.
2. The *theorems* of mathematics can be derived from logical axioms through purely logical deduction.

I. The Derivation of Mathematical Concepts

To make precise the thesis that the concepts of mathematics are derivable from logical concepts, we must specify the logical concepts to be employed in the derivation. They are the following: In propositional calculus, which deals with the relations between unanalyzed sentences, the most important concepts are: the negation of a sentence p, 'not-p' (symbolized '$\sim p$'); the disjunction of two sentences, 'p or q' ('$p \vee q$'); the conjunction, 'p and q' ('$p \cdot q$'); and the implication, 'if p, then q' ('$p \supset q$'). The concepts of functional calculus are given in the form of functions, e.g., '$f(a)$' (read 'f of a') signifies that the property f belongs to the object a. The most important concepts of functional calculus are universality and existence: '$(x)f(x)$' (read 'for every x, f of x') means that the property f belongs to every object; '$(\exists x)f(x)$' (read 'there is an x such that f of x') means that f belongs to at least one object. Finally there is the concept of identity: '$a = b$' means that 'a' and 'b' are names of the same object.

Not all these concepts need be taken as undefined or primitive, for some of them are reducible to others. For example, '$p \vee q$' can be defined as '$\sim(\sim p \cdot \sim q)$' and '$(\exists x)f(x)$' as '$\sim(x)\sim f(x)$'. It is the logicist thesis, then, that the logical concepts just given suffice to define all mathematical concepts, that over and above them no specifically mathematical concepts are required for the construction of mathematics.

Already before Frege, mathematicians in their investigations of the interdependence of mathematical concepts had shown, though often without being able to provide precise definitions, that all the concepts of arithmetic are reducible to the natural numbers (i.e., the numbers 1, 2, 3, . . . which are used in ordinary counting). Accordingly, the *main problem* which remained for logicism was to derive the natural numbers from logical concepts. Although Frege had already found a solution to this problem, Russell and Whitehead reached the same results independently of him and were subsequently the first to recognize the agreement of their work with Frege's. The crux of this solution is the correct recognition of the logical status of the natural numbers; they are logical attributes which belong, not to things, but to concepts. That a certain number, say 3, is the number of a concept means that three objects fall under it. We can express the very same thing with the help of the logical concepts previously given. For example, let '$2_m(f)$' mean that at least two objects fall under the concept f. Then we can define this concept as follows (where '$=_{Df}$' is the symbol for definition, read as "means by definition"):

$$2_m(f) =_{Df} (\exists x)(\exists y)[\sim(x = y) \cdot f(x) \cdot f(y)]$$

or in words: there is an x and there is a y such that x is not identical with y and f belongs to x and f belongs to y. In like manner, we define 3_m, 4_m, and so on. Then we define the number two itself thus:

$$2(f) =_{Df} 2_m(f) \cdot \sim 3_m(f)$$

or in words: at least two, but not at least three, objects fall under f. We can also define arithmetical operations quite easily. For example, we can define addition with the help of the disjunction of two mutually exclusive concepts. Furthermore, we can define the concept of natural number itself.

The derivation of the other kinds of numbers—i.e., the positive and negative numbers, the fractions, the real and the complex numbers—is accomplished, not in the usual way by adding to the domain of the natural numbers, but by the construction of a completely new domain. The natural numbers do not constitute a subset of the fractions but are merely correlated in obvious fashion with certain fractions. Thus the natural number 3 and the fraction $\frac{3}{1}$ are not identical but merely correlated with one another. Similarly we must distinguish the fraction $\frac{1}{2}$ from the real number correlated with it. In this paper, we will treat only the definition of the real numbers. Unlike the derivations of the other kinds of numbers which encounter no great difficulties, the derivation of the real numbers presents problems which, it must be admitted, neither logicism, intuitionism, nor formalism has altogether overcome.

Let us assume that we have already constructed the series of fractions (ordered according to magnitude). Our task, then, is to supply definitions of the real numbers based on this series. Some of the real numbers, the rationals, correspond in obvious fashion to fractions; the rest, the irrationals, correspond as Dedekind showed (1872) to "gaps" in the series of fractions. Suppose, for example, that we divide the (positive) fractions into two classes, the class of all whose square is less than 2, and the class comprising all the rest of the fractions. This division forms a "cut" in the series of fractions which corresponds to the irrational real number $\sqrt{2}$. This cut is called a "gap" since there is no fraction correlated with it. As there is no fraction whose square is two, the first or "lower" class contains no greatest member, and the second or "upper" class contains no least member. Hence, to every real number there corresponds a cut in the series of fractions, each irrational real number being correlated with a gap.

Russell developed further Dedekind's line of thought. Since a cut is uniquely determined by its "lower" class, Russell defined a real number as the lower class of the corresponding cut in the series of fractions. For example, $\sqrt{2}$ is defined as the class (or property) of those fractions whose square is less than two, and the rational real number $\frac{1}{3}$ is defined as the class of all fractions smaller than the fraction $\frac{1}{3}$. On the basis of these definitions, the entire arithmetic of the real numbers can be developed. This development, however, runs up against certain difficulties connected with so-called "impredicative definition," which we will discuss shortly.

The essential point of this method of introducing the real numbers is that they are *not postulated but constructed*. The logicist does not establish the existence of structures which have the properties of the real numbers by laying down axioms or postulates; rather, through explicit definitions, he produces logical constructions that have, by virtue of these definitions, the usual properties of the real numbers. As there are no "creative definitions," definition is not creation but only name-giving to something whose existence has already been established.

In similarly constructivistic fashion, the logicist introduces the rest of the concepts of mathematics, those of analysis (e.g., convergence, limit, continuity, differential, quotient, integral, etc.) and also those of set theory (notably the concepts of the transfinite cardinal and ordinal numbers). This "constructivistic" method forms part of the very texture of logicism.

II. The Derivation of the Theorems of Mathematics

The second thesis of logicism is that the *theorems of mathematics* are derivable from logical axioms

through logical deduction. The requisite system of
logical axioms, obtained by simplifying Russell's system, contains four axioms of propositional calculus
and two of functional calculus. The rules of inference
are a rule of substitution and a rule of implication
(the *modus ponens* of ancient logic). Hilbert and
Ackermann have used these same axioms and rules of
inference in their system.

Mathematical predicates are introduced by explicit
definitions. Since an explicit definition is nothing but
a convention to employ a new, usually much shorter,
way of writing something, the *definiens* or the new
way of writing it can always be eliminated. Therefore, as every sentence of mathematics can be translated into a sentence which contains only the primitive
logical predicates already mentioned, this second thesis can be restated thus: Every provable mathematical
sentence is translatable into a sentence which contains only primitive logical symbols and which is provable in logic.

But the derivation of the theorems of mathematics
poses certain difficulties for logicism. In the first place
it turns out that some theorems of arithmetic and set
theory, if interpreted in the usual way, require for
their proof besides the logical axioms still other special
axioms known as the *axiom of infinity* and the *axiom
of choice* (or multiplicative axiom). The axiom of infinity states that for every natural number there is a
greater one. The axiom of choice states that for every
set of disjoint non-empty sets, there is (at least) one
selection-set, i.e., a set that has exactly one member
in common with each of the member sets. But we are
not concerned here with the content of these axioms
but with their logical character. Both are existential
sentences. Hence, Russell was right in hesitating to
present them as logical axioms, for logic deals only
with possible entities and cannot make assertions
about whether something does or does not exist. Russell found a way out of this difficulty. He reasoned

The Logicist Foundations of Mathematics 181

that since mathematics was also a purely formal science, it too could make only conditional, not categorical, statements about existence: if certain structures exist, then there also exist certain other structures whose existence follows logically from the existence of the former. For this reason he transformed a mathematical sentence, say S, the proof of which required the axiom of infinity, I, or the axiom of choice, C, into a conditional sentence; hence S is taken to assert not S, but $I \supset S$ or $C \supset S$, respectively. This conditional sentence is then derivable from the axioms of logic.

A greater difficulty, perhaps the greatest difficulty, in the construction of mathematics has to do with another axiom posited by Russell, the so-called *axiom of reducibility*, which has justly become the main bone of contention for the critics of the system of *Principia Mathematica*. We agree with the opponents of logicism that it is inadmissible to take it as an axiom. As we will discuss more fully later, the gap created by the removal of this axiom has certainly not yet been filled in an entirely satisfactory way. This difficulty is bound up with Russell's *theory of types* which we shall now briefly discuss.

We must distinguish between a "simple theory of types" and a "ramified theory of types." The latter was developed by Russell but later recognized by Ramsey to be an unnecessary complication of the former. If, for the sake of simplicity, we restrict our attention to one-place functions (properties) and abstract from many-place functions (relations), then type theory consists in the following classification of expressions into different "types": To type 0 belong the names of the objects ("individuals") of the domain of discourse (e.g., a, b, . . .). To type 1 belong the properties of these objects (e.g., $f(a)$, $g(a)$, . . .). To type 2 belong the properties of these properties (e.g., $F(f)$, $G(f)$, . . .); for example, the concept $2(f)$ defined above belongs to this type. To type 3 belong the properties of properties of properties, and so on. The basic rule of type theory is that every predicate belongs to a determinate type and can be meaningfully applied only to expressions of the next lower type. Accordingly, sentences of the form $f(a)$, $F(f)$, $2(f)$ are always meaningful, i.e., either true or false; on the other hand combinations like $f(g)$ and $f(F)$ are neither true nor false but meaningless. In particular, expressions like $f(f)$ or $\sim f(f)$ are meaningless, i.e., we cannot meaningfully say of a property either that it belongs to itself or that it does not. As we shall see, this last result is important for the elimination of the antinomies.

This completes our outline of the simple theory of types, which most proponents of modern logic consider legitimate and necessary. In his system, Russell introduced the ramified theory of types, which has not found much acceptance. In this theory the properties of each type are further subdivided into "orders." This division is based, not on the kind of objects to which the property belongs, but on the form of the definition which introduces it. Later we shall consider the reasons why Russell believed this further ramification necessary. Because of the introduction of the ramified theory of types, certain difficulties arose in the construction of mathematics, especially in the theory of real numbers. Many fundamental theorems not only could not be proved but could not even be expressed. To overcome this difficulty, Russell had to use brute force; i.e., he introduced the axiom of reducibility by means of which the different orders of a type could be reduced in certain respects to the lowest order of the type. The sole justification for this axiom was the fact that there seemed to be no other way out of this particular difficulty engendered by the ramified theory of types. Later Russell himself, influenced by Wittgenstein's sharp criticism, abandoned the axiom of reducibility in the second edition of *Principia Mathematica* (1925). But, as he still believed that one could not get along without the ramified theory of types, he despaired of the situation. Thus we see how important it would be, not only for logicism but for any attempt to solve the problems of the foundations of mathematics, to show that the simple theory of types is sufficient for the construction of mathematics out of logic. A young English mathematician and pupil of Russell, Ramsey (who unfortunately died this year, i.e., 1930), in 1926 made some efforts in this direction which we will discuss later.

III. *The Problem of Impredicative Definition*

To ascertain whether the simple theory of types is sufficient or must be further ramified, we must first of all examine the reasons which induced Russell to adopt this ramification in spite of its most undesirable consequences. There were two closely connected reasons: the necessity of eliminating the logical antinomies and the so-called "vicious circle" principle. We call "logical antinomies" the contradictions which first appeared in set theory (as so-called "paradoxes") but which Russell showed to be common to all logic. It can be shown that these contradictions arise in logic if the theory of types is not presupposed. The simplest antinomy is that of the concept "impredicable." By definition a property is "impredicable" if it does not belong to itself. Now is the property "impredicable" itself impredicable? If we assume that it is, then since it belongs to itself it would be, according to the definition of "impredicable," not impredicable. If we assume that it is not impredicable, then it does not belong to itself and hence, according to the definition of "impredicable," is impredicable. According to the law of excluded middle, it is either impredicable or not, but both alternatives lead to a contradiction. Another example is Grelling's antinomy of the concept "heterological." Except that it concerns predicates rather than properties, this antinomy is completely analogous to the one just described. By definition, a

predicate is "heterological" if the property designated
by the predicate does not belong to the predicate itself. (For example, the word "monosyllabic" is heterological, for the word itself is not monosyllabic.)
Obviously both the assumption that the word "heterological" is itself heterological as well as the opposite
assumption lead to a contradiction. Russell and other
logicians have constructed numerous antinomies of
this kind.

Ramsey has shown that there are two completely
different kinds of antinomies. Those belonging to the
first kind can be expressed in logical symbols and are
called "logical antinomies" (in the narrower sense).
The "impredicable" antinomy is of this kind. Ramsey
has shown that this kind of antinomy is eliminated by
the simple theory of types. The concept "impredicable," for example, cannot even be defined if the
simple theory of types is presupposed, for an expression of the form, a property does not belong to itself
$(\sim f(f))$, is not well-formed, and meaningless according to that theory.

Antinomies of the second kind are known as "semantical" or "epistemological" antinomies. They include our previous example, "heterological," as well
as the antinomy, well-known to mathematicians, of
the smallest natural number which cannot be defined
in German with fewer than 100 letters. Ramsey has
shown that antinomies of this second kind cannot be
constructed in the symbolic language of logic and
therefore need not be taken into account in the construction of mathematics from logic. The fact that they
appear in word languages led Russell to impose certain restrictions on logic in order to eliminate them,
viz., the ramified theory of types. But perhaps their
appearance is due to some defect of our ordinary word
language.

Since antinomies of the first kind are already eliminated by the simple theory of types and those of the
second kind do not appear in logic, Ramsey declared

that the ramified theory of types and hence also the axiom of reducibility were superfluous.

Now what about Russell's second reason for ramifying the theory of types, viz., the vicious circle principle? This principle, that "no whole may contain parts which are definable only in terms of that whole," may also be called an "injunction against impredicative definition." A definition is said to be "impredicative" if it defines a concept in terms of a totality to which the concept belongs. (The concept "impredicative" has nothing to do with the aforementioned pseudo concept "impredicable.") Russell's main reason for laying down this injunction was his belief that antinomies arise when it is violated. From a somewhat different standpoint Poincaré before, and Weyl after, Russell also rejected impredicative definition. They pointed out that an impredicatively defined concept was meaningless because of the circularity in its definition. An example will perhaps make the matter clearer:

We can define the concept "inductive number" (which corresponds to the concept of natural number including zero) as follows: A number is said to be "inductive" if it possesses all the hereditary properties of zero. A property is said to be "hereditary" if it always belongs to the number $n + 1$ whenever it belongs to the number n. In symbols,

$$\text{Ind}(x) =_{\text{Df}} (f)[(\text{Her}(f) \cdot f(0)) \supset f(x)]$$

To show that this definition is circular and useless, one usually argues as follows: In the *definiens* the expression '(f)' occurs, i.e., "for all properties (of numbers)." But since the property "inductive" belongs to the class of all properties, the very property to be defined already occurs in a hidden way in the *definiens* and thus is to be defined in terms of itself, an obviously inadmissible procedure. It is sometimes claimed that the meaninglessness of an impredicatively defined concept is seen most clearly if one tries to establish whether the concept holds in an individual case. For example, to ascertain whether the number three is inductive, we must, according to the definition, investigate whether every property which is hereditary and belongs to zero also belongs to three. But if we must do this for every property, we must also do it for the property "inductive" which is also a property of numbers. Therefore, in order to determine whether the number three is inductive, we must determine among other things whether the property "inductive" is hereditary, whether it belongs to zero, and finally—this is the crucial point—whether it belongs to three. But this means that it would be impossible to determine whether three is an inductive number.

Before we consider how Ramsey tried to refute this line of thought, we must get clear about how these considerations led Russell to the ramified theory of types. Russell reasoned in this way: Since it is inadmissible to define a property in terms of an expression which refers to "all properties," we must subdivide the properties (of type 1): To the "first order" belong those properties in whose definition the expression "all properties" does not occur; to the "second order" those in whose definition the expression "all properties of the first order" occurs; to the "third order" those in whose definition the expression "all properties of the second order" occurs, and so on. Since the expression "all properties" without reference to a determinate order is held to be inadmissible, there never occurs in the definition of a property a totality to which it itself belongs. The property "inductive," for example, is defined in this no longer impredicative way: A number is said to be "inductive" if it possesses all the hereditary properties of the first order which belong to zero.

But the ramified theory of types gives rise to formidable difficulties in the treatment of the real numbers. As we have already seen, a real number is defined as a class, or what comes to the same thing, as a property of fractions. For example, we saw that $\sqrt{2}$

is defined as the class or property of those fractions whose square is less than two. But since the expression "for all properties" without reference to a determinate order is inadmissible under the ramified theory of types, the expression "for all real numbers" cannot refer to all real numbers without qualification but only to the real numbers of a determinate order. To the first order belong those real numbers in whose definition an expression of the form "for all real numbers" does not occur; to the second order belong those in whose definition such an expression occurs, but this expression must be restricted to "all real numbers of the first order," and so on. Thus there can be neither an admissible definition nor an admissible sentence which refers to all real numbers without qualification.

But as a consequence of this ramification, many of the most important definitions and theorems of real number theory are lost. Once Russell had recognized that his earlier attempt to overcome it, viz., the introduction of the axiom of reducibility, was itself inadmissible, he saw no way out of this difficulty. The *most difficult problem* confronting contemporary studies in the foundations of mathematics is this: How can we develop logic if, on the one hand, we are to avoid the danger of the meaninglessness of impredicative definitions and, on the other hand, are to reconstruct satisfactorily the theory of real numbers?

IV. *Attempt at a Solution*

Ramsey (1926) outlined a construction of mathematics in which he courageously tried to resolve this difficulty by declaring the forbidden impredicative definitions to be perfectly admissible. They contain, he contended, a circle but the circle is harmless, not vicious. Consider, he said, the description "the tallest man in this room." Here we describe something in terms of a totality to which it itself belongs. Still no one thinks this description inadmissible since the person described already exists and is only singled out, not created, by the description. Ramsey believed that the same considerations applied to properties. The totality of properties already exists in itself. That we men are finite beings who cannot name individually each of infinitely many properties but can describe some of them only with reference to the totality of all properties is an empirical fact that has nothing to do with logic. For these reasons Ramsey allows impredicative definition. Consequently, he can both get along with the simple theory of types and still retain all the requisite mathematical definitions, particularly those needed for the theory of the real numbers.

Although this happy result is certainly tempting, I think we should not let ourselves be seduced by it into accepting Ramsey's basic premise; viz., that the totality of properties already exists before their characterization by definition. Such a conception, I believe, is not far removed from a belief in a platonic realm of ideas which exist in themselves, independently of *if* and *how* finite human beings are able to think them. I think we ought to hold fast to Frege's dictum that, in mathematics, only that may be taken to exist whose existence has been proved (and he meant proved in finitely many steps). I agree with the intuitionists that the finiteness of every logical-mathematical operation, proof, and definition is not required because of some accidental empirical fact about man but is required by the very nature of the subject. Because of this attitude, intuitionist mathematics has been called "anthropological mathematics." It seems to me that, by analogy, we should call Ramsey's mathematics "theological mathematics," for when he speaks of the totality of properties he elevates himself above the actually knowable and definable and in certain respects reasons from the standpoint of an infinite mind which is not bound by the wretched necessity of building every structure step by step.

We may now rephrase our crucial question thus:

Can we have Ramsey's result without retaining his absolutist conceptions? His result was this: Limitation to the simple theory of types and retention of the possibility of definitions for mathematical concepts, particularly in real number theory. We can reach this result if, like Ramsey, we allow impredicative definition, but can we do this without falling into his conceptual absolutism? I will try to give an affirmative answer to this question.

Let us go back to the example of the property "inductive" for which we gave an impredicative definition:

$$\operatorname{Ind}(x) = {}_{\mathrm{Df}}(f)[(\operatorname{Her}(f) \cdot f(\mathrm{o})) \supset f(x)]$$

Let us examine once again whether the use of this definition, i.e., establishing whether the concept holds in an individual case or not, really leads to circularity and is therefore impossible. According to this definition, that the number two is inductive means:

$$(f)[(\operatorname{Her}(f) \cdot f(\mathrm{o})) \supset f(2)]$$

in words: Every property f which is hereditary and belongs to zero belongs also to two. How can we verify a universal statement of this kind? If we had to examine every single property, an unbreakable circle would indeed result, for then we would run headlong against the property "inductive." Establishing whether something had it would then be impossible in principle, and the concept would therefore be meaningless. But the verification of a universal logical or mathematical sentence does not consist in running through a series of individual cases, for impredicative definitions usually refer to infinite totalities. The belief that we must run through all the individual cases rests on a confusion of "numerical" generality, which refers to objects already given, with "specific" generality.[1] We

---

[1] Cf. F. Kaufmann, *Das Unendliche in der Mathematik und seine Ausschaltung* (Vienna, 1930).

do not establish specific generality by running through
individual cases but by logically deriving certain properties from certain others. In our example, that the
number two is inductive means that the property "belonging to two" follows logically from the property
"being hereditary and belonging to zero." In symbols,
'$f(2)$' can be derived for an arbitrary f from 'Her(f) ·
$f(0)$' by logical operations. This is indeed the case.
First, the derivation of '$f(0)$' from 'Her(f) · $f(0)$' is
trivial and proves the inductiveness of the number
zero. The remaining steps are based on the definition
of the concept "hereditary":

$$\text{Her}(f) =_{\text{Df}} (n)[f(n) \supset f(n+1)]$$

Using this definition, we can easily show that '$f(0 +
1)$' and hence '$f(1)$' are derivable from 'Her(f) · $f(0)$'
and thereby prove that the number one is inductive.
Using this result and our definition, we can derive
'$f(1 + 1)$' and hence '$f(2)$' from 'Her(f) · $f(0)$',
thereby showing that the number two is inductive.
We see then that the definition of inductiveness, although impredicative, does not hinder its utility. That
proofs that the defined property obtains (or does not
obtain) in individual cases can be given shows that
the definition is meaningful. If we reject the belief
that it is necessary to run through individual cases and
rather make it clear to ourselves that the complete
verification of a statement about an arbitrary property
means nothing more than its logical (more exactly,
tautological) validity for an arbitrary property, we
will come to the conclusion that impredicative definitions are logically admissible. If a property is defined
impredicatively, then establishing whether or not it
obtains in an individual case may, under certain circumstances, be difficult, or it may even be impossible
if there is no solution to the decision problem for that
logical system. But in no way does impredicativeness
make such decisions impossible in principle for all
cases. If the theory just sketched proves feasible, logi-

cism will have been helped over its greatest difficulty, which consists in steering a safe course between the Scylla of the axiom of reducibility and the Charybdis of the allocation of the real numbers to different orders.

Logicism as here described has several features in common both with intuitionism and with formalism. It shares with intuitionism a constructivistic tendency with respect to definition, a tendency which Frege also emphatically endorsed. A concept may not be introduced axiomatically but must be constructed from undefined, primitive concepts step by step through explicit definitions. The admission of impredicative definitions seems at first glance to run counter to this tendency, but this is only true for constructions of the form proposed by Ramsey. Like the intuitionists, we recognize as properties only those expressions (more precisely, expressions of the form of a sentence containing one free variable) which are constructed in finitely many steps from undefined primitive properties of the appropriate domain according to determinate rules of construction. The difference between us lies in the fact that we recognize as valid not only the rules of construction which the intuitionists use (the rules of the so-called "strict functional calculus"), but in addition, permit the use of the expression "for all properties" (the operations of the so-called "extended functional calculus").

Further, logicism has a methodological affinity with formalism. Logicism proposes to construct the logical-mathematical system in such a way that, although the axioms and rules of inference are chosen with an interpretation of the primitive symbols in mind, nevertheless, *inside the system* the chains of deductions and of definitions are carried through formally as in a pure calculus, i.e., without reference to the meaning of the primitive symbols.

RUSSELL'S MATHEMATICAL LOGIC*

Kurt Gödel

Mathematical Logic, which is nothing else but a precise and complete formulation of formal logic, has two quite different aspects. On the one hand, it is a section of Mathematics treating of classes, relations, combinations of symbols, etc., instead of numbers, functions, geometric figures, etc. On the other hand, it is a science prior to all others, which contains the ideas and principles underlying all sciences. It was in this second sense that Mathematical Logic was first conceived by Leibniz in his *Characteristica universalis,* of which it would have formed a central part. But it was almost two centuries after his death before his idea of a logi-

This essay first appeared in *The Philosophy of Bertrand Russell* in the Library of Living Philosophers, ed. by P. A. Schilpp, La Salle, Ill.: The Open Court Publishing Co. It is reprinted by permission of the author and the publishers.

* The author wishes to note (1) that since the original publication of this paper, advances have been made in some of the problems discussed and that the formulations given could be improved in several places, and (2) that the term "constructivistic" in this paper is used for a strictly nominalistic kind of constructivism such as that embodied in Russell's "no class theory." Its meaning, therefore, is very different from that used in current discussions on the foundations of mathematics, i.e., from both "intuitionistically admissible" and "constructive" in the sense of the Hilbert school. Both these schools base their constructions on a mathematical intuition whose avoidance is exactly one of the principal aims of Russell's constructivism (see the first alternative in the last sentence of footnote 23 below). What, in Russell's own opinion, can be obtained by his constructivism (which might better be called fictionalism) is the system of finite orders of the ramified hierarchy without the axiom of infinity for individuals. The explanation of the term "constructive" given in footnote 22 below is to be replaced by the remarks just made.

cal calculus really sufficient for the kind of reasoning occurring in the exact sciences was put into effect (in some form at least, if not the one Leibniz had in mind) by Frege and Peano.[1] Frege was chiefly interested in the analysis of thought and used his calculus in the first place for deriving arithmetic from pure logic. Peano, on the other hand, was more interested in its applications within mathematics and created an elegant and flexible symbolism, which permits expressing even the most complicated mathematical theorems in a perfectly precise and often very concise manner by single formulas.

It was in this line of thought of Frege and Peano that Russell's work set in. Frege, in consequence of his painstaking analysis of the proofs, had not gotten beyond the most elementary properties of the series of integers, while Peano had accomplished a big collection of mathematical theorems expressed in the new symbolism, but without proofs. It was only in *Principia Mathematica* that full use was made of the new method for actually deriving large parts of mathematics from a very few logical concepts and axioms. In addition, the young science was enriched by a new instrument, the abstract theory of relations. The calculus of relations had been developed before by Peirce and Schröder, but only with certain restrictions and in too close analogy with the algebra of numbers. In *Principia* not only Cantor's set theory but also ordinary arithmetic and the theory of measurement are treated from this abstract relational standpoint.

It is to be regretted that this first comprehensive and thorough-going presentation of a mathematical logic and the derivation of Mathematics from it is so greatly lacking in formal precision in the foundations (contained in *1–*21 of *Principia*), that it presents in this

[1] Frege has doubtless the priority, since his first publication about the subject, which already contains all the essentials, appeared ten years before Peano's.

respect a considerable step backwards as compared
with Frege. What is missing, above all, is a precise
statement of the syntax of the formalism. Syntactical
considerations are omitted even in cases where they
are necessary for the cogency of the proofs, in particular in connection with the "incomplete symbols." These
are introduced not by explicit definitions, but by rules
describing how sentences containing them are to be
translated into sentences not containing them. In
order to be sure, however, that (or for what expressions) this translation is possible and uniquely determined and that (or to what extent) the rules of inference apply also to the new kind of expressions, it is
necessary to have a survey of all possible expressions,
and this can be furnished only by syntactical considerations. The matter is especially doubtful for the rule of
substitution and of replacing defined symbols by their
definiens. If this latter rule is applied to expressions
containing other defined symbols it requires that the
order of elimination of these be indifferent. This how-
ever is by no means always the case ($\varphi!\hat{u} = \hat{u}[\varphi!u]$,
e.g., is a counter-example). In *Principia* such elimina-
tions are always carried out by substitutions in the
theorems corresponding to the definitions, so that it
is chiefly the rule of substitution which would have to
be proved.

I do not want, however, to go into any more details
about either the formalism or the mathematical content of *Principia*,[2] but want to devote the subsequent
portion of this essay to Russell's work concerning the
analysis of the concepts and axioms underlying Mathematical Logic. In this field Russell has produced a
great number of interesting ideas, some of which are
presented most clearly (or are contained only) in his
earlier writings. I shall therefore frequently refer also

[2] Cf. in this respect W. V. Quine's article in the Whitehead
volume in the Library of Living Philosophers series.

to these earlier writings, although their content may partly disagree with Russell's present standpoint.

What strikes one as surprising in this field is Russell's pronouncedly realistic attitude, which manifests itself in many passages of his writings. "Logic is concerned with the real world just as truly as zoology, though with its more abstract and general features," he says, e.g., in his *Introduction to Mathematical Philosophy* (edition of 1920, p. 169). It is true, however, that this attitude has been gradually decreasing in the course of time[3] and also that it always was stronger in theory than in practice. When he started on a concrete problem, the objects to be analyzed (e.g., the classes or propositions) soon for the most part turned into "logical fictions." Though perhaps this need not necessarily mean [according to the sense in which Russell uses this term] that these things do not exist, but only that we have no direct perception of them.

The analogy between mathematics and a natural science is enlarged upon by Russell also in another respect (in one of his earlier writings). He compares the axioms of logic and mathematics with the laws of nature and logical evidence with sense perception, so that the axioms need not necessarily be evident in themselves, but rather their justification lies (exactly as in physics) in the fact that they make it possible for these "sense perceptions" to be deduced; which of course would not exclude that they also have a kind of intrinsic plausibility similar to that in physics. I think that (provided "evidence" is understood in a sufficiently strict sense) this view has been largely justified by subsequent developments, and it is to be expected that it will be still more so in the future. It has turned out that (under the assumption that modern mathematics is consistent) the solution of certain arithmetical problems requires the use of assump-

[3] The above quoted passage was left out in the later editions of the *Introduction*.

tions essentially transcending arithmetic, i.e., the domain of the kind of elementary indisputable evidence that may be most fittingly compared with sense perception. Furthermore it seems likely that for deciding certain questions of abstract set theory and even for certain related questions of the theory of real numbers new axioms based on some hitherto unknown idea will be necessary. Perhaps also the apparently insurmountable difficulties which some other mathematical problems have been presenting for many years are due to the fact that the necessary axioms have not yet been found. Of course, under these circumstances mathematics may lose a good deal of its "absolute certainty;" but, under the influence of the modern criticism of the foundations, this has already happened to a large extent. There is some resemblance between this conception of Russell and Hilbert's "supplementing the data of mathematical intuition" by such axioms as, e.g., the law of excluded middle which are not given by intuition according to Hilbert's view; the borderline, however, between data and assumptions would seem to lie in different places according to whether we follow Hilbert or Russell.

An interesting example of Russell's analysis of the fundamental logical concepts is his treatment of the definite article "the." The problem is: what do the so-called descriptive phrases (i.e., phrases as, e.g., "the author of *Waverley*" or "the king of England") denote or signify[4] and what is the meaning of sentences in which they occur? The apparently obvious answer that, e.g., "the author of *Waverley*" signifies Walter Scott, leads to unexpected difficulties. For, if we admit the further apparently obvious axiom, that the signification of a composite expression, containing constituents

---

[4] I use the term "signify" in the sequel because it corresponds to the German word *"bedeuten"* which Frege, who first treated the question under consideration, used in this connection.

which have themselves a signification, depends only on the signification of these constituents (not on the manner in which this signification is expressed), then it follows that the sentence "Scott is the author of *Waverley*" signifies the same thing as "Scott is Scott;" and this again leads almost inevitably to the conclusion that all true sentences have the same signification (as well as all false ones).[5] Frege actually drew this conclusion; and he meant it in an almost metaphysical sense, reminding one somewhat of the Eleatic doctrine of the "One." "The True"—according to Frege's view —is analyzed by us in different ways in different propositions; "the True" being the name he uses for the common signification of all true propositions.[6]

Now according to Russell, what corresponds to sentences in the outer world is facts. However, he avoids the term "signify" or "denote" and uses "indicate" instead (in his earlier papers he uses "express" or "being a symbol for"), because he holds that the relation between a sentence and a fact is quite different from that of a name to the thing named. Furthermore, he uses "denote" (instead of "signify") for the relation between things and names, so that "denote" and "indicate" together would correspond to Frege's "*bedeuten*." So, according to Russell's terminology and view, true sentences "indicate" facts and, correspondingly, false ones indicate nothing.[7] Hence Frege's theory

[5] The only further assumptions one would need in order to obtain a rigorous proof would be: 1) that "φ (a)" and the proposition "a is the object which has the property φ and is identical with a" mean the same thing and 2) that every proposition "speaks about something," i.e., can be brought to the form φ (a). Furthermore one would have to use the fact that for any two objects a. b. there exists a true proposition of the form φ (a, b) as, e.g., a $\neq$ b or a = a. b = b.

[6] Cf. "Sinn und Bedeutung," *Zeitschrift für Philosophie und philosophische Kritik*, Vol. 100 (1892), p. 35.

[7] From the indication (*Bedeutung*) of a sentence is to be distinguished what Frege called its meaning (*Sinn*) which is

would in a sense apply to false sentences, since they
all indicate the same thing, namely nothing. But different true sentences may indicate many different
things. Therefore this view concerning sentences makes
it necessary either to drop the above mentioned principle about the signification (i.e., in Russell's terminology the corresponding one about the denotation and
indication) of composite expressions or to deny that
a descriptive phrase denotes the object described. Russell did the latter[8] by taking the viewpoint that a descriptive phrase denotes nothing at all but has meaning only in context; for example, the sentence "the
author of *Waverley* is Scotch," is defined to mean:
"There exists exactly one entity who wrote *Waverley*
and whoever wrote *Waverley* is Scotch." This means
that a sentence involving the phrase "the author of
Waverley" does not (strictly speaking) assert anything
about Scott (since it contains no constituent denoting
Scott), but is only a roundabout way of asserting something about the concepts occurring in the descriptive
phrase. Russell adduces chiefly two arguments in favor
of this view, namely (1) that a descriptive phrase may
be meaningfully employed even if the object described
does not exist (e.g., in the sentence: "The present king
of France does not exist"). (2) That one may very
well understand a sentence containing a descriptive

---

the conceptual correlate of the objectively existing fact (or
"the True"). This one should expect to be in Russell's theory
a possible fact (or rather the possibility of a fact), which would
exist also in the case of a false proposition. But Russell, as he
says, could never believe that such "curious shadowy" things
really exist. Thirdly, there is also the psychological correlate
of the fact which is called "signification" and understood to be
the corresponding belief in Russell's latest book, *An Inquiry
into Meaning and Truth.* "Sentence" in contradistinction to
"proposition" is used to denote the mere combination of symbols.

[8] He made no explicit statement about the former; but it
seems it would hold for the logical system of *Principia,* though
perhaps more or less vacuously.

phrase without being acquainted with the object described; whereas it seems impossible to understand a sentence without being acquainted with the objects about which something is being asserted. The fact that Russell does not consider this whole question of the interpretation of descriptions as a matter of mere linguistic conventions, but rather as a question of right and wrong, is another example of his realistic attitude, unless perhaps he was aiming at a merely psychological investigation of the actual processes of thought. As to the question in the logical sense, I cannot help feeling that the problem raised by Frege's puzzling conclusion has only been evaded by Russell's theory of descriptions and that there is something behind it which is not yet completely understood.

There seems to be one purely formal respect in which one may give preference to Russell's theory of descriptions. By defining the meaning of sentences involving descriptions in the above manner, he avoids in his logical system any axioms about the particle "the," i.e., the analyticity of the theorems about "the" is made explicit; they can be shown to follow from the explicit definition of the meaning of sentences involving "the." Frege, on the contrary, has to assume an axiom about "the," which of course is also analytic, but only in the implicit sense that it follows from the meaning of the undefined terms. Closer examination, however, shows that this advantage of Russell's theory over Frege's subsists only as long as one interprets definitions as mere typographical abbreviations, not as introducing names for objects described by the definitions, a feature which is common to Frege and Russell.

I pass now to the most important of Russell's investigations in the field of the analysis of the concepts of formal logic, namely those concerning the logical paradoxes and their solution. By analyzing the paradoxes to which Cantor's set theory had led, he freed them from all mathematical technicalities, thus bringing to light the amazing fact that our logical intuitions (i.e., intuitions concerning such notions as: truth, concept, being, class, etc.) are self-contradictory. He then investigated where and how these common-sense assumptions of logic are to be corrected and came to the conclusion that the erroneous axiom consists in assuming that for every propositional function there exists the class of objects satisfying it, or that every propositional function exists "as a separate entity;"[9] by which is meant something separable from the argument (the idea being that propositional functions are abstracted from propositions which are primarily given) and also something distinct from the combination of symbols expressing the propositional function; it is then what one may call the notion or concept defined by it.[10] The existence of this concept already suffices for the paradoxes in their "intensional" form, where the concept of "not applying to itself" takes the place of Russell's paradoxical class.

Rejecting the existence of a class or concept in general, it remains to determine under what further hypotheses (concerning the propositional function) these entities do exist. Russell pointed out (*loc. cit.*) two possible directions in which one may look for such a criterion, which he called the zig-zag theory and

[9] In Russell's first paper about the subject: "On Some Difficulties in the Theory of Transfinite Numbers and Order Types," *Proc. London Math. Soc.*, Second Series, Vol. 4, 1906, p. 29. If one wants to bring such paradoxes as "the liar" under this viewpoint, universal (and existential) propositions must be considered to involve the class of objects to which they refer.

[10] "Propositional function" (without the clause "as a separate entity") may be understood to mean a proposition in which one or several constituents are designated as arguments. One might think that the pair consisting of the proposition and the argument could then for all purposes play the role of the "propositional function as a separate entity," but it is to be noted that this pair (as one entity) is again a set or a concept and therefore need not exist.

the theory of limitation of size, respectively, and which might perhaps more significantly be called the intensional and the extensional theory. The second one would make the existence of a class or concept depend on the extension of the propositional function (requiring that it be not too big), the first one on its content or meaning (requiring a certain kind of "simplicity," the precise formulation of which would be the problem).

The most characteristic feature of the second (as opposed to the first) would consist in the nonexistence of the universal class or (in the intensional interpretation) of the notion of "something" in an unrestricted sense. Axiomatic set theory as later developed by Zermelo and others can be considered as an elaboration of this idea as far as classes are concerned.[11] In particular the phrase "not too big" can be specified (as was shown by J. v. Neumann[12]) to mean: not equivalent with the universe of all things, or, to be more exact, a propositional function can be assumed to determine a class when and only when there exists no relation (in intension, i.e., a propositional function with two variables) which associates in a one-to-one manner with each object, an object satisfying the propositional function and vice versa. This criterion, however, does not appear as the basis of the theory but as a consequence of the axioms and inversely can replace two of the axioms (the axiom of replacement and that of choice).

For the second of Russell's suggestions too, i.e., for the zig-zag theory, there has recently been set up a logical system which shares some essential features

11 The intensional paradoxes can be dealt with, e.g., by the theory of simple types or the ramified hierarchy, which do not involve any undesirable restrictions if applied to concepts only and not to sets.

12 Cf. "Über eine Widerspruchfreiheitsfrage in der axiomatischen Mengenlehre," *Journal für reine und angewandte Mathematik*, Vol. 160, 1929, p. 227.

with this scheme, namely Quine's system.[13] It is, more-over, not unlikely that there are other interesting pos-sibilities along these lines.

Russell's own subsequent work concerning the so-lution of the paradoxes did not go in either of the two aforementioned directions pointed out by himself, but was largely based on a more radical idea, the "no-class theory," according to which classes or concepts *never* exist as real objects, and sentences containing these terms are meaningful only to such an extent as they can be interpreted as a *façon de parler*, a manner of speaking about other things (cf. p. 212). Since in *Principia* and elsewhere, however, he formulated cer-tain principles discovered in the course of the devel-opment of this theory as general logical principles without mentioning any longer their dependence on the no-class theory, I am going to treat of these prin-ciples first.

I mean in particular the vicious circle principle, which forbids a certain kind of "circularity" which is made responsible for the paradoxes. The fallacy in these, so it is contended, consists in the circumstance that one defines (or tacitly assumes) totalities, whose existence would entail the existence of certain new elements of the same totality, namely elements defin-able only in terms of the whole totality. This led to the formulation of a principle which says that "no totality can contain members definable only in terms of this totality, or members involving or presupposing this totality" [vicious circle principle]. In order to make this principle applicable to the intensional para-doxes, still another principle had to be assumed, namely that "every propositional function presupposes the totality of its values" and therefore evidently also the totality of its possible arguments.[14] [Otherwise

[13] Cf. "New Foundations for Mathematical Logic," *Amer. Math. Monthly,* Vol. 44, p. 70.

[14] Cf. *Principia Mathematica,* Vol. I, p. 39.

the concept of "not applying to itself" would presuppose no totality (since it involves no quantifications),[15] and the vicious circle principle would not prevent its application to itself.] A corresponding vicious circle principle for propositional functions which says that nothing defined in terms of a propositional function can be a possible argument of this function is then a consequence.[16] The logical system to which one is led on the basis of these principles is the theory of orders in the form adopted, e.g., in the first edition of *Principia*, according to which a propositional function which either contains quantifications referring to propositional functions of order n or can be meaningfully asserted of propositional functions of order n is at least of order $n + 1$, and the range of significance of a propositional function as well as the range of a quantifier must always be confined to a definite order.

In the second edition of *Principia*, however, it is stated in the Introduction (pp. xi and xii) that "in a limited sense" also functions of a higher order than the predicate itself (therefore also functions defined in terms of the predicate as, e.g., in p '$\kappa \varepsilon \kappa$) can appear as arguments of a predicate of functions; and in Appendix B such things occur constantly. This means that the vicious circle principle for propositional functions is virtually dropped. This change is connected with the new axiom that functions can occur in propositions only "through their values," i.e., extensionally, which has the consequence that any propositional function can take as an argument any function of appropriate type, whose extension is defined (no matter what order of quantifiers is used in the definition of this extension). There is no doubt that these things are

[15] Quantifiers are the two symbols ($\exists$ x) and (x) meaning respectively, "there exists an object x" and "for all objects x." The totality of objects x to which they refer is called their range.

[16] Cf. *Principia Mathematica*, Vol. I, p. 47, section IV.

quite unobjectionable even from the constructive standpoint (see p. 206), provided that quantifiers are always restricted to definite orders. The paradoxes are avoided by the theory of simple types,[17] which in *Principia* is combined with the theory of orders (giving as a result the "ramified hierarchy") but is entirely independent of it and has nothing to do with the vicious circle principle (cf. p. 219).

Now as to the vicious circle principle proper, as formulated on p. 202, it is first to be remarked that, corresponding to the phrases "definable only in terms of," "involving," and "presupposing," we have really three different principles, the second and third being much more plausible than the first. It is the first form which is of particular interest, because only this one makes impredicative definitions[18] impossible and thereby destroys the derivation of mathematics from logic, effected by Dedekind and Frege, and a good

[17] By the theory of simple types I mean the doctrine which says that the objects of thought (or, in another interpretation, the symbolic expressions) are divided into types, namely: individuals, properties of individuals, relations between individuals, properties of such relations, etc. (with a similar hierarchy for extensions), and that sentences of the form: "a has the property φ," "b bears the relation R to c," etc. are meaningless, if a, b, c, R, φ are not of types fitting together. Mixed types (such as classes containing individuals and classes as elements) and therefore also transfinite types (such as the class of all classes of finite types) are excluded. That the theory of simple types suffices for avoiding also the epistemological paradoxes is shown by a closer analysis of these. (Cf. F. P. Ramsey's paper, quoted in footnote 21, and A. Tarski, *Der Wahrheitsbegriff in den formalisierten Sprachen*, Stud. phil., Vol. I, Lemberg, 1935, p. 399.)

[18] These are definitions of an object α by reference to a totality to which α itself (and perhaps also things definable only in terms of α) belong. As, e.g., if one defines a class α as the intersection of all classes satisfying a certain condition φ and then concludes that α is a subset also of such classes u as are defined in terms of α (provided they satisfy φ).

deal of modern mathematics itself. It is demonstrable that the formalism of classical mathematics does not satisfy the vicious circle principle in its first form, since the axioms imply the existence of real numbers definable in this formalism only by reference to all real numbers. Since classical mathematics can be built up on the basis of *Principia* (including the axiom of reducibility), it follows that even *Principia* (in the first edition) does not satisfy the vicious circle principle in the first form, if "definable" means "definable within the system" and no methods of defining outside the system (or outside other systems of classical mathematics) are known except such as involve still more comprehensive totalities than those occurring in the systems.

I would consider this rather as a proof that the vicious circle principle is false than that classical mathematics is false, and this is indeed plausible also on its own account. For, first of all one may, on good grounds, deny that reference to a totality necessarily implies reference to all single elements of it or, in other words, that "all" means the same as an infinite logical conjunction. One may, e.g., follow Langford's and Carnap's[19] suggestion to interpret "all" as meaning analyticity or necessity or demonstrability. There are difficulties in this view; but there is no doubt that in this way the circularity of impredicative definitions disappears.

Secondly, however, even if "all" means an infinite conjunction, it seems that the vicious circle principle in its first form applies only if the entities involved are constructed by ourselves. In this case there must clearly exist a definition (namely the description of the construction) which does not refer to a totality to which the object defined belongs, because the con-

[19] See Rudolf Carnap in *Erkenntnis,* Vol. 2, p. 103 (p. 186 of this volume), and *Logical Syntax of Language,* p. 162, and C. H. Langford, *Bulletin American Mathematical Society,* Vol. 33 (1927), p. 599.

struction of a thing can certainly not be based on a totality of things to which the thing to be constructed itself belongs. If, however, it is a question of objects that exist independently of our constructions, there is nothing in the least absurd in the existence of totalities containing members, which can be described (i.e., uniquely characterized)[20] only by reference to this totality.[21] Such a state of affairs would not even contradict the second form of the vicious circle principle, since one cannot say that an object described by reference to a totality "involves" this totality, although the description itself does; nor would it contradict the third form, if "presuppose" means "presuppose for the existence" not "for the knowability."

So it seems that the vicious circle principle in its first form applies only if one takes the constructivistic (or nominalistic) standpoint[22] toward the objects of logic and mathematics, in particular toward propositions, classes and notions, e.g., if one understands by a notion a symbol together with a rule for translating sentences containing the symbol into such sentences as do not contain it, so that a separate object denoted by the symbol appears as a mere fiction.[23]

[20] An object a is said to be described by a propositional function $\varphi(x)$ if $\varphi(x)$ is true for $x = a$ and for no other object.

[21] Cf. F. P. Ramsey, "The Foundations of Mathematics," in *Proc. London Math. Soc.*, Series 2, Vol. 25 (1926), p. 338. (Reprinted in *The Foundations of Mathematics*, New York and London, 1931, p. 1.)

[22] I shall use in the sequel "constructivism" as a general term comprising both these standpoints and also such tendencies as are embodied in Russell's "no class" theory.

[23] One might think that this conception of notions is impossible, because the sentences into which one translates must also contain notions so that one would get into an infinite regress. This, however, does not preclude the possibility of maintaining the above viewpoint for all the more abstract notions, such as those of the second and higher types, or in fact for all notions except the primitive terms which might be only a very few.

Classes and concepts may, however, also be conceived as real objects, namely classes as "pluralities of things" or as structures consisting of a plurality of things and concepts as the properties and relations of things existing independently of our definitions and constructions.

It seems to me that the assumption of such objects is quite as legitimate as the assumption of physical bodies and there is quite as much reason to believe in their existence. They are in the same sense necessary to obtain a satisfactory system of mathematics as physical bodies are necessary for a satisfactory theory of our sense perceptions and in both cases it is impossible to interpret the propositions one wants to assert about these entities as propositions about the "data," i.e., in the latter case the actually occurring sense perceptions. Russell himself concludes in the last chapter of his book on *Meaning and Truth*, though "with hesitation," that there exist "universals," but apparently he wants to confine this statement to concepts of sense perceptions, which does not help the logician. I shall use the term "concept" in the sequel exclusively in this objective sense. One formal difference between the two conceptions of notions would be that any two different definitions of the form $\alpha (x) = \varphi (x)$ can be assumed to define two different notions α in the constructivistic sense. (In particular this would be the case for the nominalistic interpretation of the term "notion" suggested above, since two such definitions give different rules of translation for propositions containing α.) For concepts, on the contrary, this is by no means the case, since the same thing may be described in different ways. It might even be that the axiom of extensionality[24] or at least something near to it holds

---

[24] I.e., that no two different properties belong to exactly the same things, which, in a sense, is a counterpart to Leibniz's *Principium identitatis indiscernibilium*, which says no two different things have exactly the same properties.

for concepts. The difference may be illustrated by the following definition of the number two: "Two is the notion under which fall all pairs and nothing else." There is certainly more than one notion in the constructivistic sense satisfying this condition, but there might be one common "form" or "nature" of all pairs.

Since the vicious circle principle, in its first form does apply to constructed entities, impredicative definitions and the totality of all notions or classes or propositions are inadmissible in constructivistic logic. What an impredicative definition would require is to construct a notion by a combination of a set of notions to which the notion to be formed itself belongs. Hence if one tries to effect a retranslation of a sentence containing a symbol for such an impredicatively defined notion it turns out that what one obtains will again contain a symbol for the notion in question.[25] At least this is so if "all" means an infinite conjunction; but Carnap's and Langford's idea (mentioned on p. 205) would not help in this connection, because "demonstrability," if introduced in a manner compatible with the constructivistic standpoint towards notions, would have to be split into a hierarchy of orders, which would prevent one from obtaining the desired results.[26] As Chwistek has shown,[27] it is even possible under certain assumptions admissible within constructivistic logic to derive an actual contradiction from the unrestricted admission of impredicative definitions. To be more specific, he has shown that the system of simple types becomes contradictory if one adds the "axiom of intensionality" which says (roughly speaking) that to different definitions belong different notions. This axiom, however, as has just been pointed

[25] Cf. Carnap, *loc. cit.*, footnote 19 above.

[26] Nevertheless the scheme is interesting because it again shows the constructibility of notions which can be meaningfully asserted of notions of arbitrarily high order.

[27] See *Erkenntnis*, Vol. 3, p. 367.

out, can be assumed to hold for notions in the constructivistic sense.

Speaking of concepts, the aspect of the question is
changed completely. Since concepts are supposed to
exist objectively, there seems to be objection neither
to speaking of all of them (cf. p. 214) nor to describing some of them by reference to all (or at least all
of a given type). But, one may ask, isn't this view re-
futable also for concepts because it leads to the "absurdity" that there will exist properties φ such that
$\varphi(a)$ consists in a certain state of affairs involving all
properties (including φ itself and properties defined
in terms of φ), which would mean that the vicious
circle principle does not hold even in its second form
for concepts or propositions? There is no doubt that
the totality of all properties (or of all those of a given
type) does lead to situations of this kind, but I don't
think they contain any absurdity.[28] It is true that such
properties φ [or such propositions $\varphi(a)$] will have to
contain themselves as constituents of their content [or
of their meaning], and in fact in many ways, because
of the properties defined in terms of φ; but this only
makes it impossible to construct their meaning (i.e.,
explain it as an assertion about sense perceptions or
any other non-conceptual entities), which is no objection for one who takes the realistic standpoint. Nor is
it self-contradictory that a proper part should be identical (not merely equal) to the whole, as is seen in
the case of structures in the abstract sense. The struc-

[28] The formal system corresponding to this view would have,
instead of the axiom of reducibility, the rule of substitution for
functions described, e.g., in Hilbert-Bernays, *Grundlagen der
Mathematik*, Vol. I (1934), p. 90, applied to variables of any
type, together with certain axioms of intensionality required
by the concept of property which, however, would be weaker
than Chwistek's. It should be noted that this view does not
necessarily imply the existence of concepts which cannot be
expressed in the system, if combined with a solution of the
paradoxes along the lines indicated on p. 221.

ture of the series of integers, e.g., contains itself as
a proper part and it is easily seen that there exist also
structures containing infinitely many different parts,
each containing the whole structure as a part. In addition there exist, even within the domain of constructivistic logic, certain approximations to this self-reflex-
ivity of impredicative properties, namely propositions
which contain as parts of their meaning not themselves
but their own formal demonstrability.[29] Now formal
demonstrability of a proposition (in case the axioms
and rules of inference are correct) implies this proposition and in many cases is equivalent to it. Furthermore, there doubtlessly exist sentences referring to a
totality of sentences to which they themselves belong
as, e.g., the sentence: "Every sentence (of a given
language) contains at least one relation word."

Of course this view concerning the impredicative
properties makes it necessary to look for another solution of the paradoxes, according to which the fallacy
(i.e., the underlying erroneous axiom) does not consist in the assumption of certain self-reflexivities of the
primitive terms but in other assumptions about these.
Such a solution may be found for the present in the
simple theory of types and in the future perhaps in
the development of the ideas sketched on pp. 200 and
222. Of course, all this refers only to concepts. As to
notions in the constructivistic sense, there is no doubt
that the paradoxes are due to a vicious circle. It is not
surprising that the paradoxes should have different
solutions for different interpretations of the terms occurring.

As to classes in the sense of pluralities or totalities
it would seem that they are likewise not created but
merely described by their definitions and that therefore the vicious circle principle in the first form does

[29] Cf. my paper in *Monatshefte für Mathematik und Physik*,
Vol. 38 (1931), p. 173, or R. Carnap, *Logical Syntax of Language*, § 35.

not apply. I even think there exist interpretations of the term "class" (namely as a certain kind of structures), where it does not apply in the second form either.[30] But for the development of all contemporary mathematics one may even assume that it does apply in the second form, which for classes as mere pluralities is, indeed, a very plausible assumption. One is then led to something like Zermelo's axiom system for set theory, i.e., the sets are split up into "levels" in such a manner that only sets of lower levels can be elements of sets of higher levels (i.e., x ε y is always false if x belongs to a higher level than y). There is no reason for classes in this sense to exclude mixtures of levels in one set and transfinite levels. The place of the axiom of reducibility is now taken by the axiom of classes [Zermelo's *Aussonderungsaxiom*] which says that for each level there exists for an arbitrary propositional function φ (x) the set of those x of this level for which φ (x) is true, and this seems to be implied by the concept of classes as pluralities.

Russell adduces two reasons against the extensional view of classes, namely the existence of (1.) the null class, which cannot very well be a collection, and (2.) the unit classes, which would have to be identical with their single elements. But it seems to me that these arguments could, if anything, at most prove that the null class and the unit classes (as distinct from their only element) are fictions (introduced to simplify the calculus like the points at infinity in geometry), not that all classes are fictions.

But in Russell the paradoxes had produced a pro-

[30] Ideas tending in this direction are contained in the following papers by D. Mirimanoff: "Les antinomies de Russell et de Buraliforte et le problème fondamental de la théorie des ensembles," *L'Enseignment mathematique,* Vol. 19 (1917), pp. 37–52, and "Remarques sur la théorie des ensembles et les antinomies Cantoriennes," *L'Enseignment mathematique,* Vol. 19 (1917), pp. 209–17 and Vol. 21 (1920), pp. 29–52. Cf. in particular Vol. 19, p. 212.

nounced tendency to build up logic as far as possible without the assumption of the objective existence of such entities as classes and concepts. This led to the formulation of the aforementioned "no class theory," according to which classes and concepts were to be introduced as a *façon de parler*. But propositions, too, (in particular those involving quantifications)[31] were later on largely included in this scheme, which is but a logical consequence of this standpoint, since e.g., universal propositions as objectively existing entities evidently belong to the same category of idealistic objects as classes and concepts and lead to the same kind of paradoxes, if admitted without restrictions. As regards classes, this program was actually carried out; i.e., the rules for translating sentences containing class names or the term "class" into such as do not contain them were stated explicitly; and the basis of the theory, i.e., the domain of sentences into which one has to translate is clear, so that classes can be dispensed with (within the system *Principia*), but only if one assumes the existence of a concept whenever one wants to construct a class. When it comes to concepts and the interpretation of sentences containing this or some synonymous term, the state of affairs is by no means as clear. First of all, some of them (the primitive predicates and relations such as "red" or "colder") must apparently be considered as real objects;[32] the rest of them (in particular according to the second edition of *Principia*, all notions of a type higher than the first and therewith all logically interesting ones) appear as something constructed (i.e., as something not belonging to the "inventory" of the world); but neither the basic domain of propositions in terms of

[31] Cf. "Les paradoxes de la logique," *Rev. de Metaph. et de Morale*, Vol. 14 (1906), p. 627.

[32] In Appendix C of *Principia* a way is sketched by which these also could be constructed by means of certain similarity relations between atomic propositions, so that these latter would be the only ones remaining as real objects.

which finally everything is to be interpreted, nor the method of interpretation is as clear as in the case of classes (see below).

This whole scheme of the no-class theory is of great interest as one of the few examples, carried out in detail, of the tendency to eliminate assumptions about the existence of objects outside the "data" and to replace them by constructions on the basis of these data.[33] The result has been in this case essentially negative; i.e., the classes and concepts introduced in this way do not have all the properties required for their use in mathematics, unless one either introduces special axioms about the data (e.g., the axiom of reducibility), which in essence already mean the existence in the data of the kind of objects to be constructed, or makes the fiction that one can form propositions of infinite (and even non-denumerable) length,[34] i.e., operates with truth-functions of infinitely many arguments, regardless of whether or not one can construct them. But what else is such an infinite truth-function but a special kind of an infinite extension (or structure) and even a more complicated one than a class, endowed in addition with a hypothetical meaning, which can be understood only by an infinite mind? All this is only a verification of the view defended above that logic and mathematics (just as physics) are built up on axioms with a real content which cannot be "explained away."

What one can obtain on the basis of the constructivistic attitude is the theory of orders (cf. p. 203); only now (and this is the strong point of the theory) the restrictions involved do not appear as *ad hoc* hypotheses for avoiding the paradoxes, but as unavoidable consequences of the thesis that classes, concepts,

[33] The "data" are to be understood in a relative sense here, i.e., in our case as logic without the assumption of the existence of classes and concepts.

[34] Cf. Ramsey, *loc. cit.*, footnote 21 above.

and quantified propositions do not exist as real objects. It is not as if the universe of things were divided into orders and then one were prohibited to speak of all orders; but, on the contrary, it is possible to speak of all existing things; only, classes and concepts are not among them; and if they are introduced as a *façon de parler*, it turns out that this very extension of the symbolism gives rise to the possibility of introducing them in a more comprehensive way, and so on indefinitely. In order to carry out this scheme one must, however, presuppose arithmetic (or something equivalent) which only proves that not even this restricted logic can be built up on nothing.

In the first edition of *Principia*, where it was a question of actually building up logic and mathematics, the constructivistic attitude was, for the most part, abandoned, since the axiom of reducibility for types higher than the first together with the axiom of infinity makes it absolutely necessary that there exist primitive predicates of arbitrarily high types. What is left of the constructive attitude is only: (1.) The introduction of classes as a *façon de parler*; (2.) the definition of $\sim$, v, ., etc., as applied to propositions containing quantifiers (which incidentally proved its fecundity in a consistency proof for arithmetic); (3.) the step by step construction of functions of orders higher than 1, which, however, is superfluous owing to the axiom of reducibility; (4.) the interpretation of definitions as mere typographical abbreviations, which makes every symbol introduced by definition an incomplete symbol (not one naming an object described by the definition). But the last item is largely an illusion, because, owing to the axiom of reducibility, there always exist real objects in the form of primitive predicates, or combinations of such, corresponding to each defined symbol. Finally also Russell's theory of descriptions is something belonging to the constructivistic order of ideas.

In the second edition of *Principia* (or to be more

exact, in the introduction to it) the constructivistic attitude is resumed again. The axiom of reducibility is dropped and it is stated explicitly that all primitive predicates belong to the lowest type and that the only purpose of variables (and evidently also of constants) of higher orders and types is to make it possible to assert more complicated truth-functions of atomic propositions,[35] which is only another way of saying that the higher types and orders are solely a *façon de parler*. This statement at the same time informs us of what kind of propositions the basis of the theory is to consist, namely of truth-functions of atomic propositions.

This, however, is without difficulty only if the number of individuals and primitive predicates is finite. For the opposite case (which is chiefly of interest for the purpose of deriving mathematics) Ramsey (*loc. cit.*) took the course of considering our inability to form propositions of infinite length as a "mere accident," to be neglected by the logician. This of course solves (or rather cuts through) the difficulties; but it is to be noted that, if one disregards the difference between finite and infinite in this respect, there exists a simpler and at the same time more far reaching interpretation of set theory (and therewith of mathematics). Namely, in case of a finite number of individuals, Russell's *aperçu* that propositions about classes can be interpreted as propositions about their elements becomes literally true, since, e.g., "$x \varepsilon m$" is equivalent to "$x = a_1, \vee x = a_2 \vee \ldots \vee x = a_k$" where the a_i are the elements of m; and "there exists a class such that . . ." is equivalent to "there exist individuals $x_1, x_2, \ldots x_n$ such that . . . ,"[36] provided n is the number of individuals in the world and pro-

[35] I.e., propositions of the form $S(a)$, $R(a,b)$, etc., where S, R are primitive predicates and a, b individuals.

[36] The x_i may, of course, as always, be partly or wholly identical with each other.

vided we neglect for the moment the null class which would have to be taken care of by an additional clause. Of course, by an iteration of this procedure one can obtain classes of classes, etc., so that the logical system obtained would resemble the theory of simple types except for the circumstance that mixture of types would be possible. Axiomatic set theory appears, then, as an extrapolation of this scheme for the case of infinitely many individuals or an infinite iteration of the process of forming sets.

Ramsey's viewpoint is, of course, everything but constructivistic, unless one means constructions of an infinite mind. Russell, in the second edition of *Principia*, took a less metaphysical course by confining himself to such truth-functions as can actually be constructed. In this way one is again led to the theory of orders, which, however, appears now in a new light, namely as a method of constructing more and more complicated truth-functions of atomic propositions. But this procedure seems to presuppose arithmetic in some form or other (see next paragraph).

As to the question of how far mathematics can be built up on this basis (without any assumptions about the data—i.e., about the primitive predicates and individuals—except, as far as necessary, the axiom of infinity), it is clear that the theory of real numbers in its present form cannot be obtained.[37] As to the theory of integers, it is contended in the second edition of *Principia* that it can be obtained. The difficulty to be overcome is that in the definition of the integers as "those cardinals which belong to every class containing 0 and containing $x + 1$ if containing x," the phrase "every class" must refer to a given order. So one obtains integers of different orders, and complete induction can be applied to integers of order n only

[37] As to the question how far it is possible to build up the theory of real numbers, presupposing the integers, cf. Hermann Weyl, *Das Kontinuum*, reprinted, 1932.

for properties of order n; whereas it frequently happens that the notion of integer itself occurs in the property to which induction is applied. This notion, however, is of order n + 1 for the integers of order n. Now, in Appendix B of the second edition of *Principia*, a proof is offered that the integers of any order higher than 5 are the same as those of order 5, which of course would settle all difficulties. The proof as it stands, however, is certainly not conclusive. In the proof of the main lemma *89.16, which says that every subset α (of arbitrary high order)[38] of an inductive class β of order 3 is itself an inductive class of order 3, induction is applied to a property of β involving α [namely $\alpha-\beta\neq\Lambda$, which, however, should read $\alpha-\beta\sim\varepsilon$ Induct$_2$ because (3) is evidently false]. This property, however, is of an order > 3 if α is of an order > 3. So the question whether (or to what extent) the theory of integers can be obtained on the basis of the ramified hierarchy must be considered as unsolved at the present time. It is to be noted, however, that, even in case this question should have a positive answer, this would be of no value for the problem whether arithmetic follows from logic, if propositional functions of order n are defined (as in the second edition of *Principia*) to be certain finite (though arbitrarily complex) combinations (of quantifiers, propositional connectives, etc.), because then the notion of finiteness has to be presupposed, which fact is concealed only by taking such complicated notions as "propositional function of order n" in an unanalyzed form as primitive terms of the formalism and giving their definition only in ordinary language. The reply may perhaps be offered that in *Principia* the notion of a propositional function of order n is neither

[38] That the variable α is intended to be of undetermined order is seen from the later applications of *89.17 and from the note to *89.17. The main application is in line (2) of the proof of *89.24, where the lemma under consideration is needed for α's of arbitrarily high orders.

taken as primitive nor defined in terms of the notion of a finite combination, but rather quantifiers referring to propositional functions of order n (which is all one needs) are defined as certain infinite conjunctions and disjunctions. But then one must ask: Why doesn't one define the integers by the infinite disjunction: $x = 0 \lor x = 0 + 1 \lor x = 0 + 1 + 1 \lor \ldots$ *. ad infinitum*, saving in this way all the trouble connected with the notion of inductiveness? This whole objection would not apply if one understands by a propositional function of order n one "obtainable from such truth-functions of atomic propositions as presuppose for their definition no totalities except those of the propositional functions of order $<$ n and of individuals;" this notion, however, is somewhat lacking in precision.

The theory of orders proves more fruitful if considered from a purely mathematical standpoint, independently of the philosophical question whether impredicative definitions are admissible. Viewed in this manner, i.e., as a theory built up within the framework of ordinary mathematics, where impredicative definitions are admitted, there is no objection to extending it to arbitrarily high transfinite orders. Even if one rejects impredicative definitions, there would, I think, be no objection to extend it to such transfinite ordinals as can be constructed within the framework of finite orders. The theory in itself seems to demand such an extension since it leads automatically to the consideration of functions in whose definition one refers to all functions of finite orders, and these would be functions of order ω. Admitting transfinite orders, an axiom of reducibility can be proved. This, however, offers no help to the original purpose of the theory, because the ordinal α—such that every propositional function is extensionally equivalent to a function of order α—is so great, that it presupposes impredicative totalities. Nevertheless, so much can be accomplished in this way, that all impredicativities are reduced to one special kind, namely the existence of certain large

ordinal numbers (or, well ordered sets) and the validity of recursive reasoning for them. In particular, the
existence of a well ordered set, of order type ω_1 already suffices for the theory of real numbers. In addition, this transfinite theorem of reducibility permits
the proof of the consistency of the Axiom of Choice,
of Cantor's Continuum-Hypothesis and even of the
generalized Continuum-Hypothesis (which says that
there exists no cardinal number between the power of
any arbitrary set and the power of the set of its subsets) with the axioms of set theory as well as of *Principia*.

I now come in somewhat more detail to the theory
of simple types which appears in *Principia* as combined with the theory of orders; the former is, however (as remarked above), quite independent of the
latter, since mixed types evidently do not contradict
the vicious circle principle in any way. Accordingly,
Russell also based the theory of simple types on entirely different reasons. The reason adduced (in addition to its "consonance with common sense") is very
similar to Frege's, who, in his system, already had
assumed the theory of simple types for functions, but
failed to avoid the paradoxes, because he operated
with classes (or rather functions in extension) without any restriction. This reason is that (owing to the
variable it contains) a propositional function is something ambiguous (or, as Frege says, something unsatu-
rated, wanting supplementation) and therefore can
occur in a meaningful proposition only in such a way
that this ambiguity is eliminated (e.g., by substituting
a constant for the variable or applying quantification
to it). The consequences are that a function cannot
replace an individual in a proposition, because the
latter has no ambiguity to be removed, and that functions with different kinds of arguments (i.e., different
ambiguities) cannot replace each other; which is
the essence of the theory of simple types. Taking a
more nominalistic viewpoint (such as suggested in the

second edition of *Principia* and in *Meaning and Truth*) one would have to replace "proposition" by "sentence" in the foregoing considerations (with corresponding additional changes). But in both cases, this argument clearly belongs to the order of ideas of the "no class" theory, since it considers the notions (or propositional functions) as something constructed out of propositions or sentences by leaving one or several constituents of them undetermined. Propositional functions in this sense are, so to speak, "fragments" of propositions, which have no meaning in themselves, but only insofar as one can use them for forming propositions by combining several of them, which is possible only if they "fit together," i.e., if they are of appropriate types. But, it should be noted that the theory of simple types (in contradistinction to the vicious circle principle) cannot in a strict sense follow from the constructive standpoint, because one might construct notions and classes in another way, e.g., as indicated on p. 215, where mixtures of types are possible. If on the other hand one considers concepts as real objects, the theory of simple types is not very plausible, since what one would expect to be a concept (such as, e.g., "transitivity" or the number two) would seem to be something behind all its various "realizations" on the different levels and therefore does not exist according to the theory of types. Nevertheless, there seems to be some truth behind this idea of realizations of the same concept on various levels, and one might, therefore, expect the theory of simple types to prove useful or necessary, at least as a stepping-stone for a more satisfactory system, a way in which it has already been used by Quine.[39] Also Russell's "typical ambiguity" is a step in this direction. Since, however, it only adds certain simplifying symbolic conventions to the theory of types, it does not *de facto* go beyond this theory.

[39] *Loc. cit.*, cf. footnote 13 above.

It should be noted that the theory of types brings in a new idea for the solution of the paradoxes, especially suited to their intensional form. It consists in blaming the paradoxes not on the axiom that every propositional function defines a concept or class, but on the assumption that every concept gives a meaningful proposition, if asserted for any arbitrary object or objects as arguments. The obvious objection that every concept can be extended to all arguments, by defining another one which gives a false proposition whenever the original one was meaningless, can easily be dealt with by pointing out that the concept "meaningfully applicable" need not itself be always meaningfully applicable.

The theory of simple types (in its realistic interpretation) can be considered as a carrying through of this scheme, based, however, on the following additional assumption concerning meaningfulness: "Whenever an object x can replace another object y in one meaningful proposition, it can do so in every meaningful proposition."[40] This of course has the consequence that the objects are divided into mutually exclusive ranges of significance, each range consisting of those objects which can replace each other; and that therefore each concept is significant only for arguments belonging to one of these ranges, i.e., for an infinitely small portion of all objects. What makes the above principle particularly suspect, however, is that its very assumption makes its formulation as a meaningful proposition impossible,[41] because x and y must then be confined to definite ranges of significance which are either the same or different, and in both cases the statement does not express the principle or

[40] Russell formulates a somewhat different principle with the same effect, in *Principia*, Vol. I, p. 95.

[41] This objection does not apply to the symbolic interpretation of the theory of types, spoken of on p. 219, because there one does not have objects but only symbols of different types.

even part of it. Another consequence is that the fact that an object x is (or is not) of a given type also cannot be expressed by a meaningful proposition.

It is not impossible that the idea of limited ranges of significance could be carried out without the above restrictive principle. It might even turn out that it is possible to assume every concept to be significant everywhere except for certain "singular points" or "limiting points," so that the paradoxes would appear as something analogous to dividing by zero. Such a system would be most satisfactory in the following respect: our logical intuitions would then remain correct up to certain minor corrections, i.e., they could then be considered to give an essentially correct, only somewhat "blurred," picture of the real state of affairs. Unfortunately the attempts made in this direction have failed so far;[42] on the other hand, the impossibility of this scheme has not been proved either, in spite of the strong inconsistency theorems of Kleene and Rosser.[43]

In conclusion I want to say a few words about the question whether (and in which sense) the axioms of *Principia* can be considered to be analytic. As to this problem it is to be remarked that analyticity may be understood in two senses. First, it may have the purely formal sense that the terms occurring can be defined (either explicitly or by rules for eliminating them from sentences containing them) in such a way that the axioms and theorems become special cases of the law

[42] A formal system along these lines is Church's (cf. "A Set of Postulates for the Foundation of Logic," *Annals of Mathematics*, Vol. 33 (1932), p. 346 and Vol. 34 (1933), p. 839), where, however, the underlying idea is expressed by the somewhat misleading statement that the law of excluded middle is abandoned. However, this system has been proved to be inconsistent. See footnote 43.

[43] Cf. S. C. Kleene and J. B. Rosser, "The Inconsistency of Certain Formal Logics," *Annals of Math.*, Vol. 36 (1935), p. 630.

of identity and disprovable propositions become negations of this law. In this sense even the theory of integers is demonstrably non-analytic, provided that one
requires of the rules of elimination that they allow one
actually to carry out the elimination in a finite number
of steps in each case.[44] Leaving out this condition by
admitting, e.g., sentences of infinite (and non-denumerable) length as intermediate steps of the process
of reduction, all axioms of *Principia* (including the
axioms of choice, infinity and reducibility) could be
proved to be analytic for certain interpretations (by
considerations similar to those referred to on p.
215).[45] But this observation is of doubtful value, because the whole of mathematics as applied to sentences of infinite length has to be presupposed in order
to prove this analyticity, e.g., the axiom of choice can
be proved to be analytic only if it is assumed to be
true.

In a second sense a proposition is called analytic if
it holds, "owing to the meaning of the concepts
occurring in it," where this meaning may perhaps be
undefinable (i.e., irreducible to anything more fundamental).[46] It would seem that all axioms of *Principia,*
in the first edition (except the axiom of infinity) are
in this sense analytic for certain interpretations of
the primitive terms, namely if the term "predicative
function" is replaced either by "class" (in the extensional sense) or (leaving out the axiom of choice)
by "concept," since nothing can express better the
meaning of the term "class" than the axiom of classes
(cf. p. 210) and the axiom of choice, and since, on the

[44] Because this would imply the existence of a decision-
procedure for all arithmetical propositions. Cf. A. M. Turing,
Proc. Lond. Math. Soc., Vol. 42 (1936), p. 230.

[45] Cf. also F. P. Ramsey, *loc. cit.,* footnote 21, where,
however, the axiom of infinity cannot be obtained, because it
is interpreted to refer to the individuals in the world.

[46] The two significations of the term *analytic* might perhaps
be distinguished as tautological and analytic.

other hand, the meaning of the term "concept" seems
to imply that every propositional function defines a
concept.[47] The difficulty is only that we don't perceive the concepts of "concept" and of "class" with
sufficient distinctness, as is shown by the paradoxes.
In view of this situation, Russell took the course of
considering both classes and concepts (except the
logically uninteresting primitive predicates) as non-
existent and of replacing them by constructions of our
own. It cannot be denied that this procedure has led
to interesting ideas and to results valuable also for
one taking the opposite viewpoint. On the whole, however, the outcome has been that only fragments of
Mathematical Logic remain, unless the things condemned are reintroduced in the form of infinite propositions or by such axioms as the axiom of reducibility
which (in case of infinitely many individuals) is demonstrably false unless one assumes either the existence
of classes or of infinitely many "*qualitates occultae.*"
This seems to be an indication that one should take a
more conservative course, such as would consist in
trying to make the meaning of the terms "class" and
"concept" clearer, and to set up a consistent theory

[47] This view does not contradict the opinion defended above
that mathematics is based on axioms with a real content, because the very existence of the concept of, e.g., "class" constitutes already such an axiom; since, if one defined, e.g., "class"
and "ε" to be "the concepts satisfying the axioms," one would
be unable to prove their existence. "Concept" could perhaps
be defined in terms of "proposition" (cf. p. 220) (although I
don't think that this would be a natural procedure); but then
certain axioms about propositions, justifiable only with reference to the undefined meaning of this term, will have to be assumed. It is to be noted that this view about analyticity makes
it again possible that every mathematical proposition could perhaps be reduced to a special case of a = a, namely if the reduction is effected not in virtue of the definitions of the terms
occurring, but in virtue of their meaning, which can never be
completely expressed in a set of formal rules.

of classes and concepts as objectively existing entities. This is the course which the actual development of Mathematical Logic has been taking and which Russell himself has been forced to enter upon in the more constructive parts of his work. Major among the attempts in this direction (some of which have been quoted in this essay) are the simple theory of types (which is the system of the first edition of *Principia* in an appropriate interpretation) and axiomatic set theory, both of which have been successful at least to this extent, that they permit the derivation of modern mathematics and at the same time avoid all known paradoxes. Many symptoms show only too clearly, however, that the primitive concepts need further elucidation.

It seems reasonable to suspect that it is this incomplete understanding of the foundations which is responsible for the fact that Mathematical Logic has up to now remained so far behind the high expectations of Peano and others who (in accordance with Leibniz's claims) had hoped that it would facilitate theoretical mathematics to the same extent as the decimal system of numbers has facilitated numerical computations. For how can one expect to solve mathematical problems systematically by mere analysis of the concepts occurring, if our analysis so far does not even suffice to set up the axioms? But there is no need to give up hope. Leibniz did not in his writings about the *Characteristica universalis* speak of a utopian project; if we are to believe his words he had developed this calculus of reasoning to a large extent, but was waiting with its publication till the seed could fall on fertile ground.[48] He went even so far[49] as to

[48] *Die philosophischen Schriften von G. W. Leibniz,* herausgegeben von C. J. Gerhardt, Vol. 7 (1890), p. 12. Cf. also G. Vacca, "La logica di Leibniz" (section VII), *Riv. di Mat.,* Vol. 8 (1902–6), p. 72, and the preface in the first volume of the first series of *Leibniz's Sämtliche Briefe und Schriften,*

estimate the time which would be necessary for his calculus to be developed by a few select scientists to such an extent "that humanity would have a new kind of an instrument increasing the powers of reason far more than any optical instrument has ever aided the power of vision." The time he names is five years, and he claims that his method is not any more difficult to learn than the mathematics or philosophy of his time. Furthermore, he said repeatedly that, even in the rudimentary state to which he had developed the theory himself, it was responsible for all his mathematical discoveries; which, one should expect, even Poincaré would acknowledge as a sufficient proof of its fecundity.

---

herausgegeben von der Preussischen Akademie der Wissenschaften (1923–   ).

[49] Leibniz, *Philosophische Schriften* (ed. Gerhardt), Vol. 7, p. 187.

WHAT IS RUSSELL'S THEORY OF DESCRIPTIONS?[1]

David Kaplan

Russell expounded his theory of descriptions in a number of places, but perhaps the best-known source is his 1905 article, "On Denoting."[2] I think it may still be fruitful to discuss the doctrine of that article since some readers may disagree as to its main point.

Theories of descriptions concern the analysis of sentences containing definite descriptions. For example, "The present Queen of England is sexy," or "The least prime number is even." Let us refer to the description itself as proper or improper according as there is or is not a unique object described. Thus the descriptions "the present Queen of England" and "the least prime number" are both proper since they uniquely describe Elizabeth Windsor and two. But the descriptions "the present King of France" and "the author of *Principia Mathematica*" are improper since the first describes nothing and the second describes Russell and Whitehead equally well. The difficulties involved in the analysis of sentences containing descriptions (I will say "description" as short for "definite description") are most apparent in connection with improper descriptions. This should not be surprising, since improper descriptions are rarely used knowingly, and thus usage does not provide a clear guide. On even the most elementary question of

This essay was read at the International Colloquium on Logic, Physical Reality, and History at the University of Denver in May 1966. It was published in the Proceedings of the Colloquium, *Physics, Logic and History*, New York: The Plenum Publishing Corporation. It is included in this volume by permission of the author and the publisher. Notes appear at the end of this paper, on p. 241.

analysis, the truth value of such sentences, we find disagreements. Consider the sentence "The present King of France is bald." According to Russell's theory it is false. According to the chosen-object theory of Frege,[3] elaborated by Carnap,[4] in which all improper descriptions are treated as if they uniquely described some previously chosen object, the sentence is true (taking Yul Brynner as chosen object). According to the truth-value gap theory of Frege,[5] elaborated by Strawson,[6] in which improper descriptions are treated as having meaning but describing nothing and sentences containing such descriptions are treated as themselves meaningful but having no truth value, the sentence is neither true nor false. I am aware of no theory according to which the sentence is both true and false, though no doubt such a theory has been or will be proposed.

This much is well known about Russell's theory: he takes the propriety of the description to be a part of the *content* of certain sentences containing descriptions and thus counts them false if they contain *improper* descriptions. More specifically, he claims that a paradigm sentence of the form "The such-and-such is so-and-so" is equivalent to "One and only one thing is a such-and-such, and that one is so-and-so." In symbols:

(1) "$F\imath xGx$" is equivalent to "$(\exists x)((y)(Gy \equiv y = x) \mathbin{\&} Fx)$."

This analysis does not provide a unique understanding of sentences of the form "The such-and-such is not this-and-that," which may be treated as equivalent to "One and only one thing is a such-and-such and that one is not this-and-that," thus assimilating "not this-and-that" to the "so-and-so" of the paradigm; but the given form may also be treated as equivalent to "It is not the case that one and only one thing is such-and-such and that one is this-and-that," thus applying the paradigm to "the such-and-such is this-and-that" and understanding the given form as its negation. This ambiguity is regarded by Russell as a simple scope problem on a par with the party invitation which reads, "Bring your wife or come stag and have a good time." And he introduces the terminology of *primary* and *secondary* (and by natural extension *tertiary, quaternary,* and so forth) occurrences to indicate the intended scope of the description in sentences of the given form. (Later, in *Principia Mathematica*[7] he introduces the more technically satisfactory device of scope indicators.)

These two features then, (i) that the sentence "The present King of France is bald" is taken to be equivalent to "One and only one thing is a present King of France and that one is bald," and (ii) that this leads to scope problems in the case of "The present King of France is not bald," which comes out true if the description is given secondary occurrence but false if the description is given primary occurrence, I take to be well known; and possibly because they provide a convenient means of comparison with other theories of descriptions, they have sometimes been thought to constitute the distinctive feature in Russell's doctrine. But this, I believe, is not so. The peculiar and interesting feature is his position on denoting. For he claims that in contrast to such proper names as "Elizabeth Windsor" which denote a certain person, a description like "the present Queen of England" doesn't *really* denote anything. If the description is proper you may want to speak *as if* it denoted the unique thing described, and that won't get you in any difficulties (if you avoid oblique contexts), but it would be misleading. For it would lead you to believe that the two sentences:

(2) Elizabeth Windsor is sexy.
(3) The present Queen of England is sexy.

have the same logical form, namely subject-predicate form, with "Elizabeth Windsor" in one case and "the present Queen of England" in the other case as subjects, both denoting the same individual, and "is sexy" as predicate, denoting, say, some class of individuals. Thus in both cases the sentence is true if and only if the given individual is a member of the given class. But nothing could be further from the Russellian truth. (2) and (3) do not have the same logical form at all, for if (3) were of subject-predicate form, so would

(4)   The present King of France is sexy.

be, by parity of form (as Russell would say). But according to Russell, the truth conditions for (4) have nothing to do with any given individual being sexy.

And now, I believe, we are at the heart of the matter. Russell's article "On Denoting" is not about a theory of descriptions comparable to Frege-Carnap or Frege-Strawson. Russell's article is about logical form, and is in the tradition of those philosophers who have warned us of the dangers of confusing the grammatical form of a sentence in ordinary language with its logical form. Such philosophers have often sought to construct a *logically perfect language* in which grammatical and logical form would always coincide.

I am dissatisfied with Russell's theory about the logical form of sentences containing descriptions, and I will try to indicate the features I find unsatisfactory by comparison with an analogous theory which I call "Russell's theory of indefinite descriptions."[8] This theory is concerned with the analysis of sentences containing *in*definite descriptions. For example:

(5)   A senator from New York is supporting Rockefeller.

Now (5) certainly has subject-predicate grammatical form in English, but if you feel that its logical form is the same as

(6)   Jacob Javits is supporting Rockefeller.

you can quickly disabuse yourself by comparing:

(7)   A senator from New York is supporting Rockefeller, and a senator from New York is not supporting Rockefeller.

with

(8)   Jacob Javits is supporting Rockefeller, and Jacob Javits is not supporting Rockefeller.

(8) is a contradiction, but (7) is true. In fact, isn't it obvious that indefinite descriptions do not even purport to denote a unique object as names do? Accordingly, Russell's theory of indefinite descriptions asserts that the logical form of a paradigm sentence like "A such-and-such is so-and-so" is represented by the equivalent sentence "Something is both a such-and-such and so-and-so." In symbols:

(9)   "$F\alpha xGx$" is equivalent to "$(\exists x)[Gx \,\&\, Fx]$".

Note that this analysis does not provide a unique understanding of certain compound sentences containing indefinite descriptions, for example:

(10)   A girl danced with every boy.
In symbols: $(y)[By \supset D(\alpha xGx, y)]$.

Depending on whether the indefinite description is taken as having primary or secondary occurrence, the sentence will be equivalent to either

(11)   Some girl is such that she danced with all the boys.
       In symbols: $(\exists x)(Gx \,\& \,(y)(By \supset D(x, y)))$

or

(12)   Each boy is such that some girl or other danced with him.
       In symbols $(y)(By \supset (\exists x)(Gx \,\& \,D(x, y)))$.

There are further parallels between Russell's theory of definite descriptions and Russell's theory of indefinite descriptions, but I think the point is made. The point is that Russell regarded definite descriptions exactly as we would regard indefinite descriptions. Although grammatically, at least from the point of view of what is now called surface grammar, indefinite descriptions are terms and function like proper names, sentences which contain indefinite descriptions and appear to have subject-predicate form should be treated as idioms and expanded as in the paradigm.[9]

Russell's theory of indefinite descriptions seems to me both correct and natural. In fact, the analysis fits indefinite descriptions so perfectly that any disanalogies between definite and indefinite descriptions throw suspicion on Russell's theory of definite descriptions. Further, I believe that the leading ideas of Russell's theory of definite descriptions are more clearly seen in connection with Russell's theory of indefinite descriptions, and thus questions about the former might be more easily answered in connection with the latter.

With respect to disanalogies between definite and indefinite descriptions, I will just mention two ways in which Russell (and everyone else I suppose) provides differential treatment. First, Russell invents a symbolic notation for definite descriptions and introduces them into the language of *Principia Mathematica*. So far as I know neither Russell nor anyone else has ever given serious consideration to the introduction of indefinite descriptions into any formalism. Not that it could not be done. The foregoing brief remarks on Russell's theory of indefinite descriptions make it clear exactly how to do it. It is even clear how scope indicators could be introduced. It is just that nobody would think it worth doing. Why? Because such a notation, rather than providing a useful and succinct means of expression for investigating logical relations, would tend to obscure the logical form of the sentence and obfuscate the issues in question. This, of course, is exactly what definite descriptions of English are said to do (by Russell), but still he introduces them into *Principia Mathematica*.

The second respect in which Russell treats definite and indefinite descriptions differently is in connection with his offhand remark that one *might* speak of proper definite descriptions *as if* they denoted the unique individual having the property in question although strictly speaking this would be incorrect. We certainly do want to treat proper descriptions in this way, and every other theory of definite descriptions with which I am familiar does so. Are there any cases (let alone, the central cases) in which it is natural to treat an indefinite description like a proper name, that is, as denoting an individual? Russell never suggests so.[10]

I wish now to raise the question of how to regard the fundamental equivalences (1) and (9) of the two theories. Russell called them *contextual definitions*. But what is a contextual definition? Ordinarily we think of definitions as being either stipulative or explicative (in an older terminology, nominal or real). That is, either a new expression is introduced and assigned the meaning of a phrase whose meaning is antecedently known, or else an old expression is given a more precise, or in some other way slightly adjusted, meaning in terms of some antecedently understood phrase. In the case in question the new expression to be introduced is the definite or indefinite description operator. But what meaning is given to it, or even to the full description? None! For the central thesis of Russell's theory is that this phrase *has* no meaning in isolation.

Another notion closely related to that of definition which is, I believe, somewhat more appropriate to Russell's contextual definitions is that of *abbreviation*. In an abbreviation a new expression is introduced to *stand for* an old phrase. But the phrase so abbreviated is not required to be meaningful; it may be any combination of signs. Abbreviation is purely a matter of syntax. Whereas only well-formed expressions can serve as *definiens*, any expression can be abbreviated. To understand the meaning of an expression in terms of the meanings of its components, we must first expand it into unabbreviated form (except, of course, insofar as the abbreviations are also definitions).

I prefer still another understanding of (1) and (9). We may treat them as rules for translating ordinary, logically imperfect, language into a logically perfect symbolism. According to this conception the symbolic descriptions "αxFx" and "$\imath xFx$" would be understood as not occurring in the perfect language at all, not even as abbreviations. They would appear only at a transitional stage in the translation process as an aid in representing the surface grammar of ordinary language. This seems to me a natural understanding of (9), since as remarked above, no one would seriously consider introducing indefinite descriptions into a logically perfect language.[11] If Russell really took his doctrine seriously and were willing to completely abjure the "misleading" surface grammar of definite descriptions, he should be willing to accept the present understanding of (1). His use of definite descriptions in *Principia Mathematica* indicates to me a lingering ambivalence.

Although I will not now attempt to make the notion of a logically perfect language absolutely precise,

I would like to clarify it somewhat. The intuitive idea is that the logical form of a sentence should mirror its grammatical form. The grammar of a language is assumed to be given in terms of certain grammatical categories such as term, formula, two-place predicate, etc. Each atomic expression is assigned to some such category, and *formation rules* are given which tell us how we can form compounds of a given grammatical category from components of certain grammatical categories. The grammatical form of an expression is then determined by the formation rules. An expression is grammatically correct if it can be "constructed" from grammatically simple components in accordance with the formation rules. Such a construction assigns a grammatical structure, or form, to the expression. To parse a sequence is to exhibit its grammatical form. Just as grammatical properties and relations such as being a noun clause or being the subject of a given sentence depend on the grammatical form of the expressions in question, so logical properties and relations such as being valid or being a logical consequence of a given sentence depend on the logical form of the expressions in question. Logical form is determined by the *evaluation rules* of the language. These rules tell us how to "construct" the semantical value of an expression in terms of the values of its logically simple components. (We here take the semantical value to be what Carnap calls "the extension," that is: a truth value for sentences, an individual for names, a class of individuals for one-place predicates, and so on.) Such a construction of the truth value of a sentence exhibits the logical structure, or form, of the sentence in a way analogous to that in which parsing a sentence exhibits its grammatical form. As shown by Tarski, the notions of validity and logical consequence can be given in terms of such constructions.[12] In ordinary language, replacements which do not change the apparent grammatical form of sentences, for example replacing a proper name

with "someone," may well introduce or obliterate relations of logical consequence between the affected
sentences, thus indicating a change in logical form.
This point, that sentences with the same apparent
grammatical form can have different logical forms, is
illustrated by (5)–(8). In a logically perfect language
the logical form of an expression must always mirror
the grammatical form. Therefore, for logical perfection we require that the logically simple expressions
coincide with the grammatically simple (but well-
formed) expressions, and that to every formation rule
there corresponds a unique evaluation rule such that
any compound formed by applying the formation rule
to given components is evaluated by applying the
corresponding evaluation rule to the values of the
components. This has the desired result that the semantical evaluation of an expression exactly recapitu-
lates its grammatical construction.[13]

Given the grammar of a language, one semantical
treatment may make it logically perfect and another
not. Take, for example, a sentential language which
contains: (1) the atomic expressions "p_1", "p_2", "p_3",
etc., all belonging to the grammatical category *sentence*, and (2) three formation rules which allow us
to form the compound sentences $\ulcorner(\phi \supset \psi)\urcorner$, $\ulcorner{\sim}\phi\urcorner$,
$\ulcorner(\phi \equiv \psi)\urcorner$ from any component sentences ϕ and ψ.
Now consider two different methods for assigning val-
ues to the sentences. Method I consists of (1) assigning a truth value to each atomic sentence in accordance with some given interpretation of the atomic
sentences, and (2) for each formation rule using a
corresponding truth function to evaluate the truth
value of the compound in terms of the truth values
of its immediate components. Method I is the standard semantical analysis of such a language. Method
II agrees with Method I for the atomic sentences but
provides two stages for the analysis of compounds,
(i) "eliminate" all biconditionals from compound sen-
tences by replacing subsentences $\ulcorner(\phi \equiv \psi)\urcorner$ by

⌜∼((φ ⊃ ψ) ⊃ ∼(ψ ⊃ φ))⌝, (ii) evaluate the result as in Method I.[14] I call the language which incorporates Method I logically perfect, but the detour from grammatical form involved in Method II renders the language incorporating that method logically imperfect. This, in spite of the fact that the two methods assign the same values to all sentences.

Let us assume that the grammar of Russell's language distinguishes *term* and *formula* and contains among its formation rules: all variables are terms; all individual constants are terms; if Φ is a formula and v is variable, ⍳vΦ is a term; if τ is any term (a variable, individual constant, or definite description), ⌜τ is bald⌝ is a formula, plus the usual formation rules for identity, quantifiers, sentential connectives, etc.[15] Following Russell's informal remarks, we will understand his semantics as involving first the elimination of all descriptions by means of (1). In accordance with the conventions for dropping scope indicators in *Principia Mathematica,* we take the scope always to be the smallest possible. Such a semantical analysis will of course make (1) true, and in a trivial way. But it makes the language logically imperfect.[16]

This brings us to another question. Does acceptance of the equivalence (1) commit us to Russell's analysis of the logical form of sentences containing definite descriptions? The answer is "No." At least two different (but closely related) analyses can make the language logically perfect. We can follow the method of Frege-Strawson in claiming that improper descriptions simply don't denote, but in the Frege-Strawson evaluation rules for atomic formulas:

(i) ⌜τ is bald⌝ is true if and only if τ denotes something which is bald.

(ii) ⌜τ is bald⌝ is false if and only if τ denotes something which is not bald.

(where τ may be any term: a variable, individual constant, or definite description); retain (i) and replace (ii) with:

(ii′) ⌜τ is bald⌝ is false if and only if it is not true.

Alternatively, we can follow the method of Frege-Carnap in stipulating that some previously chosen entity will be taken as the common *denotatum* of all improper descriptions, but put this entity *outside* the domain of discourse (possibly by just letting the chosen entity be the domain of discourse itself). According to this method we would retain the evaluation rule (ii) and replace (i) with:

(i′) ⌜τ is bald⌝ is true if and only if τ denotes something which is bald *and is within the domain of discourse.*

Note that in the unmodified Frege-Carnap theory the italicized phrase is otiose.

On both the modified Frege-Strawson analysis and the modified Frege-Carnap analysis the equivalence (1) is preserved, as is the accuracy of Russell's translation of "ɿxFx exists" by "$(\exists y)(x)(Fx \equiv x = y)$" which in turn is equivalent to "$(\exists y)(y = ɿxFx)$." And since the evaluation rules require us to look only at the evaluation of the immediate constituent term and not at whether it is a variable, individual constant or definite description, the language is rendered logically perfect.

It may be objected that all we have done is to find two ways of coding information about the syntactical character of a term (whether or not it is a definite description) into the evaluation rules. Thus if a term has no denotation or none within the domain of discourse, we know that it must be a definite description. But such an objection would be both inaccurate and shortsighted. Inaccurate, because it ignores the fact that the treatment of improper descriptions no longer distorts the treatment of proper descriptions, which now receive the natural semantical analysis; and shortsighted, because it ignores the possibility of using the semantical ideas of the modified Frege-Strawson method or the modified Frege-Carnap method to construct theories which depart still further from that of Russell but which allow a complete assimilation of definite descriptions and individual constants, and even provide for true atomic sentences about nonexisting individuals. Indeed, such theories have already been constructed by a number of authors.[17]

Russell and Frege were both interested in removing the logical imperfections of ordinary language but their methods were quite different. (For what follows, it is necessary to assume the "translation rule" interpretation of contextual definitions according to which definite descriptions do not occur at all in the perfect language.) Where grammar called for entities whose nature was obscure, Frege attempted constructions, as with numbers, or a theory about the purported entities, as with propositions. Thus he sought to preserve the integrity of ordinary language by ontological ingenuity. Russell's response, at least in the case of definite descriptions, was by grammatical reconstrual and replacement. The two methods are easily contrasted by their analyses of "the number of planets is two" (I simplify for economy). Following Frege's method, we accept the apparent grammatical form (that of an identity sentence) and translate into something like "the similarity class of the set of planets = the set of all couples." Following Russell's method (though he might not follow it in this case) we dispense altogether with singular terms purporting to refer to numbers and translate into something like "there is a planet, and there is another, and there are no others." Either method may lead to logical perfection, but Frege's way seems to me more fruitful in the long run. I see Frege's method at work in Tarski's reduction of possible worlds to models,[18] Carnap's reduction of propositions to classes of models,[19] Wiener's reduction of ordered couples to classes[20] (and hence of relations to classes), and of course Frege's own treatment of numbers.[21] I would classify as applications of Russell's method: Stevenson's emotive analysis of "x is good,"[22] Austin's reconstrual of the singular term "the-meaning-of-(the-word)-'rat,'"[23] Quine's treatment of virtual classes,[24] and, classically, Russell's own treatment of definite descriptions. The scope and limitation of Russell's method, in one of its applications, has received careful and extended discussion in Quine's *Set Theory and its Logic*.

Russell seems not to have viewed his linguistic replacements as being in sharp contrast with Frege's ontological constructions, for in his essay "Logical Atomism" he writes:

> One very important heuristic maxim which Dr. Whitehead and I found, by experience, to be applicable in mathematical logic, and have since applied in various other fields, is a form of Ockham's razor. . . . The Principle may be stated in the form: "Wherever possible, substitute constructions out of known entities for inferences to unknown entities."
>
> The uses of this principle are very various, but are not intelligible in detail to those who do not know mathematical logic. . . .
>
> A very important example of the principle is Frege's definition of the cardinal number of a given set of terms as the class of all sets that are "similar" to the given set. . . . Thus a cardinal number is the class of all those classes which are similar to a given class. This definition leaves unchanged the truth-values of all propositions in which cardinal numbers occur, and avoids the inference to a set of entities called "cardinal numbers," which were never needed except for the purpose of making arithmetic intelligible, and are now no longer needed for the purpose. . . .

Another important example concerns what I call "definite descriptions," i.e., such phrases as "the even prime," "the present King of England," "the present King of France." There has always been a difficulty in interpreting such propositions as "the present King of France does not exist." The difficulty arose through supposing that "the present King of France" is the subject of this proposition. . . . The fact is that, when the words "the so-and-so" occur in a proposition, there is no corresponding single constituent of the proposition, and when the proposition is fully analyzed the words "the so-and-so" have disappeared.[25]

Insofar as we find reconstruction of our grammatical intuitions and reconstruction of our ontological intuitions equally congenial, this conflation of ontological construction with grammatical reconstrual is harmless. But insofar as our grammatical preconceptions continue to dominate our ideas, logical perfection achieved in Russell's way will remain unsatisfactory.

REFERENCES

1. This paper has benefited from a number of sources including a seminar at Princeton, a colloquium at Cornell, Montgomery Furth, and National Science Foundation Grant GP-4594.

2. *Mind,* Vol. 14, 1905. Reprinted in Russell's *Logic and Knowledge,* ed. by R. C. Marsh, London, 1956, and also in *Readings in Philosophical Analysis,* ed. by Feigl and Sellars, New York, 1949.

3. G. Frege, "Ueber Sinn und Bedeutung," *Zeitschrift für Philosophie und philosophische Kritik,* Vol. 100, 1892. Translated as "On Sense and Reference" in Frege's *Philosophical Writings,* tr. by Geach and Black, Oxford, 1952, and also as "On Sense and

Nominatum" in *Readings in Philosophical Analysis*.
See especially footnote 9.

4. R. Carnap, *Meaning and Necessity*, Chicago,
1946. See especially §8.

5. "Ueber Sinn und Bedeutung." See especially the
discussion of sentences containing "Odysseus."

6. P. F. Strawson, *Introduction to Logical Theory*,
London, 1952.

7. Cambridge, 1910.

8. Russell's theory of indefinite descriptions is most
clearly adumbrated in Chapter XVI of his *Introduction to Mathematical Philosophy*, London, 1919.

9. Compare "It is snowing" which also appears to
have subject-predicate form.

10. At the beginning of "On Denoting," Russell
suggests as an initial understanding of indefinite descriptions that " 'a man' denotes . . . an ambiguous
man." But he quickly rejects this idea.

11. Hilbert's ϵ-operator does not produce an indefinite description in the sense herein discussed.

12. A. Tarski, "Der Wahrheitsbegriff in den formalisierten Sprachen," *Studia Philosophica*, Vol. 1,
1936; and "Über den Begriff der logischen Folgerung," *Actes du Congrès International de Philosophie
Scientifique*, Vol. 7, 1936. Translated as "The Concept
of Truth in Formalized Languages" and "On the Concept of Logical Consequence" in Tarski's *Logic, Semantics, Metamathematics*, Oxford, 1956. What I call
evaluation rules are clauses in Tarski's definition of satisfaction.

13. This relationship between formation rules and
evaluation rules is developed in somewhat greater detail in Chap. 1 of my dissertation, *Foundations of*

Intensional Logic, University Microfilms, Ann Arbor, Mich., 1964.

14. It is important for the point of the example that all three formation rules are understood as primitive, and thus that biconditionals are *not* thought of as defined expressions.

15. At this point we revert to the theory of definite descriptions and leave indefinite descriptions aside as an instructive amusement.

16. It should be noted here that I assume the grammar to be given in the way described above, essentially what is now called an *immediate constituent phrase structure grammar.* It is not implausible to regard Russell's contextual definitions as providing his language with a *transformational phrase structure grammar.* Since Russell's implied evaluation rule for sentences containing definite descriptions, like that of our Method II, might plausibly be called a *transformational evaluation rule,* we might consider this mirroring of syntactical structure a kind of perfection. But insofar as there is a natural tendency to expect a language to exhibit the simpler immediate constituent form, a language whose grammar is described by *transformational* means might, on that account alone, be considered imperfect.

17. Among others, Hintikka, "Studies in the Logic of Existence and Necessity: I. Existence," *The Monist,* Vol. 50, 1966; Lambert, "Notes on El III: A Theory of Descriptions," *Philosophical Studies,* Vol. 13, 1962; Scott, "Existence and Description in Formal Logic," forthcoming.

18. Implicit in "Über den Begriff der logischen Folgerung."

19. *Meaning and Necessity,* § 40.

20. P. P. Weiner, "Simplification of the Logic of

Relations," *Proceedings of the Cambridge Philosophical Society*, Vol. 17, 1912–1914.

21. G. Frege, *Grundlagen der Arithmetik*, Breslaw, 1884. Translated as *The Foundations of Arithmetic*, Oxford, 1950.

22. C. L. Stevenson, "The Emotive Meaning of Ethical Terms," *Mind*, Vol. 46, 1937. Reprinted in *Logical Positivism*, ed. by Ayer, Glencoe, Ill., 1959.

23. "The Meaning of a Word," in Austin's *Philosophical Papers*, Oxford, 1961.

24. W. V. O. Quine, *Set Theory and its Logic*, Cambridge, Mass., 1963.

25. First published in *Contemporary British Philosophy*, ed. by Muirhead, London, 1924. Reprinted in *Logical Positivism*.

RUSSELL'S THEORY OF TYPES

Charles S. Chihara

Russell used the expression "theory of types" to refer to his own theory about how and why we should restrict the ranges of variables in logic and mathematics. In this sense, Russell's theory of types is a theory about, among other things, what it makes sense to say. The expressions "theory of types" and "type theory" have also been used to refer to formal systems of logic and formal set theories in which the variables are restricted in such a way that the ranges of the variables form a hierarchy similar to the hierarchy of types of *Principia Mathematica* (henceforth abbreviated: *PM*).[1] In this paper, I shall be concerned with Russell's theory of types in the former sense.

1

Russell's Attitude Toward the Paradoxes

Russell developed his theory of types in response to the paradoxes of logic and mathematics which he did so much to get promulgated at the turn of the century. Of these paradoxes, perhaps the most striking and fundamental for the philosopher of mathematics is Russell's own paradox which he discovered in 1901.

Now Russell's paradox is so well known that it may be thought unnecessary or tedious to state it here. However, I think it is worth while comparing the version Russell gave in his important 1908 paper, [5], with more recent versions. Russell begins by letting

---

This paper has not been previously published.
[1] For examples of this use of "theory of types," see Wang, [2], p. 406 (references given at the end of this paper), and Wilder, [1], p. 226.

W be the set of all sets which are not members of themselves. He then infers that for any set x, $x \in W$ if and only if $x \notin x$, and hence that $W \in W$ if and only if $W \notin W$.

It is usual nowadays for Russell's paradox to be expressed making use of a first-order language somewhat as follows. It is suggested that many (or most) mathematicians of this period accepted an (unrestricted) *axiom of abstraction* which says that for every property (or condition), there is a set whose members are just those objects having the property (or satisfying the condition). This axiom is given thus

$$(\exists x)(y)(y \in x \leftrightarrow \phi y).$$

Now taking ϕy to be the property of not being a member of itself which we can express "$y \notin y$", we get

$$(\exists x)(y)(y \in x \leftrightarrow y \notin y),$$

and hence we can infer

$$x \in x \leftrightarrow x \notin x.$$

It is generally thought that the conclusion to be drawn from this derivation is simply that the set theory accepted at this time was inconsistent. Russell, however, was convinced that "the trouble lay in logic rather than mathematics and that it was logic which would have to be reformed" ([10], p. 76).

Consider the following familiar story. Three salesmen at a convention decide to stay the night at the same hotel. To save money, they agree to share a room. Since the room costs $30, each contributes $10. Later on, however, the desk clerk discovers that he should have charged the salesmen only $25 for the room and thus sends the bellhop up to their room with the $5 change. The bellhop, deciding that it is too difficult to split $5 three ways returns only $3, pocketing the remaining $2. Now, since each salesman originally contributed $10 and subsequently received

$1 back, we can conclude that each spent only $9 for the room. Thus the three salesmen spent $27 for the room, and the bellhop received $2. This makes $29. But they originally started with $30. So what happened to the other dollar?

Needless to say, there is no temptation here to attribute any sort of contradiction to mathematics. And insofar as one sees a puzzle, it is natural enough to look for some sort of solution. One need not look far, for it soon becomes apparent that the situation is described so as to mislead the reader into analyzing the financial situation improperly: it is suggested that from the original $30, $27 was spent and, in addition, $2 was given to the bellhop, whereas the $2 that went to the bellhop came out of the $27 spent. So there is no problem about what happened to the $30: $27 was spent and $3 was saved.

Now Russell evidently thought that the paradoxes troubling him were also to be solved by pointing to some sort of mistake or confusion. He tells us in his autobiography that he thought there must be "some trivial error in reasoning" responsible for the paradoxes ([11], p. 147). Russell's attitude toward the paradoxes can be likened to that of a person who is given one of the paradoxes of Euclidean geometry found floating around mathematics departments: the person does not seriously consider the possibility that geometry is contradictory or that, say, some angle really is identical to the sum of another angle plus itself; he is certain that there is some fallacy in the "proof." And just as we would say of some of these paradoxes that they rest upon an unjustified assumption that there exists a line with such and such properties or that one can construct a line with such and such properties, so Russell became convinced that the paradoxes with which he was concerned rested upon equally unwarranted assumptions regarding the existence of certain sorts of large totalities. Russell was led to this position by Poincaré's suggestion that the paradoxes resulted from definitions that were viciously circular (Poincaré, [1], pp. 307–8). Following this suggestion, Russell formulated a principle that would distinguish and, so to speak, rule out the guilty totalities. This principle became known as the *vicious-circle principle*.

2

The Vicious-Circle Principle

Russell's own statements of the principle are vague and obscure.

(1) Whatever involves *all* of a collection must not be one of the collection ([5], p. 63; *PM*, p. 37).

(2) If, provided a certain collection had a total, it would have members only definable in terms of that total, then the said collection has no total ([5], p. 63; *PM*, p. 31).

(Russell writes in a footnote: "When I say that a collection has no total, I mean that statements about all its members are nonsense" ([5], p. 63)).

(3) Given any set of objects such that, if we suppose the set to have a total, it will contain members which presuppose this total, then such a set cannot have a total. By saying that a set has "no total," we mean, primarily, that no significant statement can be made about "all its members" (*PM*, p. 37).

(4) No totality can contain members defined in terms of itself ([5], p. 75).

(5) Whatever contains an apparent variable must not be a possible value of that variable ([5], p. 75; cf. [3], p. 640).

Now examining the first three statements above, we see that (1) contains the term "involves," whereas

(2) uses "only definable in terms of," and (3) contains neither of these expressions but instead the word "presupposes." This fact prompted Gödel to claim that Russell proposed three different vicious-circle principles.[2] But admitting that "presuppose" does not ordinarily mean "only definable in terms of" or "involves," it is by no means obvious that we are dealing with three different principles; for surely there is more to getting at what Russell was driving at than merely reading his explicit statements of the principle. Thus, we can examine the applications of the principle that Russell made, and also analyze the theory of types for further clarification of his principle.

It is common nowadays for logicians to interpret the vicious-circle principle as a device for severely limiting the abstraction axiom mentioned above so as to yield a consistent set theory.[3] On this interpretation the principle requires that "impredicative specifications" be eschewed; and although one does not find complete unanimity as to how "impredicative specification" is to be defined, the general idea can be given as follows: a specification of a set A by means of the schema

$$(x)(x \in A \leftrightarrow \phi x)$$

is impredicative if the set A, were it to exist, or any set presupposing the existence of A, falls within the range of a bound variable in the specification.[4] Thus

---

[2] Fraenkel and Bar-Hillel claim that Gödel *shows* that Russell gave us three different principles rather than three different formulations of a single principle ([1], p. 175). This is an overstatement: Gödel does not *show* any such thing, he only claims it! (See Gödel, [1], p. 135, pp. 203 ff. of this volume.)

[3] See Quine, [5], p. 243; Fraenkel and Bar-Hillel, [1], p. 176; also Beth, [1], pp. 497–500.

[4] The clause "or any set presupposing the existence of A" is somewhat vague. One wants to have the abstraction axiom limited to specifications in which, not only A does not occur within the range of a bound variable in the specification, but

the vicious-circle principle is thought to restrict the abstraction axiom to just predicative specifications (i.e., specifications that are not impredicative). In other words, it is legitimate to infer the existence of a set answering to a specification only if the specification is predicative. No doubt the above statement of the principle is not as clear as one would like.[5] But it will be of some use in the following discussion, if only as an object of comparison.

Let us now see how the vicious-circle principle, as stated above, can be used to obviate Cantor's paradox. This paradox begins with the classical theorem that the cardinality of a set S is always less than the cardinality of the set of all subsets of S. Now let U be the set of all sets. Clearly, no set of sets can have cardinality greater than U. Yet, by the above theorem, its power set does have a greater cardinal number.

To see how impredicative specifications enter into this paradox, we need only examine some typical proof of the theorem used in the paradox. Somewhere along the way, it is proved that there cannot be a one-one correspondence between S and $P(S)$, the power set of S; and the proof usually proceeds along the

---

also, for example, any set containing A, any set containing a set containing A, any set that can only be defined in terms of A, etc. This clause is not always included in explications of "impredicative specification" (cf. Fraenkel and Bar-Hillel, [1], p. 176). Quine uses a clause which says "or any set whose specification might presuppose A" ([5], p. 242), but I find this clause even more vague and misleading than the above. In any case, some such clause is clearly needed not only to bring the principle closer to both Russell's statements of the principle and his actual practice in constructing his set theory, but also so that the principle is sufficiently strong to bar contradictions (see Wang, [1], pp. 640–41).

[5] Cf. J. R. Shoenfield's remark: "The study of the various possible precise notions of predicativity and their relations to one another is the chief problem of predicativity" ([1], p. 132, n.).

following lines.[6] Let us suppose that ϕ is such a one-one correspondence, i.e., suppose that ϕ is a set of ordered pairs with the properties:

(i) $\langle x,y \rangle \in \phi$ only if x is a member of S and y is a member of $P(S)$;

(ii) for every element x of S, there is one and only one element y of $P(S)$ such that $\langle x,y \rangle \in \phi$;

(iii) for every element y of $P(S)$, there is one and only one element x of S such that $\langle x,y \rangle \in \phi$.

Then let α be the set specified as follows:

$(x) (x \in \alpha \leftrightarrow x \in S \,\&\, (y) (\langle x,y \rangle \in \phi \rightarrow x \notin y))$.

It follows that α is a member of $P(S)$. Hence, there is a unique element z of S such that $\langle x,\alpha \rangle \in \phi$. If $z \in \alpha$, then by the above specification of α, $z \notin \alpha$. But if $z \notin \alpha$, then $z \in \alpha$. Hence it cannot be that there is a one-one correspondence between S and its power set.

Clearly, the above proof does not conform to the vicious-circle principle, since the specification of α is impredicative. Besides this, I shall argue, Russell intended his vicious-circle principle to rule out as illegitimate the assumption that there is such a thing as the set of all sets. So the principle stops this paradox in two ways.

In [5], Russell attempted to make plausible his principle by first presenting the reader with a cluster of paradoxes and then arguing in each case that there is a tacit assumption of a totality in terms of which, by a kind of impredicative definition,[7] a member of the totality is singled out with the paradoxical property

[6] The proof that I present here is essentially the one given by Cantor. Russell tells us that he discovered his paradox while attempting to discover some flaw in Cantor's proof ([8], p. 136). This is not very surprising in view of the obvious similarity between Cantor's proof and Russell's paradox.

[7] I use the term "impredicative definition" here, since some of the paradoxes do not involve the concept of set. Instead of an impredicatively specified set, there are impredicatively defined propositions, numbers, etc.

that this member cannot be a member of the totality. In each case, Russell analyzed the contradictions as arising from the mistaken belief that it makes sense to have bound variables ranging over these totalities. It would seem that the specific analyses were not used to provide a kind of inductive support for the general principle: rather the reader was supposed to *see* the validity of the principle from these examples. Since Russell did not analyze the paradoxes as simply arising from the mistaken assumption that there are objects answering to impredicative definitions—Russell went further in claiming that basically it was the assumption that it made sense to make statements about (to allow a bound variable to range over) some large totality that gave rise to impredicative definitions and paradoxes—it is clear that, in the case of the set-theoretical paradoxes, Russell intended his principle to do more than rule out the use of impredicative specifications in connection with the abstraction axiom.

Let me clarify this point by looking at some of the specific paradoxes that Russell discusses in [5].

> Epimenides the Cretan said that all Cretans were liars, and all other statements made by Cretans were certainly lies (p. 59).

What is peculiar about Russell's statement of the paradox is that no contradiction follows from the above as it stands. One would have to add, for example, that no distinction is to be made between lying and asserting what is false and that a liar is someone who asserts only false propositions. In any case, Russell seems to have had in mind essentially the following version. (Cf. [3], p. 643.) Epimenides asserts a unique proposition q at time t, where q is the proposition that there is a proposition asserted by Epimenides at t which is false. Since q is the unique proposition asserted by Epimenides at t, we can conclude that for every proposition p, if Epimenides asserts p at t, then $p = q$. From these premises, we can conclude that q is true if and only if q is false.

Now Russell concludes from this paradox that we must reject the assumption that there is a totality of all propositions. But notice that another way of avoiding the contradiction is by claiming that the sentence "Epimenides asserted the unique proposition q at t" does not express a genuine proposition, at least if the purported proposition is taken to imply that for every proposition p if Epimenides asserts p at t, then $p = q$. Or one might object that the sentence "there is a proposition asserted by Epimenides at t which is false" does not express a genuine proposition.[8] Evidently, Russell felt these sentences must express genuine propositions if it makes sense to quantify over all propositions.

Consider Russell's treatment of Richard's paradox. We assume that there is a class, C, of all decimals definable by means of a finite number of English words. Then, by essentially following the celebrated diagonal procedure Cantor used to prove that the set of real numbers is nondenumerable, it is easy to construct a definition (consisting of a finite number of English words) of a decimal N, which could not belong to C. The definition of N is impredicative, but again Russell does not simply declare the definition to be illegitimate—he says the definition is illegitimate because it is illegitimate to quantify over C, i.e., C is the illegitimate totality.

The Russell paradox is given a similar analysis. Russell is not content with rejecting the assumption that there is a class such as W; he claims that it is only by rejecting the assumption that there is a totality of all sets that we can avoid the contradiction.

[8] Such a position is suggested by some remarks of Wittgenstein. Cf. [1], § 691.

That there is no such class results from the fact that, if we suppose that there is, the supposition gives rise (as in the above contradiction) to new classes lying outside the supposed total of all classes ([5], p. 62).

Finally, consider Russell's treatment of the Burali-Forti paradox. It seems possible to prove in the classical theory of ordinals that the set of all ordinal numbers has an ordinal number and that this ordinal number must be greater than any ordinal number. In this case, Russell claims that the notion of "all ordinal numbers" is not legitimate.

From these examples, one can see that Russell did not simply reject some impredicative specification or definition used in producing the paradox: he always rejected, in addition, the larger totalities in terms of which the relevant impredicative specifications or definitions were made. This gives us good reason for supposing that Russell intended his vicious-circle principle to do more than simply reject impredicative specifications—it was supposed to pare down the "legitimate totalities" to some kind of manageable size. As we shall see, the underlying idea was that the "legitimate totalities" must be obtainable by a kind of process of construction (using predicative specifications) from some given totality of individuals.

3

The Need for a Positive Solution to the Paradoxes

Having agreed with Poincaré as to the source of the paradoxes—the supposed source being, in each instance, a violation of the vicious-circle principle—one might think that this would have satisfied Russell's desire for a solution to the paradoxes. This was not so: for Russell, the vicious-circle principle was "purely negative in its scope" ([5], p. 63); he felt that an adequate solution to the paradoxes must provide a *positive* theory which would "exclude" totalities in accordance with the vicious-circle principle.

> The exclusion must result naturally and inevitably from our positive doctrines, which must make it plain that "all propositions" and "all properties" are meaningless phrases ([5], p. 63).

Now why did Russell feel compelled to provide such a positive theory? Consider the following version of an elementary school puzzle. For $n = 1$, we have $2n + 5 = 7n$. Subtracting 7 from both sides of the equation, we get $2n - 2 = 7n - 7$. Factoring, we have $2(n - 1) = 7(n - 1)$. Dividing both sides by $n - 1$, we have $2 = 7$. An elementary schoolboy, genuinely puzzled by the above, would gain some understanding of the puzzle by seeing that the absurdity results from dividing by 0. He might even formulate a principle: it is illegitimate to divide by 0. But as I interpret Russell, this would provide only a *partial* solution of the puzzle: to have a satisfactory solution, the boy must also discover why dividing by 0 is illegitimate and why it gets him into trouble. To gain the required insights, it may be necessary for the boy not only to make explicit the definitions of multiplication and division, but also to gain, in terms of these definitions, a clear understanding of the algebraic operations one is allowed to perform. One can see why Russell did not feel it was enough to point out that some step in the proof of each of the paradoxes violated his vicious-circle principle and why he felt it necessary to produce a positive account of logic and mathematics in terms of which one could see both why violating the vicious-circle principle leads to contradiction, and also how to avoid such vicious-circle paradoxes in the future.[9] Thus, Russell was faced with the

[9] Cf. Russell's early statement: *"Il importe de remarquer que le principe du cercle vicieux n'est pas lui-même la solu-*

major task of "analyzing" the basic concepts of logic
and mathematics in such a way that, in the case of
each of the paradoxes, some crucial definition, specification, or proposition, could be shown to be meaningless, presupposing as it were an "illegitimate"
range of a bound variable. Furthermore, one condition of adequacy of the analysis was that the restrictions placed on the ranges of bound variables by the
theory not be *ad hoc:* "the restrictions must result
naturally and inevitably from our positive doctrines."

In the previous schoolboy puzzle, the student could
begin his task of gaining the necessary understanding
of multiplication and division by picking up an appropriate book on the subject and looking up the relevant
definitions. Russell's project had no analagous starting
point. Insofar as definitions existed of such terms as
"class" and "proposition," they were thought by Russell to be inadequate. Russell was forced to provide
his own analyses of these notions.

As for what is meant by "analysis," this is a very
difficult question indeed. There is no general agreement among philosophers as to what an analysis is
supposed to be, and it is especially difficult to say anything both accurate and precise about Russell's notion. Roughly, in analyzing the notion of class, Russell
wished to clarify and make precise what we mean
(or at least what mathematicians mean) when we
(they) make affirmations involving the term. This is
only a rough explication, as can be seen from the fact
that Russell was not always concerned with showing

*tion des paradoxes de cercle vicieux, mais seulement la consé-
quence qu'une théorie doit fournir pour apporter une solution.
Autrement dit, il faut construire une théorie des expressions
contenant des variables apparentes qui fournisse comme
conséquence le principe de cercle vicieux. C'est pour cette
raison que nous avons besoin d'une reconstruction des
premiers principes logiques, et que nous ne pouvons pas nous
contenter de ce simple fait que les paradoxes sont dus à des
cercles vicieux"* ([3], p. 640).

what we *do* mean: he was at times more intent upon showing us what we ought to mean (or what we can legitimately mean), and this latter aim sprang from his desire not only to clarify what we mean, but also to straighten out what we mean.[10] A study of the paradoxes made it obvious to Russell that our ideas of class and proposition needed straightening out, so he did not feel compelled to explicate only what we do mean. Russell would not have abandoned his analysis of class simply because it gave a distorted account, at certain points, of what mathematicians say, and he was perfectly willing to allow, as a consequence of his analysis, that mathematicians sometimes speak nonsense when they talk about classes. But although Russell was willing to allow his analysis to "deviate" from mathematical practice, he evidently felt that any adequate analysis must at least satisfy a *criterion of conservation:* the analysis must be such that the great body of mathematical truths accumulated over the centuries can be salvaged. For Russell, then, there were two necessary conditions that his analysis had to satisfy to be satisfactory: (1) it had to satisfy the criterion of conservation and in such a way that (2) the mathematics that was preserved would have a solid foundation, free of contradiction.[11]

[10] Cf. Russell's comment about his theory of descriptions: "I was concerned to find a more accurate and analyzed thought to replace the somewhat confused thoughts which most people at most times have in their heads" ([10], p. 243). Cf. also Pears, [1], pp. 18–23.

[11] Cf. [3], p. 649. Russell's reconstruction of mathematics has many points in common with his *reconstruction of empirical knowledge.* As D. Pears writes concerning the latter, "he felt himself pulled in two opposite directions. On the one hand he wanted to save as much as possible. But on the other hand he wanted what was saved to be firmly based on sound foundations, and well and truly saved" (Pears, [1], p. 23).

4

The Role of the "No-Class" Theory in Russell's Solution

Considering the magnitude of Russell's undertaking, it is not surprising that it was constructing the positive part of the solution that he found most troublesome. In [1] (Appendix B), Russell had already hit upon a device for avoiding some of the paradoxes. Roughly, the underlying idea was to restrict the range of the variables occurring in the open sentences in a way that would prevent the specification of such "classes" as the class of all classes that do not belong to themselves: variables would be restricted to entities of certain types, where individuals, classes of individuals, classes of classes of individuals, and so on, were held to be of different types. The system of set theory sketched in the *Principles*—a system which would now be roughly classified as a *simple type theory*—was not, however, free from difficulties.[12] And Russell felt that he had not yet found "the true solution" to the paradoxes. Without discussing the more technical aspects of this early version of type theory, it is easy to give some reasons for Russell's dissatisfaction: in the first place, the restrictions placed upon the ranges of variables in open sentences were devised *ad hoc* and, indeed, seemed counter-intuitive; second—and this is a reason Russell himself gives—the device of stratifying the "universe of discourse" into different types did not show him how to avoid "semantical" paradoxes of a quite similar nature, and this suggested to him that he had not yet arrived at a sufficiently deep insight into the mechanism of these paradoxes ([1], p. 527).

Russell tells us that he worked on this problem

12 See Wang, [3], § 2.

throughout 1903 and 1904 until, in the spring of 1905, he achieved what he considered a partial breakthrough: the Theory of Descriptions![13] In his important paper "On Denoting," Russell provides a method for translating sentences containing denoting phrases of the form "the such-and-such," i.e., what he later called "definite descriptions," into sentences not containing such denoting phrases.[14] In *PM*, expressions of the form "$(\imath x)\phi x$," which supposedly correspond to the definite descriptions of English, are defined contextually as follows. A sentence containing "$(\imath x)\phi x$," which I shall represent "——$(\imath x)\phi x$——,"[15] is simply an abbreviation for

$$(\exists y)\,[(x)\,(\phi x \leftrightarrow x = y)\ \&\ ——y——]$$

and no meaning is given to "$(\imath x)\phi x$" standing alone.

Now Russell's Theory of Descriptions is relevant to Russell's quest for a solution to the paradoxes for more than one reason. Not only was the theory explicitly used in *PM* in the actual development of mathematics from the axioms, but also it paved the way for his no-class theory by serving as the model

---

[13] [10], p. 79. That the discovery of the Theory of Descriptions led to Russell's solution to the paradoxes is related by Russell in several other places. In [11] he says that the Theory of Description "was the first step toward solving the difficulties which had baffled me for so long" (p. 152). In a letter to Lucy Martin Donnelly of June 13, 1905, Russell wrote: "[it] throws a flood of light on the foundations of mathematics" ([11], p. 177).

[14] I do not discuss the details of Russell's Theory of Descriptions, since the reader can find several thorough accounts elsewhere and such a discussion is not needed to understand Russell's solution to the paradoxes. Those not familiar with the intricacies of this aspect of Russell's philosophical development can find a vigorous account given in Linsky, [1]. (See David Kaplan's paper in this volume.)

[15] I follow Quine's notation in [3] here.

for his analysis of propositions involving class-referring expressions.[16] In Russell's own words:

> What was of importance in this theory was the discovery that, in analyzing a significant sentence, one must not assume that each separate word or phrase has significance on its own account. . . . It soon appeared that class-symbols could be treated like descriptions, i.e., as non-significant parts of significant sentences. This made it possible to see, in a general way, how a solution to the contradictions might be possible ([9], p. 14).

How Russell analyzed class-referring expressions can, perhaps, best be shown by stating the key definitions regarding classes in *PM*. In the following, the sentence represented as occurring to the left of the expression "$=_d$" is to be regarded as an abbreviation for the sentence represented as occurring to the right; the exclamation mark indicates that the variable immediately preceding it ranges over propositional functions called "predicative functions." (I shall discuss predicative functions shortly.)

> * 20.01 —$\hat{x}\Psi x$— $=_d$ ($\exists \phi$) [(x) $(\phi!x \leftrightarrow \Psi x)$ & —$\phi!\hat{x}$—].
> * 20.02 $x \in \phi!\hat{z} =_d \phi!x$.
> * 20.07 (α) —α— $=_d$ (ϕ) —$\hat{x}\phi!x$—.
> * 20.08 ($\exists \alpha$) —α— $=_d$ ($\exists \phi$) —$\hat{x}\phi!x$—.

Thus, in *PM*, sentences containing class-referring expressions are treated simply as abbreviations for sen-

16 Cf. Russell's comments in [8], pp. 181–82: "We must seek a definition on the same lines as the definition of descriptions, i.e., a definition which will assign a meaning to propositions in whose verbal or symbolic expression words or symbols apparently representing classes occur, but which will assign a meaning that altogether eliminates all mention of classes from a right analysis of such propositions."

tences containing expressions denoting propositional functions. It is because of this feature that the set theory of *PM* is frequently called a "no-class" theory.[17]

Before examining the relevance of the no-class theory to Russell's proposed solution to the paradoxes, it might be helpful to say something about propositional functions. Given that the *basic entities* of Russell's system of logic and set theory turn out to be not sets, but propositional functions, it is surprising that the precise nature of these propositional functions is left unclear. In *PM*, Russell admits that the "question as to the nature of a [propositional] function is by no means an easy one" (p. 39).[18] So rather than carrying on a detailed discussion of propositional functions at this point, let me merely state those salient features of propositional functions about which there can be little controversy. A propositional function has an argument range and a value range. For each argument, the value of a propositional function is a proposition, so propositional functions are similar to Fregean concepts. It should be noted, however, that whereas Frege's concepts always take *truth values,* propositional functions take truth values only indirectly, through their propositional values, so-to-speak.

In Frege's system, concepts are stratified into different levels: there are first-level concepts, second-level concepts, third-level concepts, and it would seem that one could go on to higher and higher level concepts. The variables of the system are restricted so that no variable that ranges over objects can also range over concepts; furthermore, no variable that ranges over

[17] Actually, Russell himself used the term "no-classes" to describe his theory. See [4], p. 45 and [3], p. 636.

[18] In this work, I do not always give Whitehead his share of the credit for a remark appearing in *PM*. This is primarily for stylistic reasons, although I must confess to thinking that the main philosophical ideas in *PM* are due to Russell. Russell, himself, says: "Broadly speaking, Whitehead left philosophical problems to me" ([10], p. 74).

concepts of one level can also range over concepts of another level. (One might say that Frege's system is a simple type theory for concepts.) However, Frege could see no reason for sorting the *objects* of the system into different ranges: object variables ranged over all the objects. Since the extensions of concepts were all lumped together as objects, Frege's sorting of entities into different ranges for variables did not save his system from Russell's paradox.[19]

Like Frege before him, Russell too evidently felt that logic could not prevent variables from ranging over all the objects in the universe: restricting variables to only part of the totality of objects must have seemed artificial and unmotivated to Russell.[20] This is where the "no-class" theory came in: it allowed Russell to drop the assumption that classes are objects or things, and thus gave him hope that his type-theoretical solution to the paradoxes might still be saved from the charge of arbitrariness. By making propositional functions the *basic entities* of his system, he felt he could justify the type-restrictions on the ranges of variables along the lines that Frege took—except, of course, the justifications would have to proceed in terms of the nature of propositional functions instead of concepts.

Although I have not yet discussed the actual justifications Russell gives for his type-restrictions, enough has been said to indicate the essential role the "no-class" theory plays in this justification. So we now have a partial reconstruction of the reasoning that led Russell to adopt his "no-class" theory. Let us recall at this point that Russell was dissatisfied with the *type theory* sketched in the *Principles* for various

---

[19] Cf. Carnap, [1], p. 138 f.

[20] Cf. Russell's early statement in [3]: "*Si donc le principe du cercle vicieux doit être vérifié, il faut que les classes ne soient pas parmi les valeurs possibles d'une variable entièrement illimitée, ce qui est une autre manière de dire qu'il faut qu'il n'y ait pas de classes*" (p. 646).

reasons. The principal reason for his dissatisfaction was the fact that the simple type theory did not obviate certain "semantical" paradoxes which were thought to be essentially of the same sort as the set theoretical ones. Now Russell came to believe that the "no-class" theory provided him with the means of dealing with this difficulty also, the basic idea being that, by means of the "no-class" theory, all the paradoxes could be reduced to paradoxes about propositions and propositional functions, so that the type theory would obviate them all.[21] Clearly then, the "no-class" theory was central to Russell's solution to the paradoxes.[22] It is a curious fact that mathematical logicians seeking to explicate Russell's vicious-circle principle and his predicative conception of set tend to completely ignore the "no-class" theory.

[21] Cf. *PM*, p. 38.

[22] My explanation of Russell's frequent statements to the effect that the discovery of the theory of descriptions enabled him to find his way to his solution of the paradoxes differs markedly from Quine's. In [6] (p. 300 of this volume), Quine makes the following suggestion: "If we try to be casual about the difference between use and mention as Russell was fifty and sixty years ago, we can see how he might feel that whereas a theory of types of real classes would be ontological, his theory of types of propositional functions had a notational cast. In so far, his withdrawal of classes would be felt as part of his solution of the paradoxes" (p. 308). Needless to say, I believe one can give a much more charitable interpretation: the theory of descriptions led Russell to his "no-class" theory, which in turn was thought to be the key discovery in the quest for a solution of the paradoxes since it seemed to provide him with the crucial step in finding a justification for his type restrictions, and thus for his vicious-circle principle, and it allowed him to treat all the paradoxes, including the set-theoretical ones, in terms of propositions and propositional functions.

5

The System of Orders

Before discussing Russell's justification for his type restrictions, it may be helpful to say something about the system of orders to be found in *PM*. In a *simple* type theory, the "universe" is generally sorted into mutually exclusive totalities over which variables are allowed to range, each variable being restricted to one and only one of these totalities.[23] These ranges, which I shall call "TYPES" (using uppercase letters to distinguish these ranges from *types* of *PM*), can be given as follows:

> TYPE 0: individuals (or objects as distinguished from classes);
> TYPE 1: classes of individuals;
> TYPE 2: classes of classes of individuals;
> .
> .
> .

Now the classification of ranges of variables in *PM* is more complicated than this. What are classified are not individuals and classes but individuals and propositional functions; and propositional functions contain more complexity than classes. In *PM*, propositional functions are sorted into *orders,* and indeed into *types* within orders, each type being a totality over which a variable is allowed to range. The open sentence "$x \in \alpha$" is not considered to be significant unless the variables "x" and "α" range over the appropriate types. Now each propositional function belongs to one and only one type and *a fortiori* to one and only one order. The

[23] The system envisaged by Russell in [1] did not have all these features: not all variables were restricted to one and only one of these ranges.

order of a propositional function depends upon the structure of the formula of *PM* (which contains a circumflex variable) used to denote it. To avoid clumsy and lengthy locutions, when a formula of *PM* used to denote a propositional function contains a variable or quantifier, I shall say simply that the propositional function contains the variable or quantifier. Complications arise in the theory because the system comprises not only monadic propositional functions (functions with only one argument variable), but n-adic propositional functions as well. Since relations can be handled in set theory by means of ordered pairs, it may be thought that the n-adic propositionals are unnecessary and that these complications are avoidable. Unfortunately, if we followed the usual procedure of defining functions to be sets of ordered pairs and ordered pairs to be sets (say, unordered pairs of unordered pairs), Russell's type restrictions would preclude there being any functions that take one type of entity to a different type (e.g., ordered pairs of real numbers to real numbers). However, the system becomes unwieldy and messy if n-adic propositional functions are included, so I shall simplify the following discussion by restricting it to monadic propositional functions.

In *PM*, it is assumed that there is a totality of objects called "individuals," these individuals being of order 0. Variables that range over these individuals are also said to be of order 0. Each variable ranges over one and only one type; and in general, variables of order n are variables that range over entities of order n. Now the order of a propositional function is the least integer greater than the order of all of its bound variables (quantified or circumflex). Thus, the theory of orders effectively eliminates *impredicative propositional functions* (i.e., any propositional function $\phi\hat{x}$ that contains a bound variable ranging over a totality containing either $\phi\hat{x}$ or some propositional function containing reference to $\phi\hat{x}$).

The reader can get an idea of how the orders and

types are distinguished in *PM* by the following considerations. Propositional functions of order 1 clearly can take only individuals as arguments. However, in order 2, we can distinguish two kinds of propositional functions: those that take individuals as arguments and those that take propositional functions of order 1 as arguments. Corresponding to these two kinds of propositional functions, we have two *types* in order 2. In order 3, we can distinguish four *types* of propositional functions: those that take individuals as arguments, those that take propositional functions of order 1 as arguments, and two kinds of propositional functions of order 3 that take propositional functions of order 2 as arguments, the two kinds corresponding to the two *types* of propositional functions of order 2 distinguished above. In order 4, it is easy to distinguish eight *types*, and continuing in this way, there will be 2^{n-1} different *types* of propositional functions of order n.[24]

In *PM*, only finite orders are allowed. Given the restrictions placed upon the ranges of variables, it is easy to see why Russell did not accept transfinite orders: one cannot have a variable ranging over all the finite orders (or even finitely many orders) without violating the type restrictions. Of course, one could have a propositional function of order ω if there were formulas in *PM* containing infinitely many variables, but this is explicitly not allowed (*PM*, p. 53).

A propositional function is called *predicative* when it is of the next order above that of its arguments. Hence a propositional function of order 1 is a predicative propositional function of individuals. An exclamation mark placed immediately after a variable indicates that the variable ranges over predicative

[24] There seems to be some confusion about Russell's ramified type theory. Many believe that Russell divided his ranges into TYPES, and then subdivided each TYPE into orders in accordance with the vicious-circle principle. One finds such an interpretation, for example, in Kleene [1], p. 44.

propositional functions. There is a distinct possibility of confusion as a result of the terminology adopted here, for "predicative" in the above sense does not mean "not impredicative" as one might easily suppose. All of the propositional functions of *PM* are predicative in one sense (i.e., are not impredicative), although only certain ones are predicative in the other. Generally, the context makes clear which sense is being employed.

The system of types described above can be made more perspicuous by the following notation.[25] Individuals will be of type T_0. Propositional functions of order 1 will be of type T_1. Propositional functions of order 2 taking individuals as arguments will be of type $T_{2.0}$. Propositional functions of order 2 taking propositional functions of type T_1 as arguments will be of type $T_{2.1}$. In this way we can build the hierarchy of types as follows:

.
.
.

$$T_{4.0} \quad T_{4.1} \quad T_{4.2.0} \quad T_{4.2.1} \quad T_{4.3.0} \quad T_{4.3.1} \quad T_{4.3.2.0} \quad T_{4.3.2.1}$$
$$T_{3.0} \quad T_{3.1} \quad T_{3.2.0} \quad T_{3.2.1}$$
$$T_{2.0} \quad T_{2.1}$$
$$T_1$$
$$T_0$$

In terms of this schema, a propositional function is predicative if its type is either T_1 or $T_{k.k-1.\sigma}$ (for some natural number k, with σ a sequence of the required sort).

The above exposition of the system is based primarily on section V of the introduction to the first edition of *PM*. The account given in *12 differs significantly from the above. In *12, we are told that

---

[25] This was suggested to me by Len Sasso, although it closely resembles Wang's notation for the system R described in [2], Chapter XXIV, § 10.

predicative functions are matrices, i.e., propositional functions containing no bound variables. By this definition, not all first order propositional functions would be predicative! In contradistinction to this, Russell says in the introduction that predicative functions of individuals are those that take individuals as arguments and that contain no bound variables that range over propositional functions. We are also told in *12 that the exclamation point after a variable that ranges over propositional functions indicates that the variable ranges over predicative functions (p. 164). But in the introduction, we are told that "$\phi!\hat{x}$" will denote *any* first order propositional function (p. 51). Actually, the account given in the introduction comes closer to the view put forward in [7], where it is said that all first order propositional functions are predicative and that, in general, a function of one variable is predicative if it is of order one greater than the order of its arguments (p. 78).

I do not wish to claim that the 2^{n-1} different types distinguished by the above procedure exhausts the totality of types of propositional function of order n. A set of rules for sorting propositional functions into types is given in *PM* (*9.131), which complicates the structure considerably. By these rules, even if two propositional functions have the same argument variable and are of the same order, they would still be of different types if they had different types of bound variables or if the number of occurrences of quantifiers in one differed from the number in the other. Roughly, the rationale for this enormous proliferation of types seems to be this: it is thought, for some reason, that one cannot get propositional functions of the same type from propositional functions of different types by merely changing argument variables into bound variables of quantification. It is thought that if two matrices f_1 and f_2 are of different types, and if g_j is obtained from f_j by such a change of variables ($j = 1, 2$), then g_1 and g_2 must be of different types also. But the logical justification for this principle is obscure. Notice that, by this criterion, there would be infinitely many types of monadic propositional functions of order j (j = 1, 2, 3, . . .). The arguments given in the introduction do not seem to justify such a system of types. Indeed, the system described in the introduction seems to be quite different from the one described in *9. I shall assume in the following discussions, for the sake of brevity and perspicuity, that *PM* has the simpler structure sketched above.

Despite the various restrictions on the ranges of variables, the notation of *PM* does not indicate the type over which a variable ranges. Wishing to keep the notation as simple as possible, the authors argue that for their purposes such indications are not necessary.

> In practice, we never need to know the absolute types of our variables, but only their *relative* types. That is to say, if we prove any proposition on the assumption that one of our variables is an individual, and another is a function of order n, the proof will still hold if, in place of an individual, we take a function of order m, and in place of our function of order n we take a function of order $n + m$ with corresponding changes for any other variables that may be involved (*PM*, p. 165).

Thus the reader is left to specify whatever ranges he wishes for the variables so long as he conforms to the type restriction of *PM*. Throughout *PM*, then, the formal development proceeds with sentences that are "systematically ambiguous" as to type.

6

The Justifications of the Type Restrictions

Let us now examine the Russell-Whitehead justifications for the type restrictions in *PM*. Basically, two

sorts of arguments are used: one purports to show the
need for sorting the universe into TYPES, i.e., along
the lines of a simple type theory; the other argument
aims at proving the need for the full-blown classification into orders and types. I shall begin with the
former argument, which is based upon the "direct
inspection" of a few examples. Let us scrutinize one of
these examples. In a section entitled "Why a Given
Function Requires Arguments of a Certain Type,"
the authors of *PM* claim to show that if something
that is not a propositional function can occur significantly as an argument of a propositional function,
say $\Psi\hat{x}$, then no propositional function can be an argument of $\Psi\hat{x}$.

> Take, e.g., "x is a man," and consider "$\phi\hat{x}$ is a man."
> Here there is nothing to eliminate the ambiguity which
> constitutes $\phi\hat{x}$; there is thus nothing definite which is
> said to be a man (p. 48).

Notice that this argument has some very unintuitive
consequences. First of all, it is the reason there are
no classes in *PM* containing both individuals and
classes; for if there were such a class, then (given the
"no-class" theory) there would have to be a propositional function true of both individuals and propositional functions—something that is precluded by this
appeal to "direct inspections." Second, the argument
seems to show that ($\hat{x}$ is a man) cannot be an argument of ($\hat{x}$ is a propositional function), for using the
above reasoning, we can examine "($\hat{x}$ is a man) is a
propositional function" and conclude that there is
nothing to eliminate the ambiguity which constitutes
($\hat{x}$ is a man).[26] Hence, one would think that in all consistency, Russell and Whitehead would say that if
"$\phi\hat{x}$" denotes a propositional function, then "$\phi\hat{x}$ is a

[26] I use parentheses in this section to indicate the scope of
circumflex variables.

propositional function" is meaningless. But they don't. For them, "$\phi\hat{x}$ is a function" is not a statement containing an ambiguity; it is a true statement "about an ambiguity" (*PM*, p. 40). This last point is surely plausible—the argument from direct inspection, I believe, is not.

In evaluating this argument, I find I must return again to the question, What is a propositional function? In *PM* (p. 14), we find the following definition:

> Let ϕx be a statement containing a variable x and such that it becomes a proposition when x is given any fixed determined meaning. Then ϕx is called a "propositional function." . . .

Since a variable is defined to be a symbol of a certain sort (p. 4), the above definition suggests that propositional functions are expressions or symbols, or more specifically, *open sentences* rather than what philosophers call "attributes" which are supposed to be non-linguistic in nature. The fact that Russell says explicitly ([7], p. 230; [8], p. 155) that a propositional function "is an expression" provides some confirmation of this suggestion. Further evidence of this interpretation is to be found in another place ([4], p. 30) where he says:

> A *propositional function of* x is any expression $\phi!x$ whose value, for every value of x, is a proposition; such is "x is a man" or "sin $x = 1$."

This definition parallels the following definition found in *PM* (p. 38):

> By a "propositional function" we mean something which contains a variable x, and expresses a *proposition* as soon as a value is assigned to x. . . . Thus, e.g., "x is a man" or "sin $x = 1$" is a propositional function.

Furthermore, Russell's own words on the subject provide us with an even stronger case:

> Whitehead and I thought of a propositional function as an expression containing an undetermined variable and becoming an ordinary sentence as soon as a value is assigned to the variable: "*x* is human," for example, becomes an ordinary sentence as soon as we substitute a proper name for "*x*" ([10], p. 124).

There is rather good evidence, however, that Russell also used the term "propositional function" in a quite different sense. First of all, it should be noted that Russell sometimes used the term "verb" to refer not only to a certain type of word, but also to *constituents of facts* "corresponding to verbs" ([7], p. 217). Thus, according to Russell, corresponding to the word "loves" in the proposition "John loves Mary" there is an element of the fact that John loves Mary (supposing the proposition to be true), which "loves" *means* and which Russell also calls a "verb" (see also [6], Chap. IX). Similarly, I believe, Russell used the term "propositional function" to refer, not only to open sentences, but also to something nonlinguistic which somehow corresponds to these open sentences. This is indicated by the fact that in *PM* we find quantification over propositional functions in a way that, on the most natural reading, requires propositional functions to be not open sentences, but rather qualities or attributes corresponding to open sentences.[27] For example, in *PM*, (p. 56) and in [8], (p. 189), the statement "Napoleon has all the qualities that make a great general" is symbolized

$$(\phi)[\phi!\hat{x} \text{ is a quality required in a great general} \rightarrow \phi!(\text{Napoleon})]$$

[27] Quine has made this point in several places. For more details, see [2], pp. 110 and 122; also, [1].

and "$\phi!$(Napoleon)" is understood to mean "Napoleon had the quality $\phi!\hat{x}$." Furthermore, one use of the circumflex in *PM* suggests the attribute sense. Thus we find on p. 15:

> When we wish to speak of the propositional function corresponding to "x is hurt," we shall write "$\hat{x}$ is hurt" . . . though "x is hurt" and "y is hurt" *occurring in the same context* can be distinguished, "$\hat{x}$ is hurt" and "$\hat{y}$ is hurt" convey no distinction of meaning at all.

There is another reason for thinking that Russell sometimes used the term "propositional function" to refer to things other than open sentences. Recall that his reconstruction of mathematics was supposed to satisfy a criterion of conservation. Now in attempting to fulfill this requirement, Russell felt compelled to appeal to a special axiom of reducibility

$$(\exists \Psi) (x) (\phi x \leftrightarrow \Psi!x)$$

which says that, given any propositional function $\phi\hat{x}$, regardless of its order, there is a predicative propositional function, $\Psi!\hat{x}$, extensionally identical to $\phi\hat{x}$. This axiom plays an essential role in the development of the real number system and classical analysis in *PM*. In particular, the axiom is needed to prove the theorem that every bounded class of real numbers has a least upper bound; it is also used in proving Cantor's theorems that the cardinality of a set is less than the cardinality of its power set and that the set of real numbers is uncountable. Thus, if we include this axiom among the axioms of *PM* (including the axiom of infinity), it would appear that one consequence of the axioms is that there must be uncountably many propositional functions of a certain type (since in *PM* propositional functions "go proxy" for sets and real numbers). However, if we take any natural language and construct open sentences from the sentences of this language, we get only countably many open sentences. Since we cannot get uncountably many open sentences from even a denumerable infinity of natural languages, if we regard propositional functions as being open sentences, the axiom of reducibility appears to be false (assuming that the other axioms of *PM* are true).

We should not be hasty in drawing such a conclusion, however, since we have a situation here similar to that of the Skolem paradox.[28] Assume for the present that propositional functions are open sentences. Then the theorem that we interpret as saying the set of real numbers is uncountable actually does not say that there is no one-one correspondence between the reals and the natural numbers—it says instead that there is no propositional function, i.e., open sentence, of a certain sort that "correlates" the reals one-one with the naturals. Thus, including the axiom of reducibility among the axioms of *PM* does not, by itself, provide us with grounds for thinking propositional functions are not open sentences.

However, Russell obviously thought that the theorem of *PM* that, on the usual reading, says the reals are uncountable implies that it is impossible to arrange all the real numbers in, what he calls, a "progression" ([8], p. 84); and it is difficult to see why Russell should have thought this if he interpreted the theorem in the above manner. The essential point is: if propositional functions are open sentences, then many theorems of *PM* that are supposed to express theorems of classical mathematics do not have the consequences they are supposed to have.

Let us return to the "direct-inspection" argument, keeping in mind that there seem to be two distinct senses in which the term "propositional function" is employed by Russell. If we interpret the authors of

[28] For a discussion of the Skolem paradox, see Putnam, [1], pp. 276–77.

PM to be thinking here of propositional functions as being open sentences, then the sentence "$\phi\hat{x}$ is a man" is neither meaningless nor indefinite, given that "$\phi\hat{x}$" denotes some particular propositional function. Thus, if "$\phi\hat{x}$" stands for (denotes) "x is a man," then "$\phi\hat{x}$ is a man" says that the open sentence "x is a man" is a man, and hence what the sentence says is false, not meaningless or indeterminate.

It is possible that a use-mention confusion—a type of error into which Russell was inclined to slip—has occurred in this argument. Consider first of all the following passage which occurs in the course of the statement of the argument:

> A function, in fact, is not a definite object, which could be or not be a man; it is a mere ambiguity awaiting determination, and in order that it may occur significantly it must receive the necessary determination which it obviously does not receive if it is merely substituted for something determinate in a proposition (*PM*, p. 48).

Now the sentence "$\phi\hat{x}$ is a man" can be obtained by substituting "$\phi\hat{x}$" for the occurrence of the name "Socrates" in the proposition "Socrates is a man"; but notice that what is substituted is not the propositional function itself, but rather something that stands for (denotes) the function. It is possible that Russell and Whitehead reasoned as follows: In the sentence "$\phi\hat{x}$ is a man," let us suppose that "$\phi\hat{x}$" stands for the open sentence "x is a man." Then "$\phi\hat{x}$ is a man" means the same thing as "x is a man is a man," which says nothing determinate: "it is a mere ambiguity awaiting determination."

If the authors of *PM* did reason in the above manner, then the argument can be seen to be an instance of the fallacy of equivocation. "$\phi\hat{x}$" must *stand for*, in the sense of denote, "x is a man" for the conclusion of the argument to have the force Russell and Whitehead claim for it; but on the other hand, "$\phi\hat{x}$ is a man" means the same thing as "x is a man is a man" only if "$\phi\hat{x}$" stands for, in the sense of *stands in place of* (as an abbreviation, say), "x is a man."

But could Russell and Whitehead have made such a logical slip? I shall merely contend that the above interpretation has some plausibility. Consider the following passage from *PM* (p. 7):

> . . . "implies" as used here expresses nothing else than the connection between p and q also expressed by the disjunction "not-p or q." The symbol employed for "p implies q," i.e., for "$\sim p \vee q$" is "$p \supset q$." This symbol may also be read "if p, then q."

Now how are we to treat "p" and "q" in the above passage? They are called "variable propositions." But are they variables ranging over propositions or schematic letters (to use Quine's terminology) to be regarded as standing in place of sentences "expressing propositions"? Evidently the former, since quantification over propositions is allowed (*PM*, p. 129 and p. xxii). In that case, when "p" takes as value the proposition expressed by "$2 + 2 = 4$" and "q" takes as value the proposition expressed by "$2 + 3 = 5$," "p implies q" takes as value the proposition expressed by "The proposition expressed by '$2 + 2 = 4$' implies the proposition expressed by '$2 + 3 = 5$.'" But "p implies q" may also be read, according to the above, as "if p, then q," and hence we should be able to express the above proposition by "If the proposition expressed by '$2 + 2 = 4$,' then the proposition expressed by '$2 + 3 = 5$,'" which is nonsense. And we obviously get into the same type of trouble if we treat propositions as sentences. Thus, "'$2 + 2 = 4$' implies '$2 + 3 = 5$'" cannot also be "If '$2 + 2 = 4$,' then '$2 + 3 = 5$.'" So it looks as if Quine is right in claiming ([4], p. 97) that the authors of *PM* were willing to treat "p implies q" as "if p, then *q*" because they did not distinguish clearly and keep distinct propositions from their names.

Thus, since it seems that Russell and Whitehead did commit use-mention errors in *PM*—and the above example is just one of many that I could cite in support of this claim[29]—it would not be too surprising if the source of the "direct inspection" argument were also a use-mention confusion.

On the other hand, we should explore the possibility that they did not make such a mistake. Suppose, for example, that they were thinking of propositional functions as being attributes rather than open sentences in that argument. In this case, propositional functions do not literally contain variables, although they are denoted by expressions containing bound variables. Hence, it surely cannot be determined by "direct inspection" that the sentence "($\hat{x}$ is a man) is a man" says nothing definite. For it is the attribute or, to use a term Russell sometimes used, the *quality* of being a man that is said to be a man. And in this case, too, I am inclined to say that the sentence is false, not meaningless. I fully realize, of course, that some philosophers have argued that it does not make sense to say of a *quality* that it is or is not a man. However, anyone wishing to maintain such a position regarding meaningfulness could hardly defend it by simply appealing to direct inspection.

This, perhaps, is a good reason for supposing that Russell and Whitehead meant by "propositional functions" neither open sentences nor attributes in the traditional philosophical sense. I shall return to this possibility shortly.

Now how is the "direct-inspection" argument relevant to the paradoxes? Consider the Russell paradox. The authors of *PM* argue that by examining examples such as the above, the reader will see that if "$\phi\hat{x}$" denotes some propositional function, then "$\phi(\phi\hat{x})$" must

[29] For further examples, cf. Linsky, [1], pp. 7, 79.

be meaningless. It follows that, in the logical system of *PM*, "$\alpha \in \alpha$" is also meaningless. This can be seen as follows. In virtue of the no-class theory in *PM*, "$\alpha \in \alpha$" would have to be translated

$$(\exists \Psi)[(x)(\Psi!x \leftrightarrow \phi x) \ \& \ \Psi!\hat{z} \in \Psi!\hat{z}]$$

which is the same as

$$(\exists \Psi)[(x)(\Psi!x \leftrightarrow \phi x) \ \& \ \Psi!(\Psi!\hat{z})].$$

And if "$\alpha \in \alpha$" is meaningless, so is "$\sim \alpha \in \alpha$," so we cannot have any class of all classes that do not belong to themselves.

I now turn to the argument used to support the distinctive stratification of propositional functions into orders and types that characterizes the ramified theory of types in *PM*. The argument proceeds from the principle that a propositional function always presupposes (as part of its meaning) its values and never vice versa (p. 39; cf. also p. 54), so I shall refer to this argument as *the presupposition argument*. The main idea behind this principle is that a propositional function is essentially *derivative*; it is only given a totality of propositions $\phi a, \phi b, \phi c, \ldots$ that one can then have a propositional function $\phi\hat{x}$, which, for a given argument, denotes one of the above propositions; and then the values, i.e., the propositions in its value range, are part of the meaning of the propositional function. From the above principle, it is argued that no propositional function could belong to its own argument range. Thus, if $\phi\hat{x}$ belonged to its own argument range, then one of its values would have to be $\phi(\phi\hat{x})$, and this proposition would presuppose $\phi\hat{x}$, which contradicts the above principle. For a similar reason, it is also argued that no propositional function referring to or "presupposing" $\phi\hat{x}$, e.g., $\hat{x}(\Psi x \ \& \ \sim\phi x)$, could belong to the argument range of $\phi\hat{x}$. It is easy to see how these considerations are extended to rule out the possibility of impredicative proposi-

tional functions; for in *PM*, one derives a propositional function containing quantification over some
range *R* from propositional functions containing an
argument variable ranging over *R*.

In evaluating the above argument, I think it is safe
to say that the conclusion is by no means compelling
if one takes propositional functions to be open sentences. The principle used in the argument is surely
not self-evident. Why could there not be a totality of
sentences:

> "John" contains three words.
> "John is tall" contains three words.
> "*x* contains three words" contains three words.
> .
> .
> .

from which one can extract the open sentence "*x* contains three words" and which belongs to its own argument range? Is not the sentence

> "*x* contains three words" contains three words

perfectly coherent and "well-defined" so-to-speak?

It may be argued that the expression " '*x* contains
three words' " does not denote an open sentence. I
submit that it does. If, by "open sentence" one means,
essentially, what Mates means by "sentence-form"
(in [1], Chap. 11, § 3) then "*x* contains three words"
surely is an open sentence. Furthermore, "*x* contains
three words" satisfies "*x* contains three words," given
Mates's definition of "satisfaction" ([1], p. 27).

On the other hand, if we take "propositional function" to mean "attribute" or "property," the argument
seems no more compelling, and indeed, it is difficult
to imagine how Russell and Whitehead could possibly have framed such an argument if they really
thought propositional functions were simply attributes. Thus, we seem to be driven both by the "direct-
inspection" argument and by the above argument to

search for some third interpretation of the term "propositional function."

One possibility that suggests itself is that a propositional function is essentially what one might call the *sense* or *meaning* of a predicate (or perhaps open sentence). Despite the vagueness and unclarity of the notion of sense, such an interpretation would help explain why propositional functions are supposed to be so intimately connected with the expressions of *PM* denoting them. Thus, if the propositional function denoted by $\phi\hat{x}$ is the meaning of the open sentence ϕx, then it would be easy to see how there could be a connection between the logical properties of the propositional function (e.g., its order) and the nature of the quantifiers occurring in ϕx. But will the above two arguments become sound when we interpret "propositional function" in this way? Hardly. I cannot see how this interpretation makes the arguments any more intelligible and convincing than the previous interpretations.

There are other possibilities one might try. Thus, if one concentrates on the presupposition argument, one might suppose that a propositional function is some sort of mathematical function which presupposes its range of values and its argument range. It might be argued that these ranges are presupposed by the propositional function because the ranges are literally parts of the function; or it might be suggested that a propositional function is something that correlates the objects in the argument range with the objects in the value range and hence cannot itself be one of these objects. One trouble with this interpretation, however, is that it does not enable us to get a valid, or even convincing, argument out of the "direct inspection" argument. There seems to be no way of determining by direct inspection that a propositional function (of the above sort) that takes individuals as arguments could not be an argument of another propositional function that also takes individuals as arguments. No one, so far as I can see, has come up with a satisfactory interpretation that both fits Russell's many statements about propositional functions and also makes the above arguments compelling.

Part of the difficulty lies in the apparently conflicting claims made by the authors of *PM* regarding these propositional functions. Thus, the "direct-inspection" argument is supposed to show that the sentence

$$\phi\hat{x} \text{ is a man}$$

is meaningless, since "there is nothing to eliminate the ambiguity which constitutes $\phi\hat{x}$"; on the other hand, Russell and Whitehead seem perfectly willing to assert

$$\phi\hat{x} \text{ is a function,}$$

and there seems to be nothing in the latter (not to be found in the former sentence) to eliminate the ambiguity which constitutes $\phi\hat{x}$. Furthermore, Russell saw nothing wrong with the sentence

$$(\phi)[\phi!\hat{x} \text{ is a quality required in a great general} \rightarrow \phi!(\text{Napoleon})].$$

I believe the most plausible conclusion to draw is that Russell himself did not have a clear notion of propositional function and that his use of the term was simply confused. If we drop the open-sentence interpretation, the nature of propositional functions is left extremely obscure. We have, at best, vague ideas of what they are, how many and what different kinds there are, how to distinguish one from another, and so on. (One wants to ask Russell: What makes you think there are such things?) The fact that there are such obscurities in the foundations of *PM* is no trivial matter, for it casts doubt on such fundamental statements of the system as the axiom of reducibility: one begins to wonder if the ranges of variables are well-defined totalities, and hence if the question of

whether there are nondenumerably many propositional functions in some range, even has a definite answer.[30] This is one reason for thinking that Russell's
solution to the paradoxes is defective: the attempted
reconstruction of logic and mathematics which is
aimed at bringing out the logical fallacies that un-
derlie the paradoxes, far from having set mathematics
on a firm and unshakable foundation, rests upon the
dubious notion of propositional function—a notion as
much in need of analysis and reconstruction as the
fundamental notions of mathematics with which he
dealt.

7

*An Alternative Justification for a Hierarchy of
Types*

I believe one can give a more reasonable justification for constructing a hierarchy of types of propositional functions than those discussed in § 6. Let us
suppose that propositional functions are qualities or
attributes that open sentences denote. In the following, I shall talk about "constructing" propositional
functions in stages. Actually, this is just a metaphori-
cal way of describing the process of defining (in
stages) the open sentences that are supposed to denote the propositional functions. Now suppose that
we wish to construct propositional functions that contain quantification over propositional functions. (To
simplify matters, I shall begin by restricting the discussion to propositional functions of individuals.)
Sound methodology requires that the ranges of the
bound variables be made definite. Let us assume, as
Russell did, that we can start with some definite totality of propositional functions that contain at most
quantification over the "individuals." Undoubtedly,
this assumption is infected with a significant amount

[30] Cf. H. Putnam, [1], pp. 278–81.

of vagueness, but in any case, the assumption is no more doubtful than one with which Russell began. Then, since we have a definite totality of propositional functions, we can define new propositional functions by allowing quantification over this totality. These constructed propositional functions will give us a new range over which we can quantify, so we can construct propositional functions of higher order. By defining propositional functions in stages in this way, we can erect a hierarchy of types of propositional functions. It is easy to see how one can proceed in a similar fashion to construct a hierarchy of types of propositional functions that take both individuals and propositional functions as arguments. Of course, there is nothing in the above reasoning to rule out having variables that range over more than one type of propositional functions: the hierarchy might be a sort of cumulative system. Furthermore, there seems to be no compelling reason for restricting oneself to only finite orders. In any case, such a hierarchy would bear a strong resemblance to the ramified hierarchy of *PM*.

Not surprisingly, there are passages in *PM* that do suggest thoughts similar to the above. The following is a good example:

> Consider a function whose argument is an individual. This function presupposes the totality of individuals; but unless it contains functions as apparent variables, it does not presuppose any totality of functions. If, however, it does contain a function as apparent variable, then it cannot be defined until some totality of functions has been defined. It follows that we must first define the totality of those functions that have individuals as arguments and contain no functions as apparent variables (p. 54).

Such passages supply us with hints as to why Russell thought the paradoxes were due to some sort of vicious circle. Let me first state some of the more pertinent historical facts. In 1906, Russell published [4], in which he suggested that, in view of the paradoxes, we must give up the belief that all conditions (properties, norms, or propositional functions) determine sets.[31] Using the term "predicative" to characterize those conditions that do determine sets, Russell posed the question: which conditions are predicative and which are not? Poincaré volunteered an answer to this question in [1]. He claimed that the paradoxes were due to viciously circular definitions and to the unwarranted assumption of the actual infinite. He then suggested that the predicative conditions were those that do not contain a vicious circle. Evidently, it was from this suggestion that the term "predicative" and "impredicative" came to take on the sense described earlier in this paper. Russell responded to these suggestions shortly thereafter in [3]. He said that although he disagreed with Poincaré on the question of the actual infinite, he agreed completely that the paradoxes were due to viciously circular definitions. It is also worth noting that in *PM* the reader is referred to Poincaré's article for support of the claim that the paradoxes result from some sort of vicious circle.

So one might conclude that Russell was satisfied with Poincaré's vicious-circle analysis of the paradoxes. However, Russell's "no-class" theory would seem to necessitate some differences in analysis. It would seem that, for Russell, the set-theoretical paradoxes do not result from defining some set in terms of itself as Poincaré suggested, but rather from defining some propositional function in terms of itself. Now essentially, Russell analyzed each of the paradoxes as arising from the belief in some propositional function that is supposed to fall within the range of one of its own variables. So the basic question is: why did

[31] Roughly, this suggestion can be taken to be one advocating a restricted abstraction axiom.

Russell think that such propositional functions have viciously circular definitions?

Suppose that a propositional function contains a quantifier ranging over a totality of propositional functions. It is natural to say of this propositional function that it has been defined in terms of the propositional functions of that totality. Thus, it is also natural to think that if $\phi\hat{x}$ contains a quantifier ranging over a totality to which $\phi\hat{x}$, itself, belongs, then $\phi\hat{x}$ has been defined in terms of itself, i.e., that the definition of $\phi\hat{x}$ is circular. One might then conclude that, since the paradoxes seem to result from such circular definitions, the definitions must be viciously circular.

Although the reasoning described in this section has some plausibility, in the end, Russell's claim to have solved the paradoxes simply does not ring true. There are many points at which one might question Russell's analysis of the paradoxes. Consider, for example, the set-theoretical paradoxes. Essentially, what Russell does is translate such paradoxes into paradoxes about propositional functions, and then argue, on the basis of his analysis of propositional functions, that in each case some step in the reasoning is illegitimate. But unless one is convinced that Russell's "no-class" analysis is indeed correct, why should one suppose that the illegitimate step in the paradox about propositional functions is the "fallacious step" in the corresponding set-theoretical paradox? Well, why should one doubt that statements about sets get accurately translated into statements about propositional functions by the Russellian method? There are many reasons. For one, the set theory developed in *PM* has many highly counter-intuitive features, as, for example, the existence of infinitely many null sets. Besides, the stratification of sets into types and restricting the variables to one type is not intuitive. From the point of view of those who think that there really are sets which exist independently of human thoughts and practices, the vicious-circle principle is false. (Of course, if one thinks that there are such things as sets, as distinct from propositional functions, one would reject the "no-class" theory outright.) Thus, one might have legitimate doubts about the claim made by the authors of *PM* that the theory of types "leads both to the avoidance of contradictions, and to the detection of the precise fallacy which has given rise to them" (p. 1).

REFERENCES

All page references in the text to works cited below are to the reprinted versions.

Bar-Hillel, Y.
1 and A. A. Fraenkel. *Foundations of Set Theory*, Amsterdam: North-Holland, 1958.

Beth, E. W.
1 *The Foundations of Mathematics*, Amsterdam: North-Holland, 1959.

Carnap, R.
1 *The Logical Syntax of Language*, tr. by A. Smeaton, Paterson, N.J.: Littlefield, Adams, 1959; first published in English by Routledge & Kegan Paul, London, 1937.

Fraenkel, A.
1 and Y. Bar-Hillel. *Foundations of Set Theory*, Amsterdam: North-Holland, 1958.

Gödel, K.
1 "Russell's Mathematical Logic," *The Philosophy of Bertrand Russell*, ed. by P. Schilpp, New York: Tudor, 1944, pp. 123–53.

Kleene, S. C.
1 *Introduction to Metamathematics*, New York and Toronto: Van Nostrand, 1952.

Linsky, L.

  1 *Referring,* London: Routledge & Kegan Paul, 1967.

Mates, B.

  1 *Elementary Logic,* New York: Oxford University Press, 1965.

Pears, D.

  1 *Bertrand Russell and the British Tradition in Philosophy,* London: Collins, 1967. New York: Random House, 1968.

Poincaré, H.

  1 "Les Mathématiques et la Logique," *Revue de Métaphysique et de Morale* 13 (1905), pp. 815–35; 14 (1906), pp. 17–34; 14 (1906), pp. 294–317.

Putnam, H.

  1 "The Thesis that Mathematics Is Logic," *Bertrand Russell: Philosopher of the Century,* ed. by R. Schoenman, London: Allen & Unwin, 1967, pp. 273–303.

Quine, W. V. O.

  1 "Whitehead and the Rise of Modern Logic," *The Philosophy of Alfred North Whitehead,* ed. by P. A. Schilpp, New York: Tudor, 1951, pp. 125–63.

  2 *From a Logical Point of View,* Cambridge, Mass.: Harvard University Press, 1953.

  3 *Methods of Logic,* New York: Henry Holt, 1960.

  4 "Comments," *Boston Studies in the Philosophy of Science,* ed. by M. Wartofsky, Dordrecht-Holland (D. Reidel), 1963, pp. 97–104.

  5 *Set Theory and Its Logic,* Cambridge, Mass.: Harvard University Press, 1963.

  6 "Russell's Ontological Development," *Ber-*

trand Russell: Philosopher of the Century (see Putnam [1]), pp. 304–14.

Russell, Bertrand

1   *The Principles of Mathematics,* Cambridge: Cambridge University Press, 1903; 2d ed., London: Allen & Unwin, 1937.

2   "On Denoting," *Mind,* New Series, 14 (1905), pp. 479–93; reprinted in *Logic and Knowledge,* ed. by R. Marsh, London: Allen & Unwin, 1956, pp. 39–56.

3   "Les Paradoxes de la Logique," *Revue de Métaphysique et de la Morale* 14 (1906), pp. 627–50.

4   "Some Difficulties in the Theory of Transfinite Numbers and Order Types," *Proceedings of the London Mathematical Society* 4 (1907), pp. 29–53.

5   "Mathematical Logic as Based on the Theory of Types," *American Journal of Mathematics* 30, (1908), pp. 222–62; reprinted in *Logic and Knowledge* (see Russell [2], pp. 59–102).

6   *Problems of Philosophy,* New York: Oxford University Press, 1912.

7   "The Philosophy of Logical Atomism," *Monist* 28 (1918), pp. 495–527; reprinted in *Logic and Knowledge* (see Russell, [2], pp. 177–281).

8   *Introduction to Mathematical Philosophy,* London: Allen & Unwin, 1919.

9   "My Mental Development," *The Philosophy of Bertrand Russell* (see Gödel [1]), pp. 3–20.

10   *My Philosophical Development,* New York: Simon and Schuster, 1959.

11   *Autobiography,* London: Allen & Unwin, Vol. 1 (1872–1914), 1967.

12   and A. N. Whitehead. *Principia Mathematica,* Cambridge: Cambridge University Press,

Vol. 1 (1910); paperback to *56, Cambridge: Cambridge University Press, 1967.

Shoenfield, J. R.
1 "The Problem of Predicativity," *Essays on the Foundations of Mathematics*, ed. by Y. Bar-Hillel, E. I. J. Posanaski, M. Rabin, and A. Robinson, Amsterdam: North-Holland, 1962.

Wang, H.
1 "Ordinal Numbers and Predicative Set Theory," *Zeitschrift für mathematische Logic und Grundlagen der Mathematik* 5 (1959), pp. 216–39; reprinted in Wang [2], 624–51.
2 *A Survey of Mathematical Logic*, Amsterdam: North-Holland, 1962.
3 "Russell and His Logic," *Ratio* 7 (1965), pp. 1–34.

Whitehead, A. N.
1 and B. Russell. *Principia Mathematica* (see Russell [12]).

Wilder, R.
1 *Introduction to the Foundations of Mathematics*, New York: Wiley, 1952.

Wittgenstein, L.
1 *Zettel*, ed. by G. E. M. Anscombe and G. H. von Wright, tr. by G. E. M. Anscombe, Berkeley and Los Angeles: University of California Press, 1967.

RUSSELL'S ONTOLOGICAL DEVELOPMENT

W. V. Quine

The twentieth century began, as many of you know, in 1901. Russell was 28 and had published three books: one on politics, one on mathematics, and one on philosophy. Late next summer the century will be two-thirds over. Russell's books have run to forty, and his philosophical influence, direct and indirect, over this long period has been unequalled.

Russell's name is inseparable from mathematical logic, which owes him much, and it was above all Russell who made that subject an inspiration to philosophers. The new logic played a part in the philosophical doctrines that Russell propounded during the second decade of this century—doctrines of unsensed sensa and perspectives, logical constructions and atomic facts. These doctrines affect our thinking today both directly and through supervening schools of thought. The impact of logical empiricism upon present-day philosophy is to an important degree Russell's impact at one remove, as the references in Carnap and elsewhere generously attest. Moreover, Wittgenstein's philosophy was an evolution from views that Russell and the young Wittgenstein had shared. The Oxford philosophy of ordinary language must admit, however bleakly, to a strong strain of Russell in its origins.

I think many of us were drawn to our profession by Russell's books. He wrote a spectrum of books for a graduated public, layman to specialist. We were be-

This essay first appeared in *The Journal of Philosophy*, Vol. LXIII, No. 21, November 1966. It is reprinted by permission of the author and the editor of *The Journal of Philosophy*.

guiled by the wit and a sense of new-found clarity
with respect to central traits of reality. We got mem-
orable first lessons in relativity, elementary particles,
infinite numbers, and the foundations of arithmetic.
At the same time we were inducted into traditional
philosophical problems, such as that of the reality of
matter and that of the reality of minds other than our
own. For all this emergence of problems the over-
riding sense of new-found clarity was more than a
match. In sophisticated retrospect we have had at
points to reassess that clarity, but this was a sophisti-
cation that we acquired only after we were hooked.

Russell spoke not only to a broad public, but to a
broad subject matter. The scatter of his first three
books set a precedent to which his books of the next
six decades conformed. Some treat of education, marriage, morals, and, as in the beginning, politics. I shall
not venture to guess whether the world is better for
having heeded Russell in these further matters to the
degree that it has, or whether it is better for not having heeded him more. Or both.

Instead I shall talk of Russell's ontological development. For I must narrow my scope somehow, and ontology has the virtue of being central and not unduly
narrow. Moreover Russell's ontology was conditioned
conspicuously by both his theory of knowledge and
his logic.

In *Principles of Mathematics*, 1903, Russell's ontology was unrestrained. Every word referred to something. If the word was a proper name, in Russell's
somewhat deviant sense of that phrase, its object was
a *thing;* otherwise a *concept.* He limited the term 'existence' to things, but reckoned things liberally, even
including instants and points of empty space. And
then, beyond existence, there were the rest of the entities: 'numbers, the Homeric gods, relations, chimeras, and four-dimensional spaces' (pp. 44, 449). The
word 'concept', which Russell applied to these non-

existents, connotes mereness; but let us not be put off. The point to notice, epithets aside, is that gods and chimeras are as real for Russell as numbers. Now this is an intolerably indiscriminate ontology. For, take impossible numbers: prime numbers divisible by 6. It must in some sense be false that there are such; and this must be false in some sense in which it is true that there are prime numbers. In *this* sense are there chimeras? Are chimeras then as firm as the good prime numbers and firmer than the primes divisible by 6?

Russell may have meant to admit certain chimeras (the possible ones) to the realm of being, and still exclude the primes divisible by 6 as impossibles. Or he may, like Meinong, have intended a place even for impossible objects. I do not see that in *Principles of Mathematics* Russell faced that question.

Russell's long article on Meinong came out in *Mind* in instalments the following year.[1] In it he criticized details of Meinong's system, but still protested none against the exuberance of Meinong's realm of being. In the same quarterly three issues later, however, a reformed Russell emerges: the Russell of 'On Denoting' (1905), fed up with Meinong's impossible objects. The reform was no simple change of heart; it hinged on his discovery of a means of dispensing with the unwelcome objects. The device was Russell's theory of singular descriptions, that paradigm, as Ramsey has said, of philosophical analysis. It involved defining a term not by presenting a direct equivalent of it, but by what Bentham called *paraphrasis:* by providing equivalents of all desired sentences containing the term. In this way, reference to fictitious objects can be simulated in meaningful sentences without our being committed to the objects.

The new freedom that paraphrasis confers is our reward for recognizing that the unit of communica-

[1] 'Meinong's Theory of Complexes and Assumptions', *Mind*, 1904, pp. 204–19, 33–54, 509–24.

tion is the sentence and not the word. This point of semantical theory was long obscured by the undeniable primacy, in one respect, of words. Sentences being limitless in number and words limited, we necessarily understand most sentences by construction from antecedently familiar words. Actually there is no conflict here. We can allow the sentences a monopoly of full 'meaning', in some sense, without denying that the meaning must be worked out. Then we can say that knowing words is knowing how to work out the meanings of sentences containing them. Dictionary definitions of words are mere clauses in a recursive definition of the meanings of sentences.

Bentham was perhaps the first to see the sentence thus as the primary vehicle of meaning. Frege took up the tale.[2] But Russell, in his theory of singular description, was the first to put this insight to precise and effective use. Frege and Peano had allowed singular description the status of a primitive notation; only with Russell did it become an 'incomplete symbol defined in use'. What suggested the expedient to Russell was not in fact Bentham's work, it seems, but a use of operators in the differential calculus.[3]

Russell's preoccupation with incomplete symbols began with his theory of singular descriptions in 1905. But it continued and spread, notably to classes. For background on classes we must slip back a few years. Classes were an evident source of discomfort to Russell when he was writing *Principles of Mathematics*. There was, for one thing, his epoch-making paradox. Burali-Forti had found a paradox of classes as early as 1897, but it concerned infinite ordinal numbers, and could be accommodated, one hoped, by some local adjustment of theory. On the other hand, Russell's simple paradox of the class of all classes not belonging to themselves struck at the roots. It dates from

[2] *Grundlagen der Arithmetik*, § 60.
[3] Cf. *Principia Mathematica*, I, p. 24.

1901, when, as Frege is said to have said, arithmetic tottered.

Russell's accommodation of the paradoxes, his theory of types, came only in 1908. In *Principles*, 1903, we find no more than tentative gropings in that direction. But *Principles* evinces much discomfort over classes also apart from the paradoxes. The further source of discomfort is the ancient problem of the one and the many. It seems strange now that Russell saw a problem in the fact that a single class might have many members, since he evidently saw no problem in the corresponding fact that a single attribute, or what he then called a class-concept, might apply to many things. What made the difference was that, in the bipartite ontology of *Principles of Mathematics*, classes counted as things rather than as concepts; classes existed. Russell observed against Peano that 'we must not identify the class with the class-concept', because of extensionality: classes with the same members are the same (p. 68). Since the class was not the class-concept, Russell took it not to be a concept at all; hence it has to be a thing. But then, he felt, it ought to be no more than the sum of the things in it; and here was his problem of the one and the many.

We saw that in 1905 Russell freed himself of Meinong's impossibles and the like by a doctrine of incomplete symbols. Classes were next. In his 1908 paper, 'Mathematical logic as based on the theory of types', there emerges not only the theory of types but also a doctrine of incomplete symbols for explaining classes away. This latter doctrine is designed precisely to take care of the point Russell had made against Peano in connection with extensionality. Russell's contextual definition of class notation gave the benefit of classes, namely extensionality, without assuming more than class-concepts after all.

Seeing Russell's perplexities over classes, we can understand his gratification at accommodating classes

under a theory of incomplete symbols. But the paradoxes, which were the most significant of these perplexities, were not solved by his theory of incomplete
symbols; they were solved, or parried, by his theory
of types. One is therefore startled when Russell declares in 'My mental development' that his expedient
of incomplete symbols 'made it possible to see, in a
general way, how a solution of the contradictions
might be possible'.[4] If the paradoxes had invested
only classes and not class concepts, then Russell's
elimination of classes would indeed have eliminated
the paradoxes and there would have been no call for
the theory of types. But the paradoxes apply likewise,
as Russell knew, to class concepts, or propositional
functions. And thus it was that the theory of types, in
this its first full version of 1908, was developed expressly and primarily for propositional functions and
then transmitted to classes only through the contextual definitions.

The startling statement that I quoted can be accounted for. It is linked to the preference that Russell
was evincing, by 1908, for the phrase 'propositional
function' over 'class concept'. Both phrases were current in *Principles of Mathematics;* mostly the phrase
'propositional function' was visibly meant to refer to
notational forms, namely open sentences, while concepts were emphatically not notational. But after laying waste Meinong's realm of being in 1905, Russell
trusted concepts less and favoured the more nominalistic tone of the phrase 'propositional function', which
bore the double burden. If we try to be as casual
about the difference between use and mention as Russell was fifty and sixty years ago, we can see how he
might feel that whereas a theory of types of real
classes would be ontological, his theory of types of
propositional functions had a notational cast. In so far,

[4] P. A. Schilpp, ed., *The Philosophy of Bertrand Russell,*
p. 14.

his withdrawal of classes would be felt as part of his solution of the paradoxes. This feeling could linger to 1943, when he wrote 'My mental development', even if its basis had lapsed.

We, careful about use and mention, can tell when Russell's so-called propositional functions must be taken as concepts, more specifically as attributes and relations, and when they may be taken as mere open sentences or predicates. It is when he quantifies over them that he reifies them, however unwittingly, as concepts. This is why no more can be claimed for his elimination of classes than I claimed for it above: a derivation of classes from attributes, or concepts, by a contextual definition framed to supply the missing extensionality. On later occasions Russell writes as if he thought that his 1908 theory, which reappeared in *Principia Mathematica*, disposed of classes in some more sweeping sense than reduction to attributes.

Just how much more sweeping a reduction he was prepared to claim may have varied over the years. Readers have credited him with explaining classes away in favour of nothing more than a nominalistic world of particulars and notations.[5] But Russell early and late has expressly doubted the dispensability of universals. Even if we were ingeniously to paraphrase all talk of qualities, for instance, into an idiom in which we talk rather of similarity to chosen particulars instancing those qualities, still, Russell more than once remarked, we should be left with one universal, the relation of similarity. Now here, in contrast to the class matter, I think Russell even concedes the Platonists too much; retention of the two-place predicate 'is similar to' is no evidence of assuming a corresponding abstract entity, the similarity relation, as long as that relation is not invoked as a value of a bound variable. A moral of all this is that inattention to referential semantics works two ways, obscuring some on-

[5] Hans Hahn, 'Ueberflüssige Wesenheiten', Vienna, 1928.

tological assumptions and creating an illusion of others.

What I have ascribed to confusion can be ascribed to indifference; for we are apt to take pains over a distinction only to the degree that we think it matters. Questions as to what there is were for Russell of two sorts, questions of existence in his restricted sense of the term and residual questions of being—questions of what he came to call subsistence. The questions as to what subsists evidently struck him as less substantial, more idly verbal perhaps, than questions as to what exists. This bias toward the existential would explain his indiscriminate bestowal of subsistence in *Principles of Mathematics*. True, he called a halt in 1905 with his theory of descriptions; but on that occasion he was provoked by the impossibility of Meinong's impossibles. And he had even put up with those for a time. Moreover, Russell continued to be very prodigal with subsistence even after propounding his theory of descriptions. We find him saying still in 1912 that 'nearly all the words to be found in the dictionary stand for universals'.[6]

I am suggesting that through his fourth decade Russell took a critical interest in existential questions but was relatively offhand about subsistential ones. This bias explains his glee over eliminating classes, and his indifference over the status of the surviving propositional functions; for we noted that in *Principles* the classes occupied, however uneasily, the existential zone of being. To hold that classes, if there be any, must exist, while attributes at best subsist, does strike me as arbitrary; but such was Russell's attitude.

Russell's relative indifference to subsistence shows again in his treatment of meaning. Frege's three-way distinction between the expression, what it means, and what if anything it refers to, did not come naturally to Russell. In 'On denoting', 1905, he even argued

[6] *Problems of Philosophy*, p. 146.

against it. His argument is hard to follow; at points
it seems to turn on a confusion of expressions with
their meanings, and at points it seems to turn on a
confusion of the expression with the mention of it,
while elsewhere in the same pages Russell seems clear
on both distinctions. The upshot is that 'the relation
of "C" to C remains wholly mysterious; and where
are we to find the denoting complex "C" which is
supposed to denote C? . . . This is an inextricable
tangle, and seems to prove that the whole distinction
between meaning and denotation has been wrongly
conceived' (p. 50).[7]

In other writings Russell commonly uses the word
'meaning' in the sense of 'reference'; thus '"Napoleon"
means a certain individual' and '"Man" means a whole
class of such particulars as have proper names'.[8]
What matters more than terminology is that Russell
seldom seems heedful, under any head, of a subsistent
entity such as *we* might call the meaning, over and
above the existent object of reference. He tends, as in
the 1905 paper 'On denoting', to blur that entity with
the expression itself. Such was his general tendency
with subsistents.

For my own part, I am chary of the idea of meaning and furthermore I think Russell too prodigal with
subsistent entities. So it would be odd of me to criticize Russell for not recognizing meanings as subsistent
entities. However, the outcome that wants criticizing
is just that for want of distinctions Russell tended to
blur meaninglessness with failure of reference. This
was why he could not banish the king of France without first inventing the theory of descriptions. To make
sense is to have a meaning, and the meaning is the
reference; so 'the king of France' is meaningless, and
'The king of France is bald' is meaningful only by being short for a sentence not containing 'the king of

[7] Pagination of *Logic and Knowledge*.

[8] *Analysis of Mind*, pp. 191, 194.

France'. Well, even if the theory of descriptions was not needed in quite this way, it brought major clarifications and we are thankful for it.

Russell's tendency to blur subsistent entities with expressions was noticed in his talk of propositional functions. It is equally noticeable in what he says of propositions. In *Principles of Mathematics* he describes propositions as expressions, but then he speaks also of the unity of propositions (p. 50), and of the possibility of infinite propositions (p. 145), in ways ill suited to such a version. In 'Meinong's theory', 1904, he speaks of propositions as judgments (p. 523). There is similar oscillation in *Principia Mathematica*.

But by the time of 'The Philosophy of Logical Atomism', 1918, the oscillation has changed direction. At one point in this essay we read, 'a proposition is just a symbol' (p. 185);[9] at a later point we read rather, 'Obviously propositions are nothing. . . . To suppose that in the actual world of nature there is a whole set of false propositions going about is to my mind monstrous' (p. 223). This repudiation is startling. We had come to expect a blur between expressions and subsistent entities, concepts; what we get instead of subsistence is nothingness. The fact is that Russell has stopped talking of subsistence. He stopped by 1914. What would once have counted as subsisting has been disposed of in any of three ways: identified with its expression, or repudiated utterly, or elevated to the estate of out-and-out existence. Qualities and relations come to enjoy this elevation; Russell speaks in 'The philosophy of logical atomism' of 'those ultimate simples, out of which the world is built, . . . that . . . have a kind of reality not belonging to anything else. Simples . . . are of an infinite number of sorts. There are particulars and qualities and relations of various orders, a whole hierarchy' (p. 270).

Russell's abandonment of the term 'subsistence' was

[9] Pagination of *Logic and Knowledge*.

an improvement. It is a quibbling term; its function is to limit existence verbally to space-time and so divert attention from ontological commitments of other than spatio-temporal kind. Better to acknowledge all posits under an inclusive and familiar heading. Posits too dubious for such recognition will then be dropped, as were propositions in some sense.

As for propositions, in particular, we saw Russell in this essay taking them as expressions part of the time and part of the time simply repudiating them. Dropping then the ambiguous epithet, we might take this to be Russell's net thought: there are no non-linguistic things that are somehow akin to sentences and asserted by them.

But this is not Russell's thought. In the same essay he insists that the world does contain non-linguistic things that are akin to sentences and asserted by them; he merely does not call them propositions. He calls them facts. It turns out that the existence of non-linguistic analogues of sentences offends Russell only where the sentences are false. His facts are what many of us would have been content to call true propositions. Russell himself called them that in 1904,[10] propositions then being judgments; and in the 1918 essay now under discussion he allows them full-fledged existence. 'Facts belong to the objective world' (p. 183). True, he says a page earlier that 'when I speak of a fact I do not mean a particular existing thing'; but he is here distinguishing between fact and thing only as between sorts of existents, paralleling the distinction between sentences and names. Facts you can assert and deny; things you can name (p. 270). Both exist; 'thing' has ceased to be coextensive with 'existent'.

Russell in this 1918 essay acknowledges Wittgenstein's influence. Russell's ontology of facts here is a reminder of Wittgenstein, but a regrettable one. Wittgenstein thought in his *Tractatus* days that true sen-

[10] 'Meinong's theory', p. 523.

tences mirrored nature, and this notion led him to posit things in nature for true sentences to mirror; namely, facts.

Not that Wittgenstein started Russell on facts. Russell was urging a correspondence between facts and propositions in 1912,[11] when he first knew Wittgenstein; and he equates facts with true judgments as early, we saw, as 1904. Russell had his own reason for wanting facts as entities, and Wittgenstein abetted him.

Russell was receptive to facts as entities because of his tendency to conflate meaning with reference. Sentences, being meaningful, had to stand to some sort of appropriate entities in something fairly like the relation of naming. Propositions in a non-sentential sense were unavailable, having been repudiated; so facts seemed all the more needed. They do not exactly serve as references of false sentences, but they help. For each true or false sentence there *is* a fact, which the sentence asserts or denies according as the sentence is true or false. This two-to-one variety of reference became for Russell even a central trait distinguishing sentences from names, and so facts from things.[12]

Russell continued to champion facts, right through his *Inquiry into Meaning and Truth* and into *Human Knowledge*, 1948. In *Human Knowledge* the term applies not only to what true statements assert, but to more: 'Everything that there is in the world I call a fact' (p. 143).

Russell's predilection for a fact ontology depended, I suggested, on confusion of meaning with reference. Otherwise I think Russell would have made short shrift of facts. He would have been put off by what strikes a reader of 'The Philosophy of Logical Atomism': how the analysis of facts rests on analysis of lan-

[11] *Problems of Philosophy*, pp. 198 ff.
[12] 'The Philosophy of Logical Atomism', pp. 187, 270.

guage. Anyway Russell does not admit facts as fundamental; atomic facts are atomic as facts go, but they
are compound objects.[13] The atoms of Russell's logical
atomism are not atomic facts but sense-data.

In *Problems of Philosophy*, 1912, Russell had
viewed both sense-data and external objects as irreducible existents. We are acquainted with sense-data
beyond peradventure, he held, whereas our belief in
external objects is fallible; still, speaking fallibly, both
are real. Our belief in external objects is rooted in instinct, but it is rational of us, he held, to accept such
dictates of instinct in the absence of counter-evidence
(p. 39). This cheerful resignation echoes Hume and
harmonizes also with the current Oxford way of justifying scientific method: scientific method is part
of what 'rational' means.

Two years later, in *Our Knowledge of the External
World*, Russell was more sanguine. Here it was that
sense-data became logical atoms for the construction
of the rest of the world. Already in *Problems* he had
talked of private worlds of sense-data and the public
space of physics, and of their correlations. Now we
find him using these correlations as a means of identifying external objects with classes of sense-data. He
identifies the external object with the class of all the
views of it in private worlds, actual and ideal. In so
doing he also pin-points each of the private worlds
as a point in public space.

It was a great idea. If executed with all conceivable
success, it would afford translation of all discourse
about the external world into terms of sense-data, set
theory, and logic. It would not settle induction, for
we should still be in the position of predicting sense-
data from sense-data. But it would settle the existence
of external things. It would show that assumption su-

[13] 'The Philosophy of Logical Atomism', pp. 198 f., 270; *Our
Knowledge of the External World*, p. 54.

perfluous, or prove it true; we could read the result either way.

It would neatly settle the ontology of the external world, by reducing it to that of the set theory of sense-data. In *Our Knowledge of the External World*, moreover, Russell wrote as though he had eliminated classes, and not just reduced them to attributes (cf. pp. 224 f.); so he would have looked upon the project, if successful, as resting on an ontology of sense-data alone (cf. p. 153). But by 1918 he thought better of this point, as witness the recognition of 'qualities and relations . . . a whole hierarchy' lately quoted.

In *Our Knowledge of the External World* Russell expressed no confidence that the plan he sketched could be fully realized. In his sketch, as he remarked, he took other minds for granted; moreover he broached none of the vast detail that would be needed for the further constructions, except for a few illustrative steps. But the illustrations gave a vivid sense that the concepts of *Principia Mathematica* could be helpful here and the many ingenious turns and strategies of construction that went into *Principia* could be imitated to advantage. A strategy much in evidence is definition by abstraction—what Whitehead came to call *extensive abstractions*, and Carnap *quasianalysis*.

It was left to Carnap, in 1928, to be inspired to press the plan. Russell's intervening works 'The Philosophy of Logical Atomism', *The Analysis of Matter*, and *The Analysis of Mind* might in view of their titles have been expected to further it, but they did not. The dazzling sequel to *Our Knowledge of the External World* was rather Carnap's *Der Logische Aufbau der Welt*. Carnap achieved remarkable feats of construction, starting with sense-data and building explicitly, with full *Principia* techniques and *Principia* ingenuity, toward the external world. One must in the end despair of the full definitional reduction dreamed of in recent paragraphs, and it is one of the merits of the

Aufbau that we can see from it where the obstacles
lie. The worst obstacle seems to be that the assigning
of sense qualities to public place-times has to be kept
open to revision in the light of later experience, and
so cannot be reduced to definition. The empiricist's
regard for experience thus impedes the very pro-
gramme of reducing the world to experience.[14]

Russell meanwhile was warping his logical atomism over from its frankly phenomenalistic form to
what, influenced by Perry and Holt, he called neutral monism.[15] Neutrality here has a bias, as it often
has in politics; Russell's neutral particulars are on the
side of sense-data. Still, a drift has begun, and it continues. It does not reach the physicalistic pole, even
in *Human Knowledge;* but there is an increasing naturalism, an increasing readiness to see philosophy as
natural science trained upon itself and permitted free
use of scientific findings. Russell had stated the basis
for such an attitude already in 1914: 'There is not any
superfine brand of knowledge, obtainable by the philosopher, which can give us a standpoint from which
to criticize the whole of the knowledge of daily life.
The most that can be done is to examine and purify
our common knowledge by an internal scrutiny, assuming the canons by which it has been obtained'.[16]

[14] This ironic way of putting the matter is due to Burton
Dreben.

[15] Cf. *Analysis of Mind* (1921), p. 25; *Analysis of Matter*
(1927), Chap. 37.

[16] *Our Knowledge of the External World*, p. 71.

PLATONISM IN RUSSELL'S EARLY PHILOSOPHY AND THE PRINCIPLE OF ABSTRACTION

Jules Vuillemin

"Plato's 'theory of ideas' is an attempt to solve this very problem, and in my opinion it is one of the most successful attempts hitherto made. The theory to be advocated in what follows is largely Plato's, with merely such modifications as time has shown to be necessary." (*Problems of Philosophy*, 2d edition, 1946, p. 91)

1

"Definitions by Abstraction" and "The Principle of Abstraction"

In his *Notations de Logique Mathématique*,[1] Peano introduces definitions by abstraction in the following way: "Let u be an object; we infer a new object, ϕu, by abstraction. We cannot form an equality:

$$\phi u = \text{a known expression}$$

since ϕu is an object different in kind from all those we have considered until now. So we define the equality by writing:

$$\text{D} \quad h_{u,v} \cdot \supset \cdot \phi u = \phi v \cdot = \cdot p_{u,v} \quad \text{Def.}$$

where $h_{u,v}$ is the assumption about the objects u and v; $\phi u = \phi v$ is the equality defined; it means the same thing as $p_{u,v}$, which is a condition, or relation between u and v, having a well known meaning." For

This paper was written especially for this volume. Notes appear at the end of this paper, p. 322.

instance, if "*h*" means "being a straight line," and
"*p*$_{x,y}$" means "*x* is parallel to *y*," we get the following
interpretation for D: "If *u* and *v* are straight lines,
then $\phi u = \phi v$ if and only if *u* is parallel to *v*," and the
meaning of the equality becomes clear: it means that
the direction of *u* is identical with the direction of *v*.
Similarly, if "*h*" means "being a physical object" and
if "*p*$_{x,y}$" means "*x* is exactly similar in color to *y*" we
get, "If *u* and *v* are physical objects, then $\phi u = \phi v$ if
and only if *u* is exactly similar in color to *v*," and the
meaning of the equality becomes clear in the same
way: it means that the color of *u* is the same as the
color of *v*.

From the point of view of mathematics, these definitions owe their importance to the fact that they enable us to bridge the gap which had been created by
Peano's separation of logical ideas from mathematical
ideas.[2] Thanks to them, mathematical ideas, in particular the idea of natural number, can be reduced to
logical ones,[3] the general notion of cardinal number
being defined:

$$a,b \in \text{Cls} \supset \{(\text{Num } a = \text{Num } b) = (\exists (bfa) \, rcp)\} \quad \text{Def.,}$$

which reads: "If *a* and *b* are classes, the cardinal number of *a* is equal to the cardinal number of *b* if and
only if there is a one-one correspondence between the
classes *b* and *a*."[4] In this manner, definitions by abstraction are the instrument enabling us to restore
continuity between the axiomatic method and logicism.

Against such definitions Russell makes three objections of a philosophical kind. They introduce contextually an element which is an addition to the basic
vocabulary, irreducible to it, and ineliminable. The
assumption $h_{u,v}$ restricts the use of the variables, and
re-establishes the autonomy and isolation of axiomatic domains in mathematics. Above all, the abstract
entities so defined are not determined uniquely.[5]
With the first interpretation we gave to D, we may

obtain an infinite number of variant readings, in particular, the following one: by "$\phi u = \phi v$" we mean that the direction of lines perpendicular to u is identical with the direction of lines perpendicular to v.

In order to remedy these three defects Russell introduces, in place of "definitions by abstraction," what he calls the "principle of abstraction." He defines it as follows:

(*Principle of Abstraction*) "Every transitive, symmetrical relation of which there is at least one instance, is analyzable into joint possession of a new relation to a new term, the new relation being such that no term can have this relation to more than one term, but its converse does not have this property. This principle amounts, in ordinary language, to the assertion that transitive symmetrical relations arise from a common property, with the additional stipulation that this property stands, to the terms which have it, in a relation in which nothing else stands to those terms."[6] For example, if the transitive symmetrical relation is parallelism, and if two terms u and v stand in that relation to one another, there is a one-one relation that puts them in correspondence with a unique term, the equivalence class of all straight lines parallel to u, the "direction" of u being nothing else but that class. Similarly, the color of u will be the class of all physical objects, u, v, etc., such that they are exactly similar in color to one another. Finally, the cardinal number of a will be the class of all classes that can be put in one-one correspondence with a.

According to Russell, the principle enables us to eliminate the three defects imputed to definitions by abstraction. The introduced term is neither specific nor contextual; it is a logical term belonging to the basic vocabulary ("the class of all . . ."). The restrictive assumption about the kind of entities whose unique common property is being defined disappears in favor of a universal conception of the variable: all that the principle says is that, without specifying anything about the entities constituting the field of the equivalence relation, we can analyze this relation into another one which the entities have to their equivalence class. Finally, since each equivalence class is well defined, the abstraction henceforth identified with each class turns out to be free from any ambiguity.

The philosophical interpretation of this controversy is clear. A "definition by abstraction" makes an abstraction, which it culpably fails to determine uniquely, into an entity without autonomous existence, because it is introduced only in the context of a proposition about equality. There is no need to eliminate the abstraction itself, at any rate so long as it is confined to such contexts; we can replace these contexts by an equivalent proposition dealing with individuals (straight lines, physical objects, classes). Such a view is undoubtedly nominalist. In direct opposition, although the principle of abstraction identifies the abstraction with a well-defined logical function of the individuals ("the class of all . . ."), it projects the class in question out of them, understanding it as the unique term of reference of the asymmetrical relation between the individuals and their respective equivalence classes. In other words, the principle, as Russell understands it in 1903, allows us to *infer* the existence of a common property from an equivalence relation defined on individuals. These are the characteristics of Platonism.

This philosophical confrontation has immediate consequences for our conceptions of magnitude, time, space, and number.[7] "Definitions by abstraction" lead to a relative conception of these entities, whereas the "principle of abstraction" leads to an absolute conception of them. The absolute conception has the advantage that it imposes on equivalence classes a total ordering which generates the notion of a series; this ordering holds, for example, for instants of time, but not for events in time.

2

Nominalist Criticism and Reinterpretation of the Principle of Abstraction

The three reasons adduced by Russell for rejecting "definitions by abstraction" are unacceptable. Contextual definitions are legitimate, and, in 1905, Russell was even to systematize their use for definite descriptions; if he repudiated them in 1903 that was the result of an atomistic theory of meaning which persuaded him that every word must have an entirely independent meaning. Second, the clause about the universality of the variable is fatal to the logicist system. Definitions by abstraction guarantee that, before the abstraction is constructed, the entities which will be divided into equivalence classes have already been admitted into the universe of discourse. By abolishing this clause the principle of abstraction exposes itself to the antinomies: thus, the relation of ordinal similarity, which arranges well-ordered sets in a unique series, according to the ordinal number of their equivalence classes, leads to the Burali-Forti paradox. In fact, the theory of types was to supersede the theory of the universal variable. Finally, Russell separates, as it were, an equivalence class from the whole system of partition, and it is false to say, as he does, that the abstraction is a distinctive property common to all the elements of an equivalence class, unless one adds that the property is delimited by the relation of that class to all the other equivalence classes produced by the partition that has been chosen. Let us then suppose that there are two different partitions of the same set, and that a common class belongs to both of them; being a member of this one class is obviously related to two different abstract entities, depending on the partition that we consider. For instance, being a whale corresponds to two different ab-

stract entities depending on whether the partition of
the genus Animal is determined by the criterion of
reproduction or of locomotion. It follows that, as the
partition produced by an equivalence relation is
unique, the abstract entity so defined is free from all
ambiguity in the sense that it corresponds to a well-
defined partition.

The platonism associated with the principle of abstraction seems then open to the same criticism as the
principle itself.

Aristotle criticized Plato for "separating" the forms
(that is, the universals), by making them exist not
only in particulars but also independently of them.[8]
Whatever the accuracy of Aristotle's picture of Plato
may be, it is noteworthy that we find, in the Theory of
Ideas, at least when it is presented in that form, another expression of the principle of abstraction. Indeed, the difficulty in the Theory of Ideas, as described by Aristotle, is just that the set or universal
demarcated by any propositional function is both separated as a "new object" from its elements or particulars, and located in them, because it is formed from
them by a logical construction supplied from the
basic vocabulary. Now, the mathematical antinomies
are all connected with the ambiguous use of the notion of a set. For since this notion is in itself abstract,
people were tempted to take a set of sets, considered
as a universal, and the sets that are its elements, considered as particulars, and to put them on the same
level and treat them as objects of the same kind. In
fact, the problem of defining a set is the problem of
its identity: two given sets are identical when every
element of one is an element of the other, and conversely. Now, "this question refers to a domain of existing objects, and it is unanswerable by recourse to
the meaning alone . . . But it is an illusion—to which
Dedekind, Frege, and Russell succumbed for a time,
because they apparently conceived of a 'set' as, ulti-

mately, a collective—to think that thereby a concrete representation of ideal objects has been achieved."[9]

We may presume that in Russell's works the origin of the principle of abstraction and of the confusions which crept into it was the "platonic illusion," common enough among the early set theorists. For, once the illusion was discovered, Russell turned his philosophy toward nominalism. This evolution, or rather *volte-face*, was to result in the elimination of the absolute concepts of magnitude, space, and time, which was required by the new physics. Furthermore, with an adroitness which will be taken as the stamp of heroism or inconstancy, according to taste, Russell did not hesitate to reinterpret the very same principle of abstraction, accommodated to the theory of types, in a nominalist sense. Wherever possible an inference must be replaced by a logical construction. This advice, Russell tells us explicitly, must be applied to the principle of abstraction itself: "All the relations which can naturally be represented as equality in any respect, or as possession of a common property, are transitive and symmetrical—this applies, for example, to such relations as being of the same height or weight or color. Owing to the fact that possession of a common property gives rise to a transitive symmetrical relation, we come to imagine that wherever such a relation occurs it must be due to a common property. 'Being equally numerous' is a transitive symmetrical relation of two collections; hence we imagine that both have a common property called their number. 'Existing at a given instant' . . . is a transitive symmetrical relation; hence we come to think that there really is an instant which confers a common property on all the things existing at that instant. . . . In all such cases, the class of terms that have the given transitive symmetrical relation to a given term will fulfill all the formal requisites of a common property of all the members of the class. Since there certainly is the class, while any other common property may be illusory, it is prudent, in order to avoid needless assumptions, to substitute the class for the common property which would ordinarily be assumed."[10]

What is left, then, of Russell's platonism? Is it an illusion of youth, an ill-posed problem, dissolved by analysis? Is it a remnant of a metaphysical turn of mind which we must associate with the "hegelian period" that our author claims to have passed through? Was it a conversion of the same order as his illumination one evening about the ontological argument?

Such a conclusion seems to fit the facts, but it mistakes the true spirit of Russell's early philosophy, and, perhaps, of all his philosophy. We shall now try to demonstrate this.

3

The Ambiguity of the Principle of Abstraction When It Is Considered in the Light of Quine's Criterion

The nominalist interpretation of the principle of abstraction would, in fact, run up against two objections. It is not because universals cannot be entities as particulars are, that we are forced to relegate them to the universe of words. To say, on the other hand, that "the class of all . . ." does not increase the primitive vocabulary is to speak ambiguously: as soon as we admit that the symbol for class abstraction is ineliminable when it is used to the left of the sign for membership, the question necessarily arises: when we carry out abstraction, under what conditions are we "ontologically committed"?

As far as I know, the only criterion that has been proposed for deciding this question is Quine's.[11] According to him, to be is to be the value of a variable. We must therefore distinguish two uses of universals in predicative judgments. In the first use (relation between a particular and a universal, as in: "Socrates is a man"; "The straight line *a* is parallel to the straight line *b*") there is no ontological commitment to the universal, because it is not the value of a variable. In other words, the universal is used simply and solely to group particulars (Socrates, the straight lines *a* and *b*) without being itself postulated as an object. In the second use (relation between a universal and a universal, as in: "Mankind is a species"; "Parallelism is an equivalence relation"), there is an ontological commitment to the universal to which the predicate is applied, because it is the result of assigning a value to a variable whose domain is made up of universals, rather than particulars—although these universals themselves play the same role as particulars with regard to the universal which groups them; this last universal, which groups the others, is not an object, and does not involve any commitment; the commitment applies only to the universals grouped (humanity, parallelism). In short, in the canonical notation of set theory, where "$x \epsilon y$" may be read as "x is an element of y" or, more loosely, "x is a y," we may say that the ontological commitment applies only to the variable to the left of the sign for membership, and not to the variable to the right of it.

In addition to its clarity, this doctrine has two advantages. The first advantage, which is fundamental, is connected with the different properties of theories which allow variables of quantification to range only over individuals (first order logics), and theories which allow variables to range over classes as well (second, and higher order logics). In fact, it has been shown that the former are complete, and the latter are undecidable, and that is a good reason to make an ontological division according to the different values that a theory allows for a variable. The second advantage is that it offers a precise formulation of the distinction, stated by Aristotle but not analyzed by him, between a statement predicating a universal substance of an individual substance, and a statement predicating a universal substance of a universal substance. Aristotle sometimes admits and sometimes denies the existence of universal substances. When he denies it,[12] he says explicitly: (i) that the substance of anything whatsoever is peculiar to it, but the universal is common, at least in principle, to that thing and others; (ii) that substance, insofar as it is peculiar to a thing, is not asserted of it, but the universal is asserted of it. These two arguments, however, do not apply so much to the universal itself as to its place in the relation of predication, and they hold for what is to the right of the sign for membership, but not for what is to the left of it (whatever its nature may be).

If this were correct, the principle of abstraction would be, in itself, irrelevant to the question that we asked. We could read it in a nominalist fashion—and, indeed, we ought to, according to Occam's razor—whenever the abstraction that it constitutes is used in the attributive position. And we should read it in a realist fashion whenever the abstraction is used in a substantive position, and no paraphrase can get rid of this use of it.

However, this is not Russell's view in and after 1903. The principle of abstraction seems to involve an ontological commitment about "universals," independently of the position—adjectival or substantival —that they occupy in statements. And this commitment is linked to a theory of relations which is peculiar to Russell, and which he seems never to have abandoned. We should therefore re-examine the problem in the light of the theory of relations.

4

Relations and Existential Commitment

In his *Philosophy of Leibniz* (1900), Russell has drawn attention to the preconception which is the true reason why classical logic was unable to express mathematical statements. That preconception is the theory of "internal relations": relations are nothing real; they are in principle reducible either to the terms in which they are instantiated (monadism), or to the unanalyzable "whole" which these terms constitute (monism), or to the act of understanding which relates them (Kantianism).[13] If the fundamental notions of mathematics are those of progression and series, which employ transitive and asymmetrical relations, we see at once that logicism—even understood in its minimal sense as the doctrine that mathematics may be expressed in the vocabulary of logic—remains a self-contradictory ideal so long as the prejudice of internal relations dominates philosophy. Consequently Russell fought it by putting in the field against it the principle of external relations: relations, as universals, are entities just as respectable as attributes. On the other hand, in his *Logic of Relations*, published in Peano's review, he constructed a logic of relations whose principal proposition is the principle of abstraction.

Now, from this point of view, the principle of abstraction consists in replacing an equivalence relation, and a partial ordering on a set of elements, by an asymmetrical one-one relation between these elements and their equivalence classes, which themselves become totally ordered. It is with this role of relations that Russell connects his platonism. So in order to judge it, we must investigate whether and why relations, even used in attributive positions, involve an existential commitment.

Let us consider the four "closed" statements: (1) "$(\exists x)(x \text{ is red})$"; (2) "$(\exists x)(\exists y)(x \text{ is parallel to } y)$"; (3) "$(\exists x)(\exists y)(x \text{ resembles } y);$" (4) "$(\exists x)(\exists y)(x \text{ is to the left of } y)$." These four statements, according to Quine, only commit us to recognizing the existence of individuals, which are the only variables of quantification.[14] The question is whether the use of relations does not involve another type of existential commitment.

Let us note first that a statement formed by using an equivalence relation (statement (2)) can be reduced to a statement formed by attributing a property (statement (1)). As de Morgan showed, transitive symmetrical relations "are reducible, as may be proved in each particular case, to possession of a common property, or identity of content."[15] Indeed, the statement "x is parallel to y" can, by virtue of definition by abstraction, be translated into two statements: "x is δ-directed" and "y is δ-directed," where the one-place predicate "δ-directed" designates the defining property of the equivalence class to which x and y belong. So, up to this point, we may say that, if the use of one-place predicates in the position of a verb (hence, without quantification) involves no ontological commitment, the same goes for the use of signs for equivalence relations.

But when this hypothesis is generalized, the analysis of the third case casts doubt upon it. In fact, it will be demonstrated: (1) that the elimination of signs for attributive universals in statements can be effected only by introducing, at least, a sign for a relational universal, that of resemblance (a thesis of Berkeley and Hume); (2) that the use of the sign for resemblance in an attributive—but not in a substantive—position implies its implicit use in a substantive position and, hence, ontological commitment with regard to it (a refutation of empiricism by Russell).

The first of these theses is well known and seems to be universally accepted.[16] Instead of saying that a and b are triangles, we say, according to it, that a and b resemble c where c is a particular chosen triangle. If we accept Quine's thesis, this paraphrase does not affect the ontological problem since the predicate for resemblance, appearing attributively and not substantively, involves no commitment. But let us scrutinize this accepted paraphrase more closely.

The relation of resemblance is not transitive. That is to say, resemblance may be greater or lesser; it is a comparative matter. If *a* resembles *b*, and *b* resembles *c*, but *a* does not resemble *c*, there are two, and only two, possibilities. Either *a* resembles *b* with respect to P, and *b* resembles *c* with respect to Q—we eliminate this case by making explicit the property with respect to which the resemblance holds—or else, *a* resembles *b*, and *b* resembles *c*, with respect to the same P. For example, *a* is blue, *b* is violet, and *c* is red, and we can pass imperceptibly from *a* to *c*; yet, if we can say that *a* resembles *c* in a sense, since they belong to the same scale of colors, we will refuse to say that its resemblance to *c* is the same as its resemblance to *b*, which is judged to be greater. Now this comparison[17] shows not that *more* color of a similar kind is present respectively in *a* and *b*, and *b* and *c*, than in *a* and *c*, but that there is *more resemblance* between *a* and *b*, or between *b* and *c*, than between *a* and *c*. The possibility of this comparison, which exists implicitly in all cases (as is demonstrated by the fact that Berkeley and Hume needed to refer to a standard particular), establishes a scale of sensible qualities determined by the distance between a given particular and the standard particular. Thus merely in virtue of the first thesis, "*x* is red" can be paraphrased, for example, in the following way: "there is a *y*, which is a standard red, and there is a *z*, which is still deemed red, and *x* is between *y* and *z*." It will be said that the relation "being between" is still used predicatively here, and not substantively, and hence does not yet involve any ontological commitment, so that the second thesis that we put forward (Russell's thesis) receives no support. However, we have not come to the end of our argument.

So far, we have shown that the relation of resemblance can be analyzed, when it is made explicit, in terms of "being between"; and that "x is between y and z" means, "there is a transitive asymmetrical relation which holds between x and y and between y and z";[18] and that this relation sets up a scale, with intervals, for the terms in its field. Thus, among the four cases which we distinguished, we had to move from the second to the first (from equivalence relations to properties), from the first to the third (from properties to the relation of resemblance), and from the third to the fourth (from the relation of resemblance to asymmetrical—and transitive—relations). So it will suffice if we examine the problem of ontological commitment in this last case.

Let us take, then, the relation: x is to the left of y. Let us suppose that the entire ontology implied by our statement is absorbed by the individuals x and y, as—if we except the reduction of the first case that we distinguished to the third—we assumed to be the case with the statement "x and y are red." According to this assumption, the order in which the individuals x and y figure in the statement should be immaterial—unless we suppose that this order is built into their nature as individuals. It might be objected that the role of the relation, when it is asymmetrical, is precisely to order and to give a sense to the ordering of the individuals. But this does not avoid the dilemma: either relations are external and, by ordering individuals which themselves have nothing to do with the ordering, they introduce into the universe something that is irreducible to particulars; or else they are internal, and then it is necessary to account for the asymmetrical character of the order by making it a property of each of the individuals themselves (monadistic theory), or of the whole composed of the individuals (monistic theory). But in both cases we lose the sense of the ordering which is fundamental for determining the asymmetry.[19] Thus, in either case, we are led to recognize in the sense of the relation between a and b something which cannot be absorbed either into *a* or into *b;* that something is a universal, and its irreducibility proves that it involves an ontological commitment.

The analysis of ordered pairs by Wiener and Kuratowski will be offered as an objection against this argument. But from the point of view that we are concerned with, the ordered pair is then analyzed into a set of sets and, according to Quine's criterion, this implies an ontological commitment. One can, nevertheless, by complicating the definition,[20] eliminate the type difference between (x,y) and the individuals x and y, but only by supposing that every entity is a class; this supposition is supported by the identification of individuals with their unit classes. This construction is formally irreproachable, but it has two consequences, one fatal by Quine's criterion, and the other at least paradoxical. First, it commits us ontologically to accepting classes identified with individuals. To quantify over individuals in the ordinary theory, where an individual is distinguished from the class containing it as its sole element, was to quantify over particulars without being committed to universals. But if, in order to put relations and classes on the same level, individuals are taken from the start as classes, then as soon as we quantify over individuals we quantify, in fact, over universals, and no linguistic artifice will prevent the class composed of the single element Socrates from being a universal.[21] So the price paid for simplification is a general ontological commitment with regard to classes which is alien to the theory of one-place predicates. The second consequence is that every class becomes a class of ordered pairs, that is, a relation: "The definition has also the following further advantage: *it makes everything an ordered pair.* . . . Indeed, everything comes to be at once an ordered pair, a class, and a relation. The terms 'ordered pair,' 'class,' and 'relation' fuse and become valueless as designations of categories, because they are all-embracing. . . ."[22]

This obliteration of distinctions, however, though it may have technical advantages, does not fit in with Church's theorem, according to which, although a first order logic has a decision procedure, if it is monadic, it does not have one if it is general—i.e., polyadic; for this is something that clearly distinguishes classes from relations. At the same time, from the historical point of view this account does not explain the special place of relations in the edifice of logic, a place which marks the technical difference between the logic of the Ancients, and that of the Moderns.

5

Conclusion

We may provide two solutions to the problem of ontological commitment. The first, which is Quine's, declares that to exist is to be the value of a variable. This makes it possible to draw a clear distinction between mathematical logic in the strict sense (the logic of the first order quantification) and set theory, as is required by Gödel's criterion of completeness. The second solution, which is Russell's, asserts that to exist abstractly is to impose an order and a sense on elements, which do not contain either in themselves (theory of asymmetrical relations). This makes it possible to distinguish ancient logic (syllogism and propositional calculus) from modern logic (general quantification theory), as Church's criterion of decidability requires.

Russell's logicism prevented him from linking his platonism with the first type of commitment; to do so would have been to acknowledge that logic, in the narrow sense of first order logic, is incapable of generating mathematics. Of course, Russell was a platonist in 1903 in the sense that he acknowledged the existence of classes, of classes of classes, etc. But once he accepted the theory of types, he often gives the false impression that the language he uses frees him from commitment because it is an intensional language.

The theory of relations, on the other hand, firmly and definitively linked Russell's platonism to the second type of commitment. This platonism of relations is just as authentic as the platonism of the hierarchy of individuals and classes. Thus, Aristotle states with precision that the platonic arguments lead to positing ideas of relations which in his opinion do not form an independent class in nature.[23]

It would still be necessary to examine the philosophical significance of the two kinds of ontological commitment that we have distinguished. Here we will content ourselves with stating the problem with reference to a suggestion of Russell's, which, however, is a disputed suggestion, and what is more, disputed by Russell himself.[24]

Russell affirms that, unlike the analysis of adjectives, the analysis of relations reaches a limit in the ordering of the arguments of the relation, so that we can never completely separate relations from the particulars which are their instances, to the extent that they order them. Indeed, if this were not so, we would risk confusing a relation with its converse. That is to say, there is, in the case of relations, an adherence of a universal to its domain of application which is what allows us to be acquainted with the latter in a scientific way, that is, through its structure.

Such an adherence could be removed only by treating relations as classes of classes, and so by passing from the logic of relations to set theory. Here, the universal is posited without any attachment to the particulars that are its instances, but the laws governing it obey postulates which are "stronger" and which go beyond the order of simple logic.

Can we derive from this rough and simple difference a critical theory of realism, or, in other words, a theory capable of determining the scope and limits of each ontological commitment? Such is the problem to which we seem to be led when we study Russell's platonism in 1903 and its relations with the principle of abstraction.

FOOTNOTES

1. Turin, 1894, §38, p. 45.

2. *Formulaire de Mathématique*, Paris, 1901, pp. 39 ff.

3. On this point see J. Vuillemin, *Leçons sur la Première Philosophie de Russell,* Paris: Colin, 1968, p. 176.

4. *Formulaire de Mathématique*, see above, p. 70.

5. *Principles of Mathematics,* Chap. XI, §110, pp. 114–15.

6. *Principles of Mathematics,* Chap. XXVI, §210 (2d ed., p. 220), §216, p. 226; "The Logic of Relations" (in *Logic and Knowledge,* ed. by R. C. Marsh, London, 1956, pp. 10–12). This principle is expressed in *PM* in the proposition:

$$* 72.66 : S^2 \cdot S \cdot S = \check{S} \cdot \equiv \cdot (\exists R) \cdot R \in Cls \to 1 \cdot S \cdot = R | \check{R}.$$

7. *Principles of Mathematics,* Chaps. XIX, XXVI, L–LII, XXIX; *L'idée d'ordre et la position absolue dans l'espace et le temps,* Bibliothèque du Congrès de Philosophie 1901, Paris: Colin, III, pp. 241–77.

8. W. D. Ross, *Aristotle's Metaphysics,* Oxford: Clarendon Press, 2d ed., 1948, Vol. I, p. xliii.

9. H. Weyl, *Philosophy of Mathematics and Natural Sciences,* Princeton, 1949, p. 12; Carnap, *Der Logische Aufbau der Welt,* §§37 and 40, *Die Logische Syntax der Sprache,* §38; Fraenkel, *Einleitung in die Mengenlehre,* 1928, p. 58.

10. *Our Knowledge of the External World,* pp. 133–34.

11. *From a Logical Point of View,* p. 13.

12. *Metaphysics*, 2, 13.

13. See, for example, *Principles of Mathematics*, Chap. XXVI; *Problems of Philosophy*, p. 90, and pp. 94–95.

14. See also "Russell's Ontological Development," *The Journal of Philosophy*, Vol. LXIII, No. 21, November 1966, p. 662, and reprinted in this volume, pp. 290 ff.

15. Russell, "On the Notion of Order," *Mind*, X, 1901, p. 30.

16. *The Problems of Philosophy*, pp. 95–96. It would be possible to show this thesis at work in Quine's writings; for example, in *Word and Object*: the notion of stimulation is introduced (p. 34) as a Universal—not as a dated particular, but as a repeatable event form; in consequence, stimulus meaning amounts to a disposition in a subject to assent to or dissent from a statement in response to a present stimulation. Now, the analysis of "strong" conditionals into dispositions (pp. 224–25) is done by introducing into the theory a predicate "Mxy" which is interpreted as meaning "x and y are alike in molecular structure" or, in our case (p. 223): "x and y are similar neural conditions induced by learning that disposes the subject to give his assent or dissent to a statement in response to certain given stimulations." Thus, the statement: "x and y are stimulus-synonymous" will be paraphrased by "Mxy," in which the universal of resemblance figures. According to Quine (pp. 223–24), the same goes for predicates like "red," so that we can accept the following paraphrase: "x is red" $\leftrightarrow$ "($\exists y$)(Mxy and y reflects a certain range of low frequencies selectively)" where "Mxy" is interpreted, "x and y are alike in molecular structure."

17. Russell, *Principles of Mathematics*, §159, 2d ed., pp. 170–71.

18. Russell, *Principles of Mathematics*, §207, p. 217.

19. Russell, *Principles of Mathematics*, Chap. XXVI.

20. Quine, "On Ordered Pairs and Relations" in *Selected Logic Papers*, New York: Rawdon, 1966, pp. 110–13. This definition is analogous to Wiener's, but it differs as regards types.

21. Because of their theory about "intelligible matter" and the problem of individuation, Aristotle and the scholastics insisted that a universal remains a universal even if, by its definition, it is realized in only one instance, which plays in relation to it the role of a particular.

22. Quine, "On Ordered Pairs and Relations," p. 112.

23. *Metaphysics*, A, 9, 990^b. As Ross notes (*op. cit.*, Vol. I, p. 194), the argument of the Phaedo leads to positing the idea of the equal, which is applied, in respect of length, to beds, men, and trees, and so cuts across our natural classification. There is evidently a conflict between the ontology required by mathematics and the ontology suggested by that classification.

24. *Principles of Mathematics*, Chap. IV, §55, in particular, p. 52: "Verbs, unlike adjectives, do not have instances, but are identical in all the cases of their occurrence." On this point see Weitz, "Analysis and the Unity of Russell's Philosophy," in *The Philosophy of Bertrand Russell*, P. Schilpp, ed., New York: Tudor, pp. 68–69; and Russell's reply, *ibid.*, p. 684; and Vuillemin, *op. cit.*, §14, pp. 102–6.

RUSSELL'S MORAL THEORIES

D. H. Monro

1

If Bertrand Russell had lived in an earlier century, no
one would have hesitated to call him a moral philosopher. In our more finicking age, some academics may
want to say that, great as his achievements have been
in other branches of philosophy, he is less a moral
philosopher than a moralist. That is to say, he has
consistently advocated ideals and expressed beliefs
which have made him, along with Shaw and Wells,
if not quite with Marx and Freud, one of the formative
influences on the modern mind; but he has usually
addressed these writings to the general public, and,
although writing always with great force, clarity and
skill, he has not always troubled his readers with the
minutiae of philosophical argument. But this point
should not be exaggerated. Even in his most popular
works, Russell never loses sight of the philosophical
problems in his concern for the political or psychological ones, and he certainly has views on meta-morals
and meta-politics as well as on morals and politics.
Indeed, his attempts to reconcile the two are highly
illuminating; for they show one of the clearest minds
of our time faced with one of the central problems of
our time: how to justify passionately-held moral convictions when all the evidence seems to lead to moral
scepticism. (To guard against misunderstanding, I
should perhaps say that I do not mean religious
scepticism. It is demonstrable, though it would be
irrelevant here to demonstrate, that religious beliefs,
whether justified or not, cannot provide an intellectually satisfying basis for morality.)

This essay first appeared in *Philosophy*, Vol. XXXV, 1960. It is
reprinted by permission of the author and of the editor of *Philosophy*.

Russell's moral and political doctrines themselves are too well known to need more than a brief reference. I should put first his insistence on "the scientific outlook": "the doctrine . . . that it is undesirable to believe a proposition when there is no ground whatever for supposing it true".[1] No one has insisted more cogently on the need for weighing evidence, for following the argument whithersoever it leads, for suspending judgment whenever there is reasonable ground for doubt. These doctrines seem trite only when stated, not when applied; Russell is quite right in saying that "if accepted, they would absolutely revolutionize human life".[2] It is often said that that revolution has actually been proceeding since about the seventeenth century; and there are those today who argue that the time is ripe for a counter-revolution. Article One in Russell's creed is that, on the contrary, our troubles today are caused by the partial failure of the scientific revolution, not by its too complete success.

The nature of the transformation which Russell envisages (but does not expect) is quite clear, at least in its outlines. There is to be tolerance, sympathy and understanding. There is to be equality: the good life should be possible for all men; and Russell is quite clear that under the present social and economic system most men lead cramped and frustrating lives. Above all, there is to be freedom. "Government and law, in their very essence, consist of restrictions on freedom, and freedom is the greatest of political goods. . . . I do not say freedom is the greatest of *all* goods: the best things come from within—they are such things as creative art, and love, and thought."[3] Russell's ideal state, then, will help, rather than hinder, its citizens in cultivating these goods; and to this

[1] *Sceptical Essays*, 1928, p. 11.

[2] *Ibid.*, p. 13.

[3] *Roads to Freedom*, 2d ed., 1919, p. 121.

end there will be needed a mixture of socialism and anarchism. Socialism (or at least the abolition of capitalism) is necessary to free men from the tyranny of uncongenial work; but Russell saw, much sooner than most socialists, that socialism could be a real danger to freedom. "These results are not foreseen by Socialists, because they imagine that the Socialist State will be governed by men like those who now advocate it. This is, of course, a delusion. The rulers of the State then will bear as little resemblance to the present Socialists as the dignitaries of the Church after the time of Constantine bore to the Apostles. The men who advocate an unpopular reform are exceptional in disinterestedness and zeal for the public good; but those who hold power after the reform has been carried out are likely to belong, in the main, to the ambitious executive type which has, in all ages, possessed itself of the government of nations. And this type has never shown itself tolerant of opposition or friendly to freedom."[4] These were, in 1918, prophetic words. As safeguards against this danger, Russell proposes devolution, along the lines advocated by Guild Socialists and pluralists generally; special provisions for freedom of publication, to prevent the State from acquiring a monopoly of propaganda; and the device of "the vagabond wage", by which all citizens would be given a subsistence wage whether they worked or not. This would deprive the State (or any other employer) of its most powerful coercive weapon, the threat of starvation; and it would be unlikely to deplete the labour force much, since, Russell points out, most people with small independent incomes are glad enough to increase their income by working. At the same time, the way would be open for the artist or scholar who wished to devote himself to uneconomic pursuits. This seems reasonable enough; but in general Russell treats economic problems rather cavalierly. He is content to

[4] *Roads to Freedom*, p. 117.

accept, without much examination, the view of Kropot-
kin and others that, if waste were eliminated, a very
few hours' work a day would be enough to maintain
us all at a high standard of living.

Now it is obvious that in all this Russell is committing himself to certain propositions: that love is better
than hatred, that the good life for all is better than
the good life for a few, that creative impulses are better than destructive ones, that one ought not to accept
a belief because it is useful or comforting, but only because it is true. And the question that obviously presents itself is: What is the evidence for these propositions? By what rational arguments could one defend
them against an aristocrat, an authoritarian, or a mis-
anthropist? Is the belief that one should never rely on
mere dogma itself a piece of mere dogma?

These are, of course, the problems that have always
perplexed moral philosophers, especially those who
have been imbued with the empirical spirit. And there
are, roughly, three traditional ways of tackling the
difficulty.

(1) All knowledge, it may be argued, must start
somewhere. In science we start with the evidence of
the senses. This means that there are certain "atomic
propositions", known immediately, which no one seriously doubts. Now it is arguable that in morals, too,
there are atomic propositions, known to us perhaps
through a special moral sense. If this can be made out,
the special difficulties of moral investigation vanish,
and moral philosophy is no less empirical than science.

(2) Alternatively, it may be said that morality is
not indeed concerned to establish objective facts, like
science, but to discover rules or recipes for the gratification of human desires. This is, however, a sufficiently objective study, in much the way that medicine
is objective. For the pursuit of health is simply the attempt to discover the physical conditions which men
in general find agreeable. And, although what suits
one man does not always suit another, these differ-

ences are not great enough to prevent us from regarding some physical conditions as desirable, and
others as undesirable, for all men. The pursuit of
happiness (or well-being, to use a less tendentious
term) is not significantly different from the pursuit of
health: there are some ways of life that suit human
nature, and others that do not. This is itself an objective fact; and, just as the truths of medicine apply
equally to the doctor and the Christian Scientist, so
the truths of morals apply equally to those who acknowledge them and those who do not. So that, although morality is concerned with the gratification of
desire, the rules which it lays down are objective and
applicable to all men, and their study is an empirical
one like any other.

(3) Finally, it may be contended that morality is
not objective in either of these ways and that moral
statements simply express the wishes of the person
uttering them, or possibly of the community to which
he belongs. (There are of course many refinements
of this view, as indeed of the other two, but this should
do for the present purpose.)

Russell has, at various times, adopted each of these
positions, in the order in which I have given them:
the first and the third explicitly, the second by implication. In his early paper, "The Elements of Ethics",[5]
he accepts without reserve Moore's account of morality: we know immediately that certain things are good,
and the right action is the one that produces most
good. "Good" itself is a non-natural quality, apprehended directly just as natural qualities are. But here
and there he shows traces of uneasiness.

"In this, as in all philosophical inquiries," he writes,
"after a preliminary analysis of complex data we proceed again to build up complex things from their simple constituents, starting from ideas which we understand, and from premisses which we know though

[5] Reprinted in *Philosophical Essays*, 1910.

we cannot prove them. The appearance of dogmatism in this procedure is deceptive, for the premises are such as ordinary reasoning unconsciously assumes, and there is less real dogmatism in believing them after a critical scrutiny than in employing them implicitly without examination."[6]

This procedure works well enough if the object is to explore the implications of our ordinary judgments about the external world. It would seem less serviceable for the moralist concerned to urge unpopular reforms. Of course the reformer may be able to show that his conclusions follow if only the assumptions of the man in the street are taken to their logical conclusion; and many reformers have in fact made some such claim. Nevertheless, the assumptions made in ordinary reasoning about ethics are notoriously less uniform than those made in ordinary reasoning about perception or knowledge; and it is hard to see how the moralist is to escape dogmatism except at the cost of confining himself to the safest and most tepid of generalizations. Moore, it is true, did not do this; but his account of the good life was based on the unconscious assumptions, not of the man in the street, but of the Cambridge or Bloomsbury aesthete of 1904; it seemed dogmatic enough to many of his contemporaries. And, apart altogether from this, it seems unlikely that so thoroughgoing an empiricist as Russell could long be satisfied with the notion of non-natural qualities.

2

It is perhaps significant that "The Elements of Ethics" was written before the war of 1914–18; for Russell himself has often said that it was that war that first awakened his interest in social and political reforms. Accordingly we find his next writings more concerned with practice than with theory; and the

[6] *Philosophical Essays*, p. 4.

theory that shines through seems to owe more to Freud, or perhaps even to Hobbes, than to Moore.

It is true that he begins *Principles of Social Reconstruction* by dividing human impulses into "two groups, the possessive and the creative, according as they aim at acquiring or retaining something that cannot be shared, or at bringing into the world some valuable thing, such as knowledge or art or goodwill." And he adds: "I consider the best life that which is most built on creative impulses, and the worst that which is most inspired by love of possession."[7] This is quite in accordance with Moore: some impulses just are good, and others just are bad. Moreover the list of good things (knowledge, art, goodwill), and the account of what makes an activity valuable (bringing good things into existence) are almost straight Moore.

Yet Russell was, in spite of Moore, worried by the assumption that an end can be rational or irrational in itself. "There is no objective reason to be given", he tells us, only a few pages after his Moorean beginning, "to show that one of these attitudes is essentially more rational than the other. If a man finds people repulsive, no argument can prove to him that they are not so. But both his own desires and other people's are much less likely to find satisfaction if he resembles Carlyle than if he resembles Walt Whitman."[8]

It is no longer enough, apparently, to say that goodwill has the non-natural quality of goodness. And, once this belief has been given up, there seems to be only one reason for choosing any course of action: that we want to. The obvious difficulty about this, however, is that desires conflict. Take one of Russell's own examples. "Those who believe that man is a rational animal", he writes, "will say that people boast in order that others may have a good opinion of them; but most of us can recall occasions when we

[7] *Principles of Social Reconstruction*, 1916, p. 5.
[8] *Ibid.*, p. 36.

have boasted in spite of knowing that we would be despised for it."[9] But why is this irrational? Only on the assumption that one wants to be admired and does not want to be despised. One gets satisfaction from the admiration of one's friends; moreover, that admiration may have further consequences agreeable in themselves, such as invitations to dinner. All right. But boasting itself, apparently, is a source of satisfaction. Why, then, should the one satisfaction be preferred to the other? There seems to be no reason, unless one can be shown to be greater, or more lasting, than the other.

This line of thought leads straight to the hedonic calculus. It leads straight, too, to a distinction, which Russell duly makes, between a passing impulse and a settled purpose. But Russell does not draw the conclusion that one might expect. For so far the implication is clearly that purpose, as the source of greater and more lasting satisfaction, is to be preferred to impulse. The man who acts morally is, on this view, very much in the position of the industrious apprentice: he finds it worth while to repress some inclinations, such as a taste for idleness and dissipation (or for boasting), for the sake of later but greater rewards.

What Russell actually says, however, is that this subordination of impulse to desire is to be condemned.

"Almost all paid work is done from desire, not from impulse: the work itself is more or less irksome, but the payment for it is desired. The serious activities that fill a man's working hours are, except in a few fortunate individuals, governed mainly by purposes, not by impulses, towards those activities. In this hardly anyone sees an evil, because the place of impulse in a satisfactory existence is not recognized. . . . The complete control of impulse by will, which is sometimes preached by moralists, and often enforced by economic necessity, is not really desirable. A life

[9] *Principles of Social Reconstruction*, p. 12.

governed by purposes and desires, to the exclusion of impulse, is a boring life; it exhausts vitality, and leaves a man, in the end, indifferent to the very purposes that he is trying to achieve."[10]

Now this is not necessarily inconsistent with hedonism. The point may be, not that the hedonic calculus itself is at fault, but that the accountancy methods of the calculators are often mistaken. There are unsuspected items to be added on the debit side: sources of unhappiness that Bentham never dreamed of. They had been dreamed of since, of course, by Freud. Russell's emphasis on impulse in *Principles of Social Reconstruction* undoubtedly stems from Freud: if not directly, at least from the popular Freudianism of the period. The repression of impulse, it was argued, exacted too high a price, so that lives were warped and the spontaneous joy in living killed. The industrious apprentice himself came under fire: perhaps he had nothing much, after all, to show at the end of his life except stomach ulcers and a soured disposition.

None of this would affect the hedonic calculus as such: it is still assumed that desires really do conflict and that one must choose the most satisfying and repress the others. The difference of opinion is merely about which desires are the most satisfying. But it is possible to take a different line. It is possible to argue that the conflict of desires is more apparent than real; or rather that, while the conflict is real enough, some of the desires are not. More intelligibly put, this amounts to a distinction between desires or impulses which are an innate part of "human nature" (the "real self") and those which are socially acquired.

Some such distinction was forced on the Freudians fairly early. Sexual desire, for example, is innate; but the feelings of horror and guilt often roused by sex are socially acquired. Eliminating such feelings, then, is not repression. On the contrary, it is a kind of lib-

[10] *Ibid.*, pp. 17–18.

eration. We are to think of the "natural" man as having been cramped or warped by social conventions; the task is simply to remove the fetters. It should be emphasized that this is not so much Freud as popular Freudianism. But the point at the moment is that Russell seems at least partly inclined to adopt this view. As he develops it, there are interesting echoes, both of the eighteenth-century view that man is naturally good and corrupted by society and, rather surprisingly, of the Idealist view that moral rules are prescriptions for "realizing" the true self.

In the first place, he makes a good deal of the point that the repression of impulse is not merely tiring and destructive of vitality but also the source of "new impulses . . . of cruelty and destruction". These impulses, then, are socially acquired. The suggestion is that men will not behave aggressively unless their "natural" development has been thwarted. And, secondly, this leads Russell to say, quite in the manner of the Idealists, that men have "a central principle of growth, an instinctive urgency leading them in a certain direction, as trees seek the light".[11] It looks, then, as if the initial division into good (or creative) and bad (or possessive) impulses really rests on another: into natural impulses, which proceed from the principle of growth within, and artificial ones, which are produced when these natural impulses are cramped, checked and distorted.

Russell agrees with the men of the eighteenth century, and disagrees with the Idealists, in suggesting that social institutions are responsible for the cramping or distorting. It may be said of the Freudian Revolution (though somewhat misleadingly) that, like the Marxist one, it stood Idealism on its head. The Idealist view was, roughly, that "the real self" is what Freud came to call the super-ego: the moral sentiments of parents, teachers and society generally so far as these

[11] *Principles of Social Reconstruction*, p. 24.

are taken over by the individual and made part of himself. The Freudians (though not, perhaps, Freud) declared that, on the contrary, it is the id that is the real self. Russell seems to share this view, at least to the extent of being suspicious of the super-ego. He tells us, for example, that we should not try to "mould" the young, but to "equip and strengthen" them "for the ends which the child's own spirit is obscurely seeking". And he goes on: "Certain mental habits are commonly instilled by those who are engaged in educating: obedience and discipline, ruthlessness in the struggle for worldly success, contempt towards opposing groups, and an unquestioning credulity, a passive acceptance of the teacher's wisdom. All these habits are against life."[12] It is clear that, in Russell's opinion, a man is cramped, not merely by being prevented from taking a mistress, travelling abroad, sleeping in on a week-day, fishing in a privately owned stream, or taking up art and literature instead of going into an office, but also by having certain prejudices and habits of thought instilled into him. To follow the argument whithersoever it leads, to examine the opinions of others with complete tolerance and impartiality, is, apparently, part of what he means by "nourishing the growth within".

Now one may certainly doubt whether it is "natural", as the Idealists seemed to think, to submerge oneself selflessly in the ends of society. There were good grounds for arguing that society's rules about sexual indulgence imposed a considerable strain on human nature; and one could even write cogently, as Russell did, "in praise of idleness", and argue that the industrious apprentice, too, was doing violence to his "real self". But is it really more natural to be tolerant than to be intolerant, or to acquire the habit of careful and critical thinking than to accept uncritically the dicta of authority?

[12] *Ibid.*, p. 155.

The truth is that it is not really possible to maintain that the sort of world that Russell wants to see can be obtained merely by giving free rein to the id. It is very doubtful, indeed, whether this policy will even lead to the happiness of the individual, or whether Freud himself ever advocated it. "The poor ego", Freud tells us, "has to serve three harsh masters, and has to do its best to reconcile the claims and demands of all three. The three tyrants are the external world, the super-ego and the id."[13] The id, so far from being the source of all freedom, is, it seems, itself a tyrant. The point is that the "pleasure-principle", which alone governs the id, needs to be modified by the "reality-principle". Left to itself, impulse drives blindly towards its ends without taking account of those factors in the outside world (including the existence of other men with impulses of their own) which make those ends unattainable. The external world, too, is a tyrant, no doubt, but one not to be denied. The tendency of the id to believe only what it wants to believe is to be resisted, if only in its own interests.

Now Russell recognizes this. "Instinct," he says towards the end of *Principles of Social Reconstruction,* "is the source of vitality . . . but instinct by itself leaves us powerless to control the forces of nature, either in ourselves or in our physical environment, and keeps us in bondage to the same unthinking impulse by which the trees grow."[14] So it now appears that to allow "the natural principle of growth" to have its way is, after all, to be in bondage, not to be free. For the way to control the forces of nature is, at least in part, to adapt ourselves to them. If we are to gratify our impulses it must be in ways which do not attempt to flout the laws of physics (or physiology, including,

[13] *New Introductory Lectures in Psycho-analysis,* 1933, p. 103.

[14] *Principles of Social Reconstruction,* p. 209.

for example, digestion). A rational morality will certainly need to take account of this.

Moreover, it seems to follow that a rational morality will also take account of the super-ego. For the external world, let us repeat, includes other human beings, whose likes and dislikes affect us quite as inexorably as the laws of physics; so that we are also forced to gratify our impulses only in the ways that our fellow-men will tolerate. And the super-ego, at least in part, embodies the demands which other men, in their own interests, are bound to make upon us.

Only in part, it is true. The super-ego may often enforce irrational taboos, based on false beliefs about nature, including human nature. Nevertheless, a rational man will certainly take account of the super-ego, so far as it merely represents the demands which the reality-principle makes upon the pleasure-principle. For other men are certainly real.

So far I have argued that, in *Principles of Social Reconstruction,* Russell at least dallies with the view that the way of life he believes in is the one which the id will adopt once it is freed from the corrupting influences of superstition and indoctrination. But, for all his lauding of "impulses", his "principle of growth within" is not quite Freud's id. Sometimes at least he seems to be putting forward the more moderate view that his version of the good life is the one that will result if the demands of the id are modified by nothing but the demands of reality. This gives us ample ground for rejecting superstition; and indoctrination, too, so far as it is unsupported by valid argument. Moreover, it provides justification for the scientific outlook, and the open, enquiring attitude of mind, which is necessary if we are to know what the reality-principle really does enjoin upon us.

A rational morality will, on this view, take the maximum possible satisfaction of desire as its aim. It will recognize the need to suppress some impulses: when they conflict with too many others, or when the nature of the external world (including the demands of other men) makes their realization impossible; but it will also recognize, more fully than the earlier utilitarians did, that the suppression of impulse is a very potent source of misery. And for that reason the alleged demands of the external world must be scrutinized very carefully. Many of the alleged facts which have been advanced in the past as reasons for repressing impulse can be shown not to be facts at all. And many of the restrictions imposed by other men can be shown to be quite unnecessary for the happiness of those men.

All this fits in well enough, up to a point, with Russell's beliefs: with his advocacy of tolerance and freedom, his impatience with asceticism considered as an end in itself. Certainly it is much more in accordance with his whole-hearted belief in reason than the other view we have been considering. But it is doubtful if he is really prepared to accept all its implications. For one of Russell's fundamental beliefs is that we ought to desire the good life for others as well as for ourselves; and the view we are considering does not really justify this belief. The tolerance and freedom it justifies is, after all, tolerance and freedom for oneself, not necessarily for other people. It is true that we must, in accordance with the reality principle, pay attention to other men's search for happiness as well as our own; but only so far as they will make things unpleasant for us if we don't. For the only rational ground we have found for action is still the satisfaction of desire: our own desire, not anyone else's.

We are, in short, back with Hobbes. We might, indeed, call this theory Freudian Hobbism. And the Hobbist belief that most people have found most objectionable is precisely this one: that there is no good reason to consider other people's happiness unless it affects our own. It is, of course, arguable that Hobbes is right about this; and it may even be said that Freud's discoveries about the super-ego explain why we are so reluctant to believe that he is right. For the super-ego is essentially a means by which the demands of society are impressed upon us so that they become "internalized", part of ourselves. This means that we feel guilty if we entertain any beliefs likely to undermine their influence; for it is the super-ego which, in Freud's system, plays the important role of censor. It is easy to see, then, why it should censor the view that the happiness of other men is not important in its own right. Nevertheless, if we are to submit the dictates of the super-ego to rational criticism, it is hard to see what reason there can be for considering the interests of other men except that advanced by Hobbes.

But whether Hobbes is right or not is hardly the point. The point is that Russell does not think he is. Towards the end of *Principles of Social Reconstruction* he introduces us to a rather curious mental entity which he calls "Spirit". He has been talking about the clash between "instinct" and "mind". To leave instinct unchecked, it will be remembered, is after all to be in bondage; and the function of mind is to "liberate us from this bondage, by the power of impersonal thought, which enables us to judge critically the purely biological purposes towards which instinct more or less blindly tends".[15] Unfortunately, mind exacts a high price for its liberating services. "Mind", we are told, "in its dealings with instinct is *merely* critical: so far as instinct is concerned, the unchecked activity of the mind is apt to be destructive and generate cynicism."[16] The choice, then, would seem to be between blindly pursuing the ends instinct sets before us and refusing to be a mere tool in the hands of natural impulses. If we choose the first alternative we are happy but deluded: we find ourselves, for example, cherishing such patently false beliefs as that the girl next door is the most beautiful in the world, or that

[15] *Principles of Social Reconstruction*, p. 209.
[16] *Ibid.*, p. 209.

the country we happen to have been born in is far superior to any other. If we choose the second, our eyes
are opened but there is nothing much worth looking
at: we are left quite passionless, and, consequently,
aimless.

"Spirit" comes in to release us from this dilemma.
Spirit enables us to preserve intact the emotions that
spring from instinct and at the same time "makes them
impervious to mental criticism". How does it do this?
Quite easily, it seems: all it needs to do is to "univer-
salize" these emotions.

"The man who has the life of the spirit within him",
Russell says, "views the love of man and woman, both
in himself and in others, quite differently. . . . He
sees, in his moments of insight, that in all human beings there is something deserving of love, something
mysterious."[17]

But will this satisfy "mind"? "Mind" may well object
that "spirit" (or Russell) has shifted his ground. The
original false belief was that Angelina is more beautiful, etc., than other women: "spirit" renders this impervious to criticism by substituting the belief that
Angelina is worthy to be loved. But Edwin might believe this, rationally enough, without subscribing to
the further belief that all other women are worthy to
be loved too. It is true that, so far as Angelina is no
more beautiful, intelligent, good-tempered, etc., than
other women, it may be argued that she cannot be
worthy to be loved unless they are equally so. But
this argument rests on certain highly dubious assumptions. It is assumed that emotions are fitting or rational
only if called forth by certain qualities and that, if
other objects possess the same qualities, it is irrational
not to feel the same emotions for them. But these are
assumptions which "mind", if thoroughly imbued with
the empirical spirit, may well question. For what is
meant by saying that some qualities are *to be loved*,

[17] *Principles of Social Reconstruction*, p. 219.

or worthy of love, and others to be hated? We can attach meaning to these expressions if we interpret them on Hobbist lines: a quality is to be loved if it is important for our own happiness. And, if this is what is meant, then Edwin (or his instinct, with the full approval of his mind) can retort that Angelina is important to his happiness in a way that other women are not.

It is clear, however, that this is precisely what Russell does not mean. For, he tells us, "the life of the spirit centres round impersonal feeling, as the life of the mind centres round impersonal thought. . . . It is possible to feel the same interest in the joys and sorrows of others as in our own, to love and hate independently of all relation to ourselves, to care about the destiny of man and the development of the universe without a thought that we are personally involved".[18]

It is clear, I think, that Russell is clinging here to the conviction, which most of us want to urge against Hobbes, that the happiness of other men is desirable for its own sake. I think it is clear, too, that he has not found any rational ground for this conviction other than the Moorean one we had supposed him to be rejecting. For what he is saying really amounts to this: that the attitude recommended by spirit just is good, and is impervious to the criticism of mind just because mind recognizes this. It is significant that, in one of the passages quoted, he contrasts blind subservience to the ends of Nature with being a willing minister to the impersonal desires that one *sees to be good*.

I have discussed *Principles of Social Reconstruction* at length, because I think that it shows very clearly the different and inconsistent moral theories that Russell was struggling with at this period. It shows this the more clearly because moral theory is in the back-

[18] *Ibid.*, p. 205.

ground; the book is mainly concerned with social and
political problems. Consequently the theoretical inconsistencies were allowed to appear, whereas if the
book had been explicitly devoted to moral theory Russell would presumably have done something to eliminate them. He was to do this later. But the inconsistencies are illuminating, because they are those of
which most of us are guilty when we come to *use*
moral concepts, however neatly we may tidy them up
when we are merely talking about them. It is worth
while, then, seeing clearly what the opposing positions
are. There is first of all the conviction, which most of
us have, that some ways of behaving just are good and
others bad. There is, secondly, the uneasy suspicion
that this may be a mere dogma, which anyone with
a scientific outlook is bound to question, especially
since people do genuinely disagree about which ways
of behaving are good and which bad. This leads one
to take the safer line that, finally, the only justification
for doing anything is that one wants to do it. But this
is not really very helpful, since the problem is often
to choose between conflicting desires. But perhaps
some of these desires may turn out not to be real ones?
This comforting hypothesis seems to be supported by
the Freudian discovery that, on the one hand, we have
many desires of which we are unconscious, and that,
on the other, many purposes we think we have are
the products of convention and leave us unsatisfied
when we have attained them. The conclusion is drawn
that it is safer to trust instinct, from which these unconscious desires spring, than conventional notions of
what we ought to do. But then it appears that to follow instinct is, as Spinoza pointed out, to be in bondage to the passions: in particular, we are led to cherish
beliefs which are demonstrably false. Instinct, then,
needs to be corrected by reason, if only in its own
interests. But reason, it seems, can do nothing but
dampen enthusiasm, leaving us cynical and aimless.
What we need are passions of which reason can ap-

prove. But it is the function of reason to pass judgment on the truth or falsity of propositions: so that if reason approves of some passions or purposes this must mean that we apprehend the truth or falsity of propositions of the form: *This emotion is fitting* or *This end is good.* We are back, then, where we started; and the cycle of argument and counter-argument begins once more.

3

In the other books on social and political problems written about this time, Russell's underlying moral theory does not develop very much. In *The Practice and Theory of Bolshevism* (1920) he seems to abandon his never very wholehearted belief that men would be tolerant, affectionate and full of zeal for disinterested learning if only their impulses were not repressed by a tyrannical social system. In that book he lists four fundamental passions, which (apart from the instinctive desires for food, sex and shelter) dominate human nature. They are acquisitiveness, vanity, rivalry and love of power; and the prime error of Marxist theory, he tells us, is that it concentrates on the first to the exclusion of the other three. All of these, presumably, would rank among the "possessive", or bad, impulses; so that the "creative" impulses from which he hoped so much in *Principles of Social Reconstruction* appear to have vanished entirely. In that book he had said: "I consider . . . the worst [life] that which is most inspired by love of possession";[19] so that it is a little startling to find him now writing: "The progress or retrogression of the world depends, broadly speaking, upon the balance between acquisitiveness and rivalry. The former makes for progress, the latter for retrogression."[20] It is true that he is speaking here of material progress; the point is that, as scientific discov-

[19] *Principles of Social Reconstruction*, p. 5.
[20] *Practice and Theory of Bolshevism*, p. 131.

eries "provide improved methods of production, these
may be employed either to increase the general share
of goods, or to set apart more of the labour power of
the community for the business of killing its rivals".
But he can hardly be using "progress" wholly in this
sense when he declares: "One who believes, as I do,
that the free intellect is the chief engine of human
progress, cannot but be fundamentally opposed to
Bolshevism, as much as to the Church of Rome."[21]

Russell's view of the good life has not changed: he
objects to the Soviet régime mainly because it stifles
free inquiry and fosters bigotry and a rigid orthodoxy.
But he now sees little sign that "the love of mental
adventure" or the "creative instincts" are among the
basic forces in human nature. He may have been confirmed in this more pessimistic view by the way in
which Freudianism was developing. Freud himself
was beginning to elaborate the hypothesis that the
impulse to hate was as fundamental as the impulse
to love; that the primary tendencies of the id included
the death-wish, with its accompanying desire for destruction and aggression. If this is accepted it seems
to dispose finally of the view that the good life can
be attained by liberating the id from the repression
of society. On the other hand, it provides an added
reason for being suspicious of the super-ego; for the
super-ego, Freud tells us, is influenced, not merely by
the reality-principle, but also by the sadistic and
masochistic tendencies that rise from the id. But, once
it is admitted that the id is not dominated solely by
the pleasure-principle, doubt is cast on the whole basis
of Freudian Hobbism. The contention was that the
rational way of life consists in following the pleasure-
principle, as modified (of necessity) by the reality-
principle. But this does not involve the assumption
that pleasure is, in the Moorean sense, good, but simply that pleasure is the goal at which human beings

[21] *Practice and Theory of Bolshevism,* p. 114.

do, as a matter of fact, aim. But it now appears that it is only one of the things at which they aim; the other is death and destruction. "The meaning of the evolution of culture", Freud writes, "is no longer a riddle to us. It must present to us the struggle between Eros and Death, between the instincts of life and the instincts of destruction, as it works itself out in the human species."[22] But why prefer one of these to the other, unless one is (in the Moorean sense) good and the other evil?

Yet the objections to Moore remain. When he comes to write *Power,* in 1938, we find Russell repeating emphatically that Reason cannot determine the ends of life. The whole passage is worth quoting:

"It is customary nowadays to decry Reason as a force in human affairs, yet the rise of science is an overwhelming argument on the other side. The men of science proved to intelligent laymen that a certain kind of intellectual outlook ministers to military prowess and wealth; these ends were so ardently desired that the new intellectual outlook overcame that of the Middle Ages, in spite of the force of tradition and the revenues of the Church and the sentiments associated with Catholic theology. The world ceased to believe that Joshua caused the sun to stand still, because Copernican astronomy was useful in navigation; it abandoned Aristotle's physics, because Galileo's theory of falling bodies made it possible to calculate the trajectory of a cannon-ball; it rejected the story of the flood, because geology is useful in mining, and so on. . . .

"From this example, something may be learned as to the power of Reason in general. In the case of Science, Reason prevailed over prejudice because it provided means of realizing existing purposes, and because the proof that it did so was overwhelming. Those who maintain that Reason has no power in hu-

[22] *Civilisation and Its Discontents,* 1930, p. 103.

man affairs overlook these two conditions. If, in the name of Reason, you summon a man to alter his fundamental purposes—to pursue, say, the general happiness rather than his own power—you will fail, and you will deserve to fail, since Reason alone cannot determine the ends of life. . . . But if you can prove, by evidence which is convincing to every sane man who takes the trouble to examine it, that you possess a means of facilitating the satisfaction of existing desires, you may hope, with a certain degree of confidence, that men will ultimately believe what you say."[23]

By this time, it is clear, Russell no longer believes either that some ends are good in themselves, and so recommended by Reason alone, or that the ends which men actually pursue (or would pursue, if they followed Reason in the sense of allowing the pleasure-principle to be modified by nothing but the reality-principle) are those which he himself advocates. Moore and Freudian Hobbism have both failed him. It is not surprising then, to find him turning to the third method of reconciling empiricism with morality —subjectivism. In *Power* he outlines a subjectivist ethic, quite explicitly. In doing so he merely repeats, and expands a little, the chapter on "Science and Ethics" in the little volume called *Religion and Science*[24] which he had published in 1935. There is a further statement of this position in *Human Society in Ethics and Politics;* but the chapter in *Religion and Science* is probably his clearest and most forceful exposition of it.

Moral beliefs, Russell now tells us, are essentially expressions of desire. But it is important to distinguish between two different kinds of desire: purely personal ones, like my desire for a glass of wine with my dinner, and impersonal ones, like my desire for a peace-

23 *Power,* 1938, pp. 142–43.
24 Home University Library, 1935.

ful world in which men will refrain from dropping bombs on one another. The point about impersonal desires is that we want something for others as well as for ourselves; moreover, we want others to want it. The Tolstoyan, for example, wants other men (and himself as well, of course) to want to be kindly and peaceable; the Nietzschean wants himself and others to pursue a life of strenuous heroism. This is just a matter of personal preference: the Tolstoyan happens to prefer to live in one kind of world, the Nietzschean in another. There is no objective reason for preferring one to the other; no reason, that is to say, for calling one better than the other except that one happens to prefer it. In precisely the same way, there is no reason, except one's own preference, for saying that it is better to drink wine than beer. It is true that we do not regard our taste in drinks as a matter of morality; but this is because a desire for wine or beer is a personal desire. We reserve the category "moral" for impersonal desires; but there is no other important difference.

It has commonly been thought that this is an ethical theory which destroys morality. If people are convinced that the difference between good and evil is a mere matter of taste, it is argued, they will lose all incentive to do good (which is often hard) and to avoid evil (which is tempting and easy). Russell argues, with considerable cogency, against this contention. If I desire something, I have every incentive to pursue it; ultimately, indeed, no other incentive is possible. Morality may, in a sense, be a matter of taste; but people are, after all, eager enough to gratify their tastes. This is true, he might have pointed out, even of purely personal desires. If I want wine with my dinner rather than beer, I may join a campaign to compel restaurants to provide it at a reasonable price, vote in favour of a European Common Market, and turn a deaf ear to the arguments of the Hopgrowers' Association and the Brewers' Federation. If you prefer beer to wine, I may find you opposing me in these controversies. Personal tastes, that is to say, will lead each of us to join movements, propound social policies, extol some proposals and denounce others. The same is true, to an even greater extent, of impersonal desires. If I want the kind of world in which men live comfortably and at peace with their neighbours, I will advocate one kind of social policy; if you want a world made fit for Nietzschean heroes to live in, you will advocate a different kind of policy. Neither of us, then, will sink into the mood of cynical indifference which, according to the critics, necessarily accompanies a subjectivist ethic. It is true, Russell adds, that neither of us will think the other wicked and sinful; one's opponent is seen as simply someone whose impersonal desires are different from one's own, not as a monster of corruption. Subjectivism, then, makes for tolerance; but not for any lack of moral zeal. And this is, of course, a gain rather than a loss.

Subjectivism is a highly important, and in many ways a highly attractive, moral theory. There is obviously no space here to discuss it at all fully. But I should like to make three comments on Russell's version of it.

(1) Is it true that subjectivism makes for tolerance? There is no room, Russell tells us, for "sin" in the subjectivist vocabulary. But why not? True, the sinner has lost his bad eminence and become simply a person whose tastes are different from mine. But why should that lead me to tolerate him? On the subjectivist view, to say that something is good means that it is in accordance with my impersonal desires; and to say that something is evil means that it is opposed to my impersonal desires. My opponent, then, is a wilful seeker of evil and so, one would think, sinful. If we persist in feeling that it is not after all very sinful merely to have aims opposed to our own, doesn't this mean that we are not really subjectivists? Objectivists, no doubt, believe that we ought not to condemn anyone merely

because his desires differ from ours, but only because
his desires are bad. But, on the subjectivist view, to say
that desires are "bad" is just to say that they are "different from mine".

Well, then, it may be argued, it follows that the
subjectivist does not condemn anyone; for he believes
that desires are never bad in the objectivist sense, but
only in the sense of "different from mine". It is true
that this subjectivist sense of "bad" carries with it some
of the implications of the objectivist sense: e.g. "to
be avoided", "to be opposed". (Not to recognize this
is to be exposed to Moore's strictures on the natural-
istic fallacy.) But it does not carry with it one further
implication: "to be condemned". The subjectivist con-
demns no one; he merely opposes, firmly but with
good humour, policies which don't happen to chime
with his own.

This may be true, as a psychological generalization
about subjectivists. They may all be tolerant and charitable in their treatment of opponents. But there is
no reason why they should be: tolerance does not follow, as Russell seems to think it does, as a logical consequence of their ethical theory. It can be made to
follow only if we accept the premiss: "We ought not
to condemn anyone merely because his desires differ
from ours, but only because his desires are bad." Then
it might be added: But no desires are bad (in this
sense); therefore no one is to be condemned. But
there seems no special reason why a subjectivist should
accept the first premiss. It is doubtful, indeed, whether
that premiss is consistent with subjectivism at all.

(2) Russell, then, is mistaken in supposing that tolerance necessarily follows from subjectivism. But there
is, I think, a more fundamental, though quite inconclusive, objection to his position. There can be no
doubt that his subjectivism stems, ultimately, from his
firm belief in "the scientific outlook". We apply the
scientific attitude to our moral and political beliefs as
well as to our beliefs about the external world, and we

find that there is no sound reason for accepting one set of moral beliefs rather than another. Or, at least, there is no sound reason for regarding any set of moral beliefs as objectively valid, in the sense that our belief that water flows downhill is objectively valid. Now, what follows from this? Why, that we ought not to regard any set of moral beliefs as objectively valid. But does it? Only if we make a prior assumption, viz. that one ought not to accept any proposition unless the evidence appears to support it. And, if no moral propositions are objectively valid, this one is not.

There are, no doubt, several possible replies to this objection. Russell might simply reply that he is not concerned to draw the conclusion that one ought not to regard moral beliefs as objectively valid. As a philosopher, he is not concerned to tell his readers what they ought to do, but what is the case. It is the case that moral beliefs are not objectively valid; but if his readers choose to ignore this disturbing truth and continue to nourish comforting fictions, that is purely their own concern.

This is, I say, a possible reply. I am not sure how relevant it is that, in Russell's mouth, the reply is not very convincing. For, in fact, much of his writing is concerned with a quite passionate advocacy of "the scientific outlook": facing the facts, following the argument whithersoever it leads, and so on. Certainly most readers will carry away the conviction that this is, in some sense, what they ought to do.

But, of course (and here we have a second possible reply) it is part of Russell's case that subjectivism is quite compatible with advocacy. Russell himself, it may be said, happens to prefer a world in which people do follow the argument whithersoever it leads, at whatever cost to their own comfort. Naturally, he tries to persuade other people to adopt this attitude.

But how, on this view, can he hope to persuade them, since there is no objective principle whose truth may be brought home to them? All that Russell can do is to play on a belief that they themselves already hold. If they do not already hold it, there is no earthly reason (and still less any transcendental reason) why they should, except that Russell would like them to.

Now it probably is true that most people do believe, to a greater or less degree, in following the argument whithersoever it leads. It is also true, I think, that, except in the comparatively small minority with the academic temperament, this is one of the very weakest of human passions. To give one illustration, there are very many people who, convinced that a belief in God is comforting, conducive to good actions, and incapable of causing any harm, simply cannot understand anyone who passionately attacks this belief for no other reason than that he believes it to be false. Russell himself, it will be remembered, says that people were brought to accept the teachings of scientists only because of their practical utility. It is highly doubtful, however, whether a belief in subjectivism has any practical utility. Russell says it makes men tolerant, but most men probably do not want to be made tolerant. And there seems little doubt that, in the game of trying to persuade others to adopt one's own impersonal desires, it is a great advantage to believe that one's own desires (but not one's opponent's) are eternal and immutable verities. It may be said, in general, that a grasp of the truth about any state of affairs, however unpalatable, always helps one to cope with that state of affairs; but this is not always true, and it may be doubted whether it is ever true about the nature of moral beliefs.

What follows from this is not merely that Russell, and subjectivists generally, have little chance of winning adherents, and that any they may win will belong to the small class of academics in whom the disinterested desire for truth has become hypertrophied. This is probably true anyway and to that extent confirms

Russell's views. What also follows from the subjectivist position is that there is no sound reason why other people should accept subjectivism, even if it is true.

This objection is certainly not conclusive. It is no more than a special case of an objection which Russell himself considers and perhaps refutes: that a belief in subjectivism undermines moral zeal. The earlier Russell, no doubt, believed that everyone had a duty to follow the argument wheresoever it led, and to suspend judgment where the evidence was inconclusive; he certainly thought these things good in themselves. It is from these beliefs, applied to ethics, that his subjectivism springs. The later Russell no doubt believes merely that he happens to have an abnormally keen desire to follow the argument whithersoever it leads, and that this is an impersonal desire—he wants others to want it too. There is, however, no reason why those others, if they do not already share this desire, should try to acquire it. In a sense his subjectivism has kicked away the ladder by which it climbed; but this does not really matter, since it does not need the ladder for support. All the same, the paradox is, I think, worth noticing.

(3) The final comment I want to make is of a rather different kind. Consider the following passage from *Power*:

"The great ethical innovators have not been men who *knew* more than others; they have been men who *desired* more, or, to be more accurate, men whose desires were more impersonal and of larger scope than those of average men. . . .

"All great moralists, from Buddha and the Stoics down to recent times, treated the good as something to be, if possible, enjoyed by all men equally. They did not think of themselves as princes or Jews or Greeks; they thought of themselves merely as human beings. Their ethic had always a two-fold source: on the one hand, they valued certain elements in their own lives; on the other hand, sympathy made them desire for others what they desired for themselves. . . . Sympathy is in some degree instinctive; a child may be made unhappy by another child's cry. But limitations of sympathy are also natural. The cat has no sympathy for the mouse. . . . Where there is limitation of sympathy there is a corresponding limitation in the concept of the good: the good becomes something to be enjoyed only by the magnanimous man, or only by the superman, or the Aryan, or the proletarian, or the Christadelphian. All these are cat-and-mouse ethics. . . . Such creeds, inevitably, appeal only to the cat, not to the mouse; they are imposed on the mouse by naked power."[25]

So far the point might be simply that the proponents of cat-and-mouse ethics cannot expect to have as many adherents as those moralists whose sympathies are universal: "great" in "the great ethical innovators" may simply mean "most influential". But there is little doubt that Russell means more than this; that he wants to condemn narrowness of sympathy, and hence cat-and-mouse ethics, as such. Speaking of the great religions, he says: "Their founders were men whose sympathy was universal, and who were felt, on this account, to be possessed of a wisdom surpassing that of temporary and passionate despots. The result was not all that the founders could have wished. . . . Nevertheless, the principle of universal sympathy conquered first one province, then another. It is the analogue, in the realm of feeling, of impersonal curiosity in the realm of intellect; both alike are essential elements in mental growth."[26]

And a little later he says, still more definitely: "Whatever our *politics* may be, there can be no valid argument for an undemocratic *ethic*. I mean by an undemocratic ethic one which singles out a certain portion of mankind and says: 'these men are to enjoy

[25] *Op. cit.*, pp. 238–39.
[26] p. 260.

the good things, and the rest are merely to minister to them'."[27]

The use of the expression "valid argument" here, and, rather less clearly, of "mental growth" in the earlier passage, suggest that Russell still regards "democratic" ethical systems as intrinsically better, in some objective sense, than undemocratic ones. This seems clearly inconsistent with his subjectivism.

It will be noticed, moreover, that the "principle of universal sympathy" which he speaks of here is identical with the "spirit" which, in *Principles of Social Reconstruction*, is to reconcile instinct with reason. Further, there is a close resemblance between the qualities of "the great ethical innovators" and the *defining characteristics* of moral principles. A moral principle is, properly understood, the expression of an impersonal desire: i.e. something one desires for others as well as for oneself. Now it is clear that Russell approves of breadth of sympathy and disapproves of cat-and-mouse ethics; and he seems to think of this approval and the accompanying disapproval as more than a personal idiosyncrasy. Earlier, it will be remembered, he had said that the impersonal desires of "spirit" were the only ones Reason (or "Mind") could approve of. Now he has come to believe that Reason cannot approve of any desire more than any other; but he is reluctant to relinquish these earlier beliefs. Consequently he resorts, as other contemporary moral philosophers in the same difficulty have resorted, to the device of a loaded definition. Only impersonal desires are to be called "moral". Russell thinks of men as genuinely wanting others to have the type of good life which they want for themselves. This does not necessarily exclude cat-and-mouse ethics, since a man might want to spend his life abasing himself before the superman; or he might be genuinely convinced that he would want to do this, if he did not have the good

[27] *Op. cit.*, p. 282.

luck to be a superman himself. But the man who genuinely wants to make exceptions in his own favour is ruled out, simply by definition. And to rule him out in this way is, in effect, to assume the objective validity of a basic principle: that one ought not to make exceptions in one's own favour.

. . . . .

It is fairly easy to pick holes in any of the three main ethical theories which Russell has, in the course of his development, put forward. It is much harder to find a more satisfactory theory to put in their place. The importance of Russell is that he is not only exceptionally clear-headed, but also exceptionally candid. And any candid person who tackles seriously the problem of finding a philosophical basis for his moral beliefs will, I think, find himself doing what Russell did: inclining to each of these three theories in turn, and in the end finding that none of them is wholly acceptable, but also that it is difficult to dispense with any of them. (Russell does appear, in the end, to be satisfied with subjectivism; but we have seen that his subjectivism incorporates—illegitimately—elements of the two earlier theories.) This is, I think, the central problem that confronts moral philosophers in our time. If Russell has not been able to solve it, at least it is illuminating to see what happens when a mind of the calibre of his grapples with the problem.

A SELECTIVE, CLASSIFIED
BERTRAND RUSSELL
BIBLIOGRAPHY

Harry Ruja

This bibliography for the most part lists only those of Russell's writings which are primarily philosophical. Items in foreign languages are cited sparingly. Reprints are not cited. Articles and monographs which, subsequent to their original publication, were incorporated into one of Russell's books are not separately cited unless their original form differed significantly from their reprinted form. Where publication in British and other journals was simultaneous, only the British publication is cited.

I have learned much from fellow Russell-bibliographers Kenneth M. Blackwell of McMaster University, Lester E. Denonn, and Pierre van Cutsem, though they were not directly involved in this present project. I express my gratitude to them here.

JOURNAL ABBREVIATIONS

Am.	American
Assn.	Association
Astron.	Astronomical
Brit.	British
Bull.	Bulletin
Cong.	Congress
Educ.	Education, Educational
Int.	International
J.	Journal
Math.	Mathematics, Mathématiques
Met.	Metaphysics, Métaphysique
Mor.	Morale
N.S.	New Series
O.S.	Old Series
Phil.	Philosophy, Philosophie, Philosophical

Pol.	Political, Politics
Proc.	Proceedings
Psych.	Psychology, Psychological
Q.	Quarterly
Rev.	Review, Revista, Revue
Sci.	Science, Scientific
Soc.	Société, Society
Sup.	Supplement, Supplementary

I. HISTORY OF PHILOSOPHY. PHILOSOPHY OF HISTORY. BIOGRAPHY.

The Autobiography of Bertrand Russell, 1872–1914. London: Allen & Unwin; Boston: Little, Brown; Toronto: McClelland & Stewart, 1967.

The Autobiography of Bertrand Russell, 1914–1944. London: Allen & Unwin; Boston: Little, Brown; Toronto: McClelland & Stewart, 1968.

The Autobiography of Bertrand Russell, 1944–1967. London: Allen & Unwin; New York: Simon and Schuster, 1969.

A Critical Exposition of the Philosophy of Leibniz. Cambridge: Cambridge University Press; London: Clay, 1900; 2d ed., London: Allen & Unwin, 1937.

Dear Bertrand Russell . . . Ed. by Barry Feinberg & R. Kasrils. London: Allen & Unwin; Boston: Houghton Mifflin, 1969.

A History of Western Philosophy. New York: Simon and Schuster, 1945; London: Allen & Unwin, 1946.

My Philosophical Development. London: Allen & Unwin; New York: Simon and Schuster; Toronto: Nelson, 1959.

The Philosophy of Bergson. Cambridge: Bowes & Bowes; London: Macmillan; Glasgow: MacLehose, 1914.

Portraits from Memory. London: Allen & Unwin; New York: Simon and Schuster, 1956.

Understanding History. New York: Philosophical Library, 1957.

Wisdom of the West. Ed. by Paul Foulkes. London: Macdonald; Garden City, N.Y.: Doubleday, 1959.

Review of P. Boutroux, *L'imagination et les mathématiques selon Descartes. Mind,* 1901, Vol. 10, p. 274.

"Recent Work on the Philosophy of Leibniz." *Mind*, 1903, Vol. 12, pp. 177–201.

Review of L. Couturat, *Opuscules et fragments inédits de Leibniz*. *Mind*, 1904, Vol. 13, pp. 131–32.

Review of *Essays Philosophical and Psychological in Honor of William James*. *Hibbert J.*, 1908, Vol. 7, pp. 203–4.

"The Philosophy of William James." *Nation* (London), 1910, Vol. 7, pp. 793–94.

"Spinoza." *Nation* (London), 1910, Vol. 8, pp. 278, 280.

Review of W. James, *Memories and Studies*. *Cambridge Rev.*, 1911, Vol. 33, p. 118.

Review of H. Bergson, *Laughter*. *Cambridge Rev.*, 1912, Vol. 33, pp. 193–94.

Review of W. James, *Essays in Radical Empiricism*. *Mind*, 1912, Vol. 21, pp. 571–75.

Review of G. E. Moore, *Philosophical Studies*, and of K. Stephen, *The Misuse of Mind*. *Nation & Athenaeum*, 1922, Vol. 31, pp. 538–39.

Review of G. Santayana, *Soliloquies in England*. *Dial*, 1922, Vol. 73, pp. 559–62.

Review of J. A. Gunn, *Modern French Philosophy*. *Nation & Athenaeum*, 1922, Vol. 32, p. 426.

Review of G. Santayana, *The Life of Reason*. *Outlook* (London), 1923, Vol. 51, pp. 365, 368.

Review of S. Radhakrishnan, *Indian Philosophy*, and of J. P. Bruce, *Chu Hsi and His Masters*. *Nation & Athenaeum*, 1923, Vol. 33, pp. 748–49.

Review of Hu Shih, *The Development of Logical Method in Ancient China*. *Nation & Athenaeum*, 1923, Vol. 33, pp. 778–79.

"Morris R. Cohen." *A Tribute to Professor Morris Raphael Cohen*. New York: "The Youth Who Sat At His Feet," 1928, pp. 46–49.

"How I Came by My Creed." *The Realist*, September 1929, Vol. 1, No. 6, pp. 14–21.

Review of J. Laird, *Recent Philosophy*. *Listener*, October 14, 1936, Vol. 16, No. 405, Sup. p. iii.

"Plato in Modern Dress." *New Statesman & Nation,* 1937, Vol. 13, p. 850.

"The Philosophy of Santayana." Paul A. Schilpp, ed., *The Philosophy of George Santayana.* Chicago: Northwestern University Press, 1940, pp. 453–74.

"Hegel's *Philosophy of History.*" Huntington Cairns, et al., eds., *Invitation to Learning.* New York: Random House; Toronto: Macmillan, 1941, pp. 410–22.

"Spinoza, *Ethics.*" Mark Van Doren, ed., *The New Invitation to Learning.* New York: Random House, 1942, pp. 107–18.

"Descartes, *Discourse on Method.*" *Ibid.,* pp. 93–104.

"My Mental Development." Paul A. Schilpp, ed., *The Philosophy of Bertrand Russell.* Evanston, Ill.: Northwestern University Press; Cambridge: Cambridge University Press; Toronto: Macmillan, 1944, pp. 3–20.

Foreword. James K. Feibleman, *An Introduction to Peirce's Philosophy.* New York: Harper, 1946, pp. xv–xvi.

"A Turning-Point in My Life." Leonard Russell, ed., *The Saturday Book,* Vol. 8. London: Hutchinson, 1948, pp. 142–46.

"Ideas and Beliefs of the Victorians." *Listener,* February 5, 1948, Vol. 39, pp. 211–12.

"John Stuart Mill." *Listener,* May 13, 1948, Vol. 39, p. 785.

Review of John Bowle, *The Unity of European History. Listener,* October 7, 1948, Vol. 40, p. 537.

"William of Occam." *Listener,* December 1, 1949, Vol. 42, pp. 949–51.

Autobiographical remarks. Milton Shulman, *How to Be a Celebrity.* London: Reinhardt & Evans, 1950, pp. 189–99.

"John Stuart Mill, *On Liberty.*" *Invitation to Learning,* 1951, Vol. 1, pp. 356–63.

"My First Eighty Years." *New York Post,* May 25, 1952, Sec. 2, pp. 10–11.

Review of L. Price, *Dialogues of Alfred North Whitehead.* London *Sunday Times,* November 14, 1954, p. 6.

Review of M. St. J. Packe, *The Life of John Stuart Mill.* London *Observer,* April 4, 1954, p. 9.

"Sous l'influence de Voltaire." *Table Ronde,* February 1958, No. 122, pp. 159–63.

"Prof. G. E. Moore." London *Times,* October 28, 1958, p. 14.

"The Influence and Thought of G. E. Moore." *Listener,* 1959, Vol. 61, pp. 755–56.

Allers, R. Review of *A History . . . Franciscan Studies,* 1947, Vol. 7, pp. 219–42.

Beerling, R. F. "Russell and Historical Truth." *Kant-Studien,* 1964, Vol. 55, pp. 385–93.

Bergmann, Gustav. "Russell's Examination of Leibniz Examined." *Phil. Science,* 1956, Vol. 23, pp. 175–203.

Berlin, Isaiah. Review of *A History . . . Mind,* 1947, Vol. 56, pp. 151–66.

Boas, George. Review of *A History . . . J. Hist. Ideas,* 1947, Vol. 8, pp. 117–23.

Bosanquet, Bernard. Review of *. . . Leibniz. Arch. f. System. Phil.,* 1902, N.S. Vol. 8, pp. 123–28.

Broad, C. D. "Bertrand Russell's First Forty-two Years, in Self-portraiture." *Phil. Rev.,* 1968, Vol. 77, pp. 455–73.

Buranelli, Vincent. "Bertrand Russell: an Impression." *Prairie Schooner* (Lincoln, Neb.), 1955, Vol. 29, pp. 44–48.

Collins, J. Review of *A History . . . Franciscan Studies,* 1947, Vol. 7, pp. 193–219.

Costelloe, Karin. "An Answer to Mr. Bertrand Russell's Article on the Philosophy of Bergson." *Monist,* 1914, Vol. 24, pp. 145–55.

Dewey, John, and H. M. Kallen, eds. *The Bertrand Russell Case.* New York: Viking, 1941.

Duncan, George M. Review of *. . . Leibniz. Phil. Rev.,* 1901, Vol. 10, pp. 288–97.

Edwards, Paul. "How Bertrand Russell Was Prevented from Teaching at the College of the City of New York." In Russell, *Why I Am Not a Christian,* pp. 207–59.

Feuer, Lewis S. "Bertrand Russell: the Pilgrimage of Scientific Philosophy." *Univ. of Toronto Q.,* 1955, Vol. 24, pp. 217–33.

Gottschalk, Herbert. *Bertrand Russell, a Life*. London: Baker, 1965; New York: Roy, 1966.

Hampshire, Stuart. "The Education of Bertrand Russell." *New York Rev. of Books*, April 20, 1967, Vol. 8, No. 7, pp. 3–4.

Idem. "Bertrand Russell; His Contribution to Philosophy." Manchester *Guardian*, May 17, 1952, pp. 4, 6.

Hardy, G. H. *Bertrand Russell & Trinity*. Cambridge, Eng.: Author, 1942.

Hussey, Charles. "Earl, Philosopher, Logician, Rebel." *The New York Times*, May 13, 1962, Sec. 6, pp. 10, 102, 104.

Jarrett, James L. "D. H. Lawrence and Bertrand Russell." In Harry T. Moore, ed., *A D. H. Lawrence Miscellany*, Carbondale, Ill.: Southern Illinois University Press, 1959, pp. 168–87.

Joad, C. E. M. "Bertrand Russell's 'History of Western Philosophy.'" *Proc. of Aristotelian Soc.*, 1946–47, Vol. 47, pp. 85–104.

Latta, R. Review of . . . *Leibniz*. *Mind*, 1901, Vol. 10, pp. 525–33.

Lawrence, D. H. *Letters to Bertrand Russell*, ed. by H. T. Moore. New York: Gotham Book Mart, 1948.

Leggett, Harry W. *Bertrand Russell, O.M.* London: Lincolns-Prager, 1949; New York: Philosophical Library, 1950; Toronto: McLeod, 1950.

Purcell, Victor (Myra Buttle, pseud.). *Bitches' Brew; or, The Plot Against Bertrand Russell*. New York: Watts, 1960.

Randall, John Herman, Jr. Review of *Wisdom of the West*. *J. Phil.*, 1960, Vol. 57, pp. 365–68.

Reed, Muriel. "England's Angry Old Man." *Réalités* (English ed.), August 1963, No. 153, pp. 44–49.

Santayana, George. "The Philosophy of Mr. Bertrand Russell." *Winds of Doctrine*. New York: Scribner's, 1913; London: Dent, 1913, pp. 110–54.

Scheer, Robert. "Lord Russell." *Ramparts*, May 1967, Vol. 5, No. 11, pp. 16–23.

Schilpp, Paul A., ed. *The Philosophy of Bertrand Russell*. Evanston, Ill.: Northwestern University Press, 1944; Cambridge, Eng.: Cambridge University Press, 1944; Toronto: Macmillan, 1944.

Schoenman, Ralph, ed. *Bertrand Russell, Philosopher of the Century*. London: Allen & Unwin, 1967; Boston: Little, Brown, 1968.

Somerville, John. "An Open Letter to Bertrand Russell." *Phil. Sci.*, 1946, Vol. 13, pp. 67–71. (Re dialectical materialism.)

Sparshott, F. E. Review of *Portraits . . . Tamarack Rev.*, Winter 1968, No. 6, pp. 90–94.

Tongue, William R. Review of *A History . . . Franciscan Studies*, 1947, Vol. 7, pp. 72–89.

Warnock, Geoffrey J. "Bertrand Russell." *English Philosophy Since 1900*. New York, London: Oxford University Press, 1958, Chap. 3.

Wood, Alan. *Bertrand Russell, the Passionate Skeptic*. London: Allen & Unwin, 1957; New York: Simon and Schuster, 1958.

Into the Tenth Decade; Tribute to Bertrand Russell (no pub., no date).

Obituaries, memorial notices, assessments

Signed
Ayer, Alfred J., *New Statesman*, 1970, Vol. 79, pp. 182–83.
Boyle, Sir Edward, London *Daily Telegraph*, February 7, 1970, p. 16.
Braithwaite, R. B., *Brit. J. Phil. Sci.*, 1970, Vol. 21, pp. 129–31.
Brogan, Sir Denis, *Spectator*, 1970, Vol. 224, pp. 208–9.
Bronowski, J., *Nation*, 1970, Vol. 210, p. 166.
Burns, Michael, London *Times*, February 10, 1970, p. 12.
Downie, Leonard, Jr., Washington *Post*, February 4, 1970, p. C 5.
Dutt, R. Palme, *Labour Mo.* (London), 1970, Vol. 52, pp. 97–110.
Jackson, Leonard, *Times Educ. Sup.*, February 6, 1970, p. 91.
Johnson, Dennis, Manchester *Guardian*, February 4, 1970, p. 20.
Perrot, Roy, London *Observer*, February 8, 1970, p. 21.
Steiner, George, London *Sunday Times*, February 8, 1970, p. 12.
Unwin, Philip, *Bookseller* (London), February 7, 1970, p. 388.

Walsh, John, *Science*, 1970, Vol. 167, pp. 1110–11.

Whitman, Alden, *The New York Times*, February 3, 1970, pp. 1, 30.

Unsigned

Boston *Christian Science Monitor*, February 5, 1970, p. 16.

Denver *Post*, February 4, 1970, p. 18.

Dublin *Irish Times*, February 3, 1970, p. 9; February 4, 1970, p. 9.

Edinburgh *Scotsman*, February 4, 1970, p. 5.

Life, February 13, 1970, Vol. 68, No. 5, pp. 31–32.

London *Times*, February 4, 1970, pp. 11, 12.

Manchester *Guardian*, February 4, 1970, pp. 4, 10.

Montreal *Star*, February 4, 1970, p. 8.

Newsweek, February 16, 1970, Vol. 75, No. 7, pp. 62–63.

The New York Times, February 5, 1970, p. 38.

Paris *Le Monde*, February 4, 1970, p. 6.

Seattle Times, February 4, 1970, p. A 12.

Der Spiegel, February 9, 1970, Vol. 24, No. 7, p. 134.

Time, February 16, 1970, Vol. 95, No. 7, pp. 22, 24.

Washington Post, February 6, 1970, p. A 18.

II. SURVEY OF PHILOSOPHY. MISCELLANEOUS.

The Art of Philosophizing. New York: Philosophical Library, 1968.

The Basic Writings of Bertrand Russell. Ed. by Robert E. Egner and L. E. Denonn. London: Allen & Unwin; New York: Simon and Schuster, 1961.

Bertrand Russell Speaks His Mind. London: Barker; Cleveland: World, 1960.

Essays in Skepticism. New York: Philosophical Library, 1962.

Fact and Fiction. London: Allen & Unwin, 1961; Toronto: Nelson, 1961; New York: Simon and Schuster, 1962.

In Praise of Idleness. London: Allen & Unwin; New York: Norton, 1935.

Mysticism and Logic. London and New York: Longmans, Green, 1918.

An Outline of Philosophy. London: Allen & Unwin; New York: Norton, 1927. Title of New York ed.: *Philosophy*.

Philosophical Essays. London: Allen & Unwin, 1910; 2d ed., London: Allen & Unwin, 1966; New York: Simon and Schuster, 1967.

The Problems of Philosophy. London: Williams & Norgate; New York: Holt, 1912.

Selected Papers of Bertrand Russell. New York: Modern Library, 1927.

Skeptical Essays. London: Allen & Unwin; New York: Norton, 1928.

Unpopular Essays. London: Allen & Unwin; New York: Simon and Schuster, 1950.

Review of A. Ruge, *Encyclopaedia of the Philosophical Sciences. Cambridge Rev.,* 1913, Vol. 35, p. 161.

Review of C. E. M. Joad, *Essays in Common-sense Philosophy. Athenaeum,* 1919, pp. 652–53.

Review of *Proc. of Aristotelian Soc., Vol. 19. Athenaeum,* 1919, pp. 1149–50.

"What I Believe." *Nation,* 1931, Vol. 132, pp. 469–71.

Review of H. Levy, *A Philosophy for a Modern Man. New Statesman & Nation,* 1938, Vol. 15, pp. 252–54.

"Philosophy and Common Sense." *New Statesman & Nation,* 1938, Vol. 15, p. 365.

["My Philosophy"]. *I Believe.* New York: Simon and Schuster, 1939, pp. 409–12.

"Reply to Criticisms." Paul A. Schilpp, ed., *The Philosophy of Bertrand Russell.* Evanston, Ill.: Northwestern University Press; Cambridge: Cambridge University Press; Toronto: Macmillan, 1944, pp. 681–741.

"Teaching Philosophy." *Univ. Q.,* 1947, Vol. 1, p. 367.

[Comments]. Clara Urquhart, ed., *Last Chance.* Boston: Beacon, 1948, *passim.*

"Rewards of Philosophy." *Listener,* 1948, Vol. 39, p. 459.

"Little Wisdom in the World Today." *Glasgow Herald,* October 5, 1950, p. 4.

"Notes on *Philosophy,* January, 1960." *Philosophy,* 1960, Vol. 35, pp. 146–47.

Blackwell, Kenneth. "The Importance to Philosophers of the Bertrand Russell Archive." *Dialogue* (Kingston, Ont.), 1969, Vol. 7, pp. 608–15.

Bosanquet, B. Review of *Problems of Philosophy. Mind,* 1912, Vol. 21, pp. 556–64.

Broad, C. D. Review of *Mysticism and Logic. Mind,* 1918, Vol. 27, pp. 484–92.

Copleston, Frederick C. *A History of Philosophy.* Westminster, Md.: Newman, 1966, Vol. 8, Chaps. 19–21.

Dorward, Alan. *Bertrand Russell; a Short Guide to His Philosophy.* London: Longmans, 1951.

Edwards, Paul, W. P. Alston, and A. N. Prior. "Russell, Bertrand Arthur William." In Edwards, ed., *The Encyclopedia of Philosophy,* New York: Macmillan & Free Press, 1967; London: Collier-Macmillan, 1967, Vol. 7, pp. 235–58.

Feinberg, Barry, ed. *A Detailed Catalogue of the Archives of Bertrand Russell.* London: Continuum, 1967.

Jacob, Gertrude. "Bertrand Russell; an Essay Toward a Bibliography." *Bull. Bibliog.* (Boston), December 1929, Vol. 13, pp. 198–99; May–August 1930, Vol. 14, pp. 28–30.

Jourdain, Philip E. B. *The Philosophy of Mr. B*rtr*nd R*s-s*ll.* London: Allen & Unwin, 1918; Chicago: Open Court, 1918.

Klemke, E. D., ed. *Essays on Bertrand Russell.* Urbana, Ill.: University of Illinois Press, 1970.

Lewis, John. *Bertrand Russell: Philosopher and Humanist.* London: Lawrence & Wishart, 1968; New York: International Publishers, 1968.

O'Connor, Daniel J. "Bertrand Russell." In O'Connor, ed., *A Critical History of Western Philosophy,* New York: Free Press, 1964; London: Collier-Macmillan, 1964, pp. 473–91.

Park, Joe. "An Annotated Bibliography of Some of the Principal Writings of Bertrand Russell on Education." *Hist. Educ. J.,* 1959, Vol. 10, pp. 103–15.

III. LOGIC. FOUNDATIONS OF MATHEMATICS.

An Essay on the Foundations of Geometry. Cambridge: Cambridge University Press, 1897.

Introduction to Mathematical Philosophy. London: Allen & Unwin; New York: Macmillan, 1919.

Logic and Knowledge. Ed. by Robert C. Marsh. London: Allen & Unwin; New York: Macmillan, 1956.

With Alfred N. Whitehead. *Principia Mathematica.* Cambridge: Cambridge University Press, Vol. 1, 1910 (2d ed., 1925); Vol. 2, 1912; Vol. 3, 1913.

"The *A Priori* in Geometry." *Proc. of Aristotelian Soc.*, 1895–96, O.S., Vol. 3, pp. 97–112.

"The Logic of Geometry." *Mind*, 1896, Vol. 5, pp. 1–23.

Review of L. Couturat, *De l'infini mathématique. Mind*, 1897, Vol. 6, pp. 112–19.

"On the Relations of Number and Quantity." *Mind*, 1897, Vol. 6, pp. 326–41.

"Les axiomes propres à Euclide, sont-ils empiriques?" *Rev. de Met. et de Mor.*, 1898, Vol. 6, pp. 759–76.

"Sur les axiomes de la géométrie." *Rev. de Met. et de Mor.*, 1899, Vol. 7, pp. 684–707.

Review of J. Schulz, *Psychologie der Axiome. Mind*, 1900, Vol. 9, pp. 120–21.

"L'idée d'ordre et la position absolue dans l'espace et dans le temps." *Int. Cong. Phil., 1st, Paris, 1900*, Paris: Colin, 1901, Vol. 3, pp. 241–77.

"On the Notion of Order." *Mind*, 1901, Vol. 10, pp. 30–51.

"Geometry, Non-Euclidean." *The New Volumes of the Encyclopaedia Britannica.* London: Black; New York: Encyclopaedia Britannica, 1902, Vol. 4, pp. 664–74.

"Théorie générale des séries bien-ordonnées." *Rev. de Math.*, 1902, Vol. 8, pp. 12–43.

"The Teaching of Euclid." *Math. Gazette*, 1902, Vol. 2, pp. 165–67.

[The Russell Paradox]. Jean van Heijenoort, ed., *From Frege to Gödel.* Cambridge: Harvard University Press, 1967, pp. 124–25.

"On Finite and Infinite Cardinal Numbers." *Am. J. Math.*, 1902, Vol. 24, pp. 378–83.

Review of K. Geissler, *Die Grundsätze und das Wesen des Unendlichen. Mind*, 1903, Vol. 12, pp. 267–69.

Review of L. J. Delaporte, *Essai philosophique sur les géo-métries non-Euclidiennes*. *Mind*, 1904, Vol. 13, pp. 132–33.

"The Axiom of Infinity." *Hibbert J.*, 1904, Vol. 2, pp. 809–12.

"Non-Euclidean Geometry." *Athenaeum*, 1904, pp. 592–93.

"Sur la relation des mathématiques à la logistique." *Rev. de Met. et de Mor.*, 1905, Vol. 13, pp. 906–16.

"On Some Difficulties in the Theory of Transfinite Numbers and Order Types." *London Math. Soc., Proc.*, 1906, 2d Ser., Vol. 4, pp. 29–53.

"The Theory of Implication." *Am. J. Math.*, 1906, Vol. 28, pp. 159–202.

Review of H. MacColl, *Symbolic Logic and Its Applications*. *Mind*, 1906, Vol. 15, pp. 255–60.

Review of A. Pastore, *Logica formale dedotta dalla considera-zione di modelli meccanici*. *Mind*, 1906, Vol. 15, p. 277.

"Les paradoxes de la logique." *Rev. de Met. et de Mor.*, 1906, Vol. 14, pp. 627–50.

"Mr. Haldane on Infinity." *Mind*, 1908, Vol. 17, pp. 238–42.

" 'If' and 'Imply.' " *Mind*, 1908, Vol. 17, pp. 300–1.

Review of A. Reymond, *Logique et mathématiques*. *Mind*, 1909, Vol. 18, pp. 299–301.

Review of P. Carus, *The Foundations of Mathematics*. *Math. Gazette*, 1909, Vol. 5, pp. 103–4.

Review of G. Mannoury, *Methodologisches und Philosophisches zur Elementar-Mathematik*. *Mind*, 1910, Vol. 19, pp. 438–39.

"Some Explanations in Reply to Mr. Bradley." *Mind*, 1910, Vol. 19, pp. 373–78.

[Number]. *Rev. de Met. et de Mor.*, 1912, Vol. 20, pp. 725–26.

"The Philosophical Importance of Mathematical Logic." *Monist*, 1913, Vol. 23, pp. 481–93.

[*Principia Mathematica*'s Notation]. *Mind*, 1919, Vol. 28, p. 124.

"Professor Dewey's 'Essays in Experimental Logic.' " *J. Phil.*, 1919, Vol. 16, pp. 5–26.

Review of B. Bosanquet, *Implication and Linear Inference*. *Athenaeum*, 1920, pp. 514–15.

"Mathematical Philosophy." *Sci. Progress*, 1920, Vol. 15, p. 101.

Introduction. Ludwig Wittgenstein, *Tractatus Logico-Philosophicus*. London: Paul, Trench, & Trubner; New York: Harcourt, Brace, 1922, pp. 7–23.

Preface. Jean Nicod, *Foundations of Geometry and Induction*. London: Paul, Trench, & Trubner; New York: Harcourt, Brace, 1930, pp. 5–9.

"Heads or Tails." *Atlantic Mo.*, 1930, Vol. 146, pp. 163–70.

Review of F. P. Ramsey, *The Foundations of Mathematics*. *Mind*, 1931, Vol. 40, pp. 476–82.

Idem. Philosophy, 1932, Vol. 7, pp. 84–86.

"The Relevance of Psychology to Logic." *Aristotelian Soc.*, Sup., Vol. 17, 1938, pp. 42–53.

"On the Importance of Logical Form." *International Encyclopedia of Unified Science*, Vol. 1, Part 1, No. 1, ed. by Otto Neurath. Chicago: University of Chicago Press, 1938, pp. 39–41.

"Whitehead and *Principia Mathematica*." *Mind*, 1948, Vol. 57, pp. 137–38.

"Ludwig Wittgenstein." *Mind*, 1951, Vol. 60, pp. 297–98.

"Mathematical Infinity." *Mind*, 1958, Vol. 67, p. 385.

Preface. Jean Nicod, *Le problème logique de l'induction*. Paris: Presses Universitaires de France, 1961, pp. v–vii.

"False and True." London *Observer*, March 12, 1967, p. 33.

Bedau, Hugo. Review of *Logic and Knowledge*. *Phil. Sci.*, 1958, Vol. 25, pp. 136–39.

Behmann, Heinrich. "Das Russelsche Paradoxen und die formale Logik." *Int. Cong. Phil.*, 12th, Venice, 1958. Florence: Sansoni, 1960, Vol. 5, pp. 45–54.

Carus, Paul. "Professor Russell's Views on Mathematics." *Monist*, 1910, Vol. 20, pp. 46–70.

Charlesworth, Maxwell J. "Bertrand Russell: Logical Form and the Ideal Language." *Philosophy and Linguistic Analysis.* Pittsburgh: Duquesne University, 1959, pp. 47–73.

Church, Alonzo. Review of *Principia Mathematica*, Vols. 2 and 3. *Bull. Am. Math. Soc.*, 1928, Vol. 34, pp. 237–40.

Conway, P. H. "The 'Barber' Paradox." *Laval Théol. Phil.* (Quebec), 1962, Vol. 18, pp. 161–76.

Couturat, Louis. Review of *Essay on the Foundations of Geometry. Rev. Mét. Mor.*, 1898, Vol. 6, pp. 354–80.

Couturat, Louis. Review of *Principles of Mathematics. Bull. Sci. Math.*, 1904, 2d Ser., Vol. 28, Part 1, pp. 129–47.

Darbon, André. *La philosophie des mathématiques; étude sur la logistique de Russell.* Paris: Presses Universitaires de France, 1949.

Dufumier, Henri. "La philosophie des mathématiques de MM. Russell et Whitehead." *Rev. Mét. Mor.*, 1912, Vol. 20, pp. 538–66.

Hansson, Bengt. "Some Incompatibilities in Russell's 'Introduction to Mathematical Philosophy.'" *Theoria*, 1967, Vol. 33, pp. 133–38.

Hay, William H. "Bertrand Russell on the Justification of Induction." *Phil. Sci.*, 1950, Vol. 17, pp. 266–77.

Henkin, Leon. "Are Logic and Mathematics Identical?" *Science*, 1962, Vol. 138, pp. 788–94.

Jeffreys, Harold. "Bertrand Russell on Probability." *Mind*, 1950, Vol. 59, pp. 313–19.

Lee, H. N. "Note on '⊃' and '⊢' in Whitehead and Russell's *Principia Mathematica.*" *Mind*, 1958, Vol. 67, pp. 250–53.

Montague, William P. "The Meaning of Identity, Similarity, and Non-entity; a Criticism of Mr. Russell's Logical Puzzles." *J. Phil.*, 1906, Vol. 3, pp. 127–31.

Moore, G. E. Review of *Essay on the Foundations of Geometry. Mind*, 1899, Vol. 8, pp. 397–405.

Nelson, E. J. "Whitehead and Russell's Theory of Deduction as a Nonmathematical Science." *Bull. Am. Math. Soc.*, 1934, Vol. 40, pp. 478–86.

Pears, David F. "Logical Atomism: Russell and Wittgenstein."

The Revolution in Philosophy. London: Macmillan, 1956; New York: St. Martin's Press, 1956, pp. 41–55.

Peters, Franz. "Russell on Class Theory." *Synthèse*, 1963, Vol. 15, pp. 327–35.

Prior, A. N. "Existence in Leśniewski and Russell." Logic Colloquium, 8th, Oxford, 1963. *Formal Systems and Recursive Functions* . . . Amsterdam: North-Holland, 1965, pp. 149–55.

Ruja, Harry. "Principles of Polemic in Russell." *Inquiry*, 1968, Vol. 11, pp. 282–94.

Sellars, Wilfrid. "Classes as Abstract Entities and the Russell Paradox." *Rev. Met.*, 1963, Vol. 17, pp. 67–90.

Shaw, James B. Review of *Principia Mathematica. Am. Math. Soc., Bull.*, 1912, Vol. 18, pp. 386–411.

Shearman, A. T. Review of *Principles of Mathematics. Mind*, 1907, Vol. 16, pp. 254–65.

Sheffer, Henry M. Review of *Principia Mathematica. Isis*, 1926, Vol. 8, pp. 226–31.

Smart, J. J. C. "Whitehead and Russell's Theory of Types." *Analysis*, 1950, Vol. 10, pp. 93–96.

Tallon, Hugh J. "Russell's Doctrine of the Logical Proposition." *New Scholasticism*, 1939, Vol. 13, pp. 31–48.

Wang, Hao. "Russell and His Logic." *Ratio*, June 1965, Vol. 7, No. 1, pp. 1–34.

Waterlow, S. ". . . Russell's Logical Theory of Mathematics." *Aristotelian Soc., Proc.*, 1909–10, Vol. 10, pp. 132–88.

Wilson, Edwin B. Review of *Principles of Mathematics. Am. Math. Soc., Bull.*, 1904, Vol. 11, pp. 74–93.

Weiss, Paul. "The Theory of Types." *Mind*, 1928, Vol. 37, pp. 338–48.

IV. THEORY OF KNOWLEDGE. PHILOSOPHY OF SCIENCE.

The Future of Science. New York: Philosophical Library, 1959.

Human Knowledge, Its Scope and Limits. London: Allen & Unwin; New York: Simon and Schuster, 1948.

The Impact of Science on Society. London: Allen & Unwin; New York: Simon and Schuster, 1952.

An Inquiry into Meaning and Truth. London: Allen & Unwin; New York: Norton, 1940.

Our Knowledge of the External World. Chicago, London: Open Court, 1914; London: Allen & Unwin, 1922.

The Scientific Outlook. London: Allen & Unwin; New York: Norton, 1931.

Review of G. Heymans, *Die Gesetze und Elemente des Wissenschaftlichen Denkens*. *Mind*, 1895, Vol. 4, pp. 245–49.

Review of E. Goblot, *Essai sur le classification des sciences*. *Mind*, 1898, Vol. 7, pp. 567–68.

"Meinong's Theory of Complexes and Assumptions." *Mind*, 1904, Vol. 13, pp. 204–19, 336–54, 509–24.

"The Existential Import of Propositions." *Mind*, 1905, Vol. 14, pp. 398–401.

Definition of "evidence." *Soc. Française de Phil.*, *Bull.*, Paris, 1905, Vol. 5, p. 235.

Review of H. H. Joachim, *The Nature of Truth*. *Independent Rev.*, 1906, Vol. 9, pp. 349–53.

Review of A. Meinong, *Ueber die Erfahrungsgrundlagen unseres Wissen*. *Mind*, 1906, Vol. 15, pp. 412–15.

"The Nature of Truth." *Mind*, 1906, Vol. 15, pp. 528–33.

Review of G. Santayana, *Reason in Science*. *Speaker*, April 7, 1906, Vol. 14, pp. 14–15.

Letters to Meinong, 1904–7. Rudolf Kindinger, ed. *Philosophenbriefe aus der Wissenschaftlicher Korrespondenz von Alexius Meinong*. Graz: Akademische Druck- u. Verlagsanstalt, 1965, pp. 150–53.

"On the Nature of Truth." *Proc. of Aristotelian Soc.*, 1906–7, Vol. 7, pp. 28–49.

Review of A. Meinong, *Über die Stellung der Gegenstandstheorie*. *Mind*, 1907, Vol. 16, pp. 436–39.

"Le réalisme analytique." *Soc. Française de Phil.*, *Bull.*, Paris, 1911, Vol. 11, pp. 53–64.

"The Basis of Realism." *J. Phil.*, 1911, Vol. 8, pp. 158–61.

Review of F. C. S. Schiller, *Formal Logic. Nation* (London), 1912, Vol. 11, pp. 258–59.

"The Nature of Sense-Data." *Mind*, 1913, Vol. 22, pp. 76–81.

Preface. Jules H. Poincaré, *Science and Method*. London: Nelson, 1914, pp. 5–8.

"Definitions and Methodological Principles in Theory of Knowledge." *Monist*, 1914, Vol. 24, pp. 582–93.

[Sense datum]. *J. Phil.*, 1915, Vol. 12, pp. 391–92.

"Pure Reason at Koenigsberg." *Nation* (London), 1918, Vol. 23, pp. 426, 428.

Review of C. D. Broad, *Perception, Physics, and Reality. Mind*, 1918, Vol. 27, pp. 492–98.

Review of N. O. Lossky, *The Intuitive Basis of Knowledge. Athenaeum*, 1919, pp. 524–25.

Review of H. H. Joachim, *Immediate Experience and Mediation. Athenaeum*, 1920, p. 43.

"The Meaning of 'Meaning.'" *Mind*, 1920, Vol. 29, pp. 398–404.

"Physics and Perception." *Mind*, 1922, Vol. 31, pp. 478–85.

"Lord Balfour on Methodological Doubt." *Nation & Athenaeum*, 1923, Vol. 32, pp. 542–44.

"The Mastery of Words." *Nation & Athenaeum*, 1923, Vol. 33, pp. 87–89.

"Vagueness." *Australasian J. Psych. & Phil.*, 1923, Vol. 1, pp. 84–92.

[Review of G. Santayana, *Scepticism and Animal Faith*]. *Nation & Athenaeum*, 1923, Vol. 33, p. 457.

Review of G. Santayana, *Scepticism and Animal Faith. New Statesman*, 1923, Vol. 21, p. 596.

"Knowledge, Theory of." *Encyclopaedia Britannica*, 13th ed. London & New York: Encyclopaedia Britannica, 1926, Vol. 2, pp. 642–45.

"Relativity: Philosophical Consequences." *Ibid.*, Vol. 3, pp. 331–32.

"Perception." *J. Phil. Studies*, 1926, Vol. 1, pp. 78–86.

"The Meaning of Meaning." *Dial*, 1926, Vol. 81, pp. 114–21.

"Science." Charles A. Beard, ed., *Whither Mankind*. New York: Longmans, Green, 1928, pp. 63–82.

"How Will Science Change Morals?" *Menorah J.*, 1928, Vol. 14, pp. 321–29.

"The Twilight of Science." *Century Mag.*, 1929, Vol. N.S. 96, pp. 311–15.

Review of A. S. Eddington, *New Pathways in Science. Time & Tide*, 1935, Vol. 16, pp. 550–51.

"The Limits of Empiricism." *Proc. of Aristotelian Soc.*, 1935–36, Vol. 36, pp. 131–50.

"The Congress of Scientific Philosophy." *Int. Cong. for the Unity of Science*, 1st, Paris, 1935. Paris: Hermann, 1936, Part 1, pp. 10–11.

"On Verification." *Proc. of Aristotelian Soc.*, 1937–38, Vol. 38, pp. 1–20.

"Logical Positivism." *Polemic*, 1945, No. 1, pp. 6–13.

Preface. William K. Clifford, *The Common Sense of the Exact Sciences*. New York: Knopf, 1946; Toronto: Ryerson, 1946; London: Sigma, 1947, pp. v–x.

Review of A. J. Ayer, *Language, Truth and Logic*, 2d ed. *Horizon*, 1947, Vol. 15, pp. 71–72.

"Science as a Product of Western Europe." *Listener*, 1948, Vol. 39, pp. 865–66.

"Einstein and the Theory of Relativity." *Listener*, 1949, Vol. 41, pp. 452–53.

"The Science to Save us from Science." *The New York Times*, March 19, 1950, Sec. 6, pp. 9, 31 ff.

[Comments on J. Z. Young, "Doubt and Certainty in Science"]. London *Observer*, December 24, 1950, p. 4.

"Reason and Passion." *Listener*, 1952, Vol. 48, pp. 495–96.

"The Divorce of Science and Culture." *UNESCO Courier*, February 1958, Vol. 11, No. 2, p. 4.

"The Role of Science in Society." *Int. Affairs* (Moscow), March 1958, No. 3, p. 42.

"The World and the Observer." *Listener*, 1958, Vol. 59, p. 451.

Introduction. Ernest Gellner, *Words and Things*. London: Gollancz, 1959; Boston: Beacon, 1960, pp. 13–15.

"Review Refused." London *Times*, November 5, 1959, p. 13.

"Review Refused." London *Times*, November 24, 1959, p. 13.

Ambrose, Alice. "Finitism and 'The Limits of Empiricism.'" *Mind*, 1937, Vol. 46, pp. 379–85.

Ayer, A. J. "On the Scope of Empirical Knowledge." *Erkenntnis*, 1938, Vol. 7, pp. 267–74.

Bar-Hillel, Yehoshua. "Theory of Types." In Paul Edwards, ed., *op. cit.*, Vol. 8, pp. 168–72.

Beck, Lewis W. "Constructions and Inferred Entities." *Phil. Sci.*, 1950, Vol. 17, pp. 74–86.

Bosanquet, B. Review of *Our Knowledge of the External World*. *Phil. Rev.*, 1915, Vol. 24, pp. 431–39.

Bradley, F. H. *Essays on Truth and Reality*. Oxford: Oxford University Press, 1914, *passim*.

Butler, Ronald J. "The Scaffolding of Russell's Theory of Descriptions." *Phil. Rev.*, 1954, Vol. 63, pp. 350–64.

Dewey, John. "The Existence of the World as a Problem." *Phil. Rev.*, 1915, Vol. 24, pp. 357–70.

Eames, Elizabeth R. "The Consistency of Russell's Realism." *Phil. Phenomenol. Res.*, 1967, Vol. 27, pp. 502–11.

Idem. "Contemporary British Criticism of Bertrand Russell." *Southern J. Phil.*, 1968, Vol. 6, pp. 45–51.

Idem. *Bertrand Russell's Theory of Knowledge*. London: Allen & Unwin, 1969.

Edwards, Paul. "Russell's Doubts About Induction." *Mind*, 1949, Vol. 58, pp. 141–63.

Fritz, Charles A., Jr. *Bertrand Russell's Construction of the External World*. London: Routledge & Kegan Paul, 1952; New York: Humanities, 1952.

Geach, P. T. "Russell's Theory of Descriptions." *Analysis*, 1950, Vol. 10, pp. 84–88.

Granger, Gilles-Gaston. "Le scepticisme passioné de Bertrand Russell." *Critique*, 1963, Vol. 19, pp. 1068–82.

Hawkins, Denis J. B. "The Scope and Limits of Bertrand Russell." *Month* (London), 1949, Vol. 1, pp. 322–31.

Hayner, Paul. "Knowledge by Acquaintance." *Phil. Phenomenol. Res.*, 1969, Vol. 29, pp. 423–31.

Hicks, G. Dawes; G. E. Moore, Beatrice Edgell, and C. D. Broad. "Is There 'Knowledge by Acquaintance'?" *Arist. Soc.*, *Sup.* Vol. 2, 1919, 159–220.

Hoernlé, Reinhold F. A. "On the Theory of Error in Bertrand Russell's 'Problems of Philosophy.'" *Studies in Philosophy*. Cambridge, Mass.: Harvard University Press, 1952, pp. 98–124.

Jager, Ronald. "Russell's Denoting Complex." *Analysis*, 1960, Vol. 20, pp. 53–62.

James, William. "Two English Critics." *The Meaning of Truth*. New York: Longmans, Green, 1909, pp. 272–80.

Kneale, William. Review of *Human Knowledge. Mind*, 1949, Vol. 58, pp. 369–87.

Lejewski, C. "A Re-examination of the Russellian Theory of Descriptions." *Philosophy*, 1960, Vol. 35, pp. 14–29.

Levien, Max. "Bertrand Russell and Modern Physics." *Labour Mo.*, 1927, Vol. 9, pp. 241–49, 303–13.

McLendon, Hiram J. "Has Russell Answered Hume?" *J. Phil.*, 1952, Vol. 49, pp. 145–59.

Idem. "Has Russell Proved Naïve Realism Self-contradictory?" *J. Phil.*, 1956, Vol. 53, pp. 289–302.

Malcolm, Norman. Review of *Human Knowledge. Phil. Rev.*, 1950, Vol. 59, pp. 94–106.

Mirsky, D. S. "The Outlook of Bertrand Russell." *Labour Mo.*, 1932, Vol. 14, pp. 113–19.

Nagel, Ernest. Review of *Inquiry into Meaning and Truth. J. Phil.*, 1941, Vol. 38, pp. 253–70.

Newman, M. H. A. "Mr. Russell's Causal Theory of Perception." *Mind*, 1928, Vol. 37, pp. 137–48.

Parker, DeWitt H. "Knowledge by Acquaintance." *Phil. Rev.*, 1945, Vol. 54, pp. 1–18.

Pears, David F. *Bertrand Russell and the British Tradition in*

Philosophy. New York: Random House, 1967; London: Collins, 1967.

Prichard, H. A. "Mr. Bertrand Russell on Our Knowledge of the External World." *Mind,* 1915, Vol. 24, pp. 145–85.

Prior, A. N. "Russell's Correspondence Theory." In Paul Edwards, ed., *op. cit.,* Vol. 2, pp. 226–28.

Reichenbach, Hans. "A Conversation Between Bertrand Russell and David Hume." *J. Phil.,* 1949, Vol. 46, pp. 545–49.

Searle, J. R. "Russell's Objections to Frege's Theory of Sense and Preference." *Analysis,* 1958, Vol. 18, pp. 137–43.

Smith, Helen M. "Bertrand Russell on Perception." *Proc. of Aristotelian Soc.,* 1932, Vol. 32, pp. 207–26.

Stephen, Karin C. "Comparison of the Data and Philosophical Methods of Mr. Russell and M. Bergson." *Proc. of Aristotelian Soc.,* 1914–15, Vol. 15, pp. 271–303.

Stout, George F. "Mr. Russell's Theory of Judgement." *Proc. of Aristotelian Soc.,* 1915, Vol. 15, pp. 332–52.

Strawson, P. F. "On Referring." *Mind,* 1950, Vol. 59, pp. 320–44.

Strong, Charles A. "Mr. Russell's Theory of the External World." *Mind,* 1922, Vol. 31, pp. 307–20.

Suter, Ronald. "Russell's 'Refutation' of Meinong in 'On Denoting.'" *Phil. Phenomenol. Res.,* 1967, Vol. 27, pp. 512–16.

Thalheimer, Ross. *A Critical Examination of the Epistemological and Psycho-physical Doctrines of Bertrand Russell.* Baltimore, Md.: Johns Hopkins Press, 1931.

Thayer, H. S. "The Relation Between the Theories of John Dewey and Bertrand Russell." *J. Phil.,* 1947, Vol. 44, pp. 516–27.

Torrence, Donald L. "A Philosophy for Rhetoric from Bertrand Russell." *Q. J. Speech,* 1959, Vol. 45, pp. 153–65.

Urmson, J. O. "Russell on Acquaintance with the Past." *Phil. Rev.,* 1969, Vol. 78, pp. 510–15.

Wedberg, A. "Bertrand Russell's Empiricism." In Ingemar Hedenius, et al., eds., *Philosophical Essays.* Uppsala: Almquist & Wiksell, 1937, pp. 345–87.

Williams, Donald C. "Having Ideas in the Head." *Principles of Empirical Realism*. Springfield, Ill.: C. C. Thomas, 1966, Chap. 11.

Woodger, J. H. "Russell's Theory of Perception." *Monist*, 1930, Vol. 40, pp. 621–36.

V. METAPHYSICS. PHILOSOPHY OF RELIGION.

The Analysis of Matter. London: Paul, Trench, & Trubner; New York: Harcourt, Brace, 1927.

Analysis of Mind. London: Allen & Unwin; New York: Macmillan, 1921.

Religion and Science. London: Butterworth; New York: Holt, 1935.

Why I Am Not a Christian. Edited by Paul Edwards. London: Allen & Unwin; New York: Simon and Schuster, 1957.

Review of G. Lechalas, *Étude sur l'espace et le temps*. *Mind*, 1896, Vol. 5, p. 128.

Review of A. Hannequin, *Essai critique sur l'hypothèse des atomes dans la science contemporaine*. *Mind*, 1896, Vol. 5, pp. 410–17.

Review of A. Meinong, *Ueber die Bedeutung des Weberschen Gesetzes*. *Mind*, 1899, Vol. 8, pp. 251–56.

Review of W. Hastie, ed., *Kant's Cosmogony*. *Mind*, 1901, Vol. 10, pp. 405–7.

"Is Position in Time and Space Absolute or Relative?" *Mind*, 1901, Vol. 10, pp. 293–317.

Definitions of "cause," "contenu," "convergence." *Soc. Française de Phil., Bull.*, Paris, 1903, Vol. 3, pp. 163, 192–93, 197.

Review of C. H. Hinton, *The Fourth Dimension*. *Mind*, 1904, Vol. 13, pp. 573–74.

"Religion and Metaphysics." *Independent Rev.*, 1906, Vol. 9, pp. 109–16.

"Freethought, Ancient and Modern." *Speaker*, 1906, Vol. N.S. 14, pp. 402–3.

"Metaphysics for the Man of Action." *Nation* (London), 1907, Vol. 1, pp. 44–45.

"Newton's Philosophy." *Nature,* 1908, Vol. 78, pp. 99–100.

"Metaphysics and Intuition." *Cambridge Rev.,* 1913, Vol. 34, pp. 376–77.

"Mr. Balfour's Natural Theology." *Cambridge Rev.,* 1914, Vol. 35, pp. 338–39.

"On the Experience of Time." *Monist,* 1915, Vol. 25, pp. 212–33.

"Idealism on the Defensive." *Nation* (London), 1917, Vol. 21, pp. 588, 590.

"The Mystic Vision." *Athenaeum,* 1919, pp. 487–88, 599.

"The Anatomy of Desire." *Athenaeum,* 1919, pp. 1340–41, 1372–73, 1402–3.

"The Relativity Theory of Gravitation." *English Rev.,* 1920, Vol. 30, pp. 11–18.

"Religious Evolution." *Nation* (London), 1920, Vol. 27, pp. 116, 118.

"Philosophic Idealism at Bay." *Nation & Athenaeum,* 1922, Vol. 31, pp. 625–26.

[Review of A. A. Luce, *Bergson's Doctrine of Intuition*]. *Nation & Athenaeum,* 1922, Vol. 31, p. 770.

"Relativity, Scientific and Metaphysical." *Nation & Athenaeum,* 1922, Vol. 31, pp. 796–97.

"Instinct and the Unconscious." *New Leader* (London), November 3, 1922, Vol. 1, No. 5, p. 12.

Dr. Schiller's analysis of *The Analysis of Mind. J. Phil.,* 1922, Vol. 19, pp. 645–51.

"Science and Metaphysics." *Nation & Athenaeum,* 1923, Vol. 33, p. 716.

"Biology and Religion." *Nation & Athenaeum,* 1923, Vol. 34, pp. 223–24.

"The Dogmas of Naturalism." *Nation & Athenaeum,* 1925, Vol. 37, p. 326.

"Mind and Matter." *Nation & Athenaeum,* 1925, Vol. 38, p. 323.

Review of C. D. Broad, *The Mind and Its Place in Nature. Mind,* 1926, Vol. 35, pp. 72–80.

"Relativity and Religion." *Nation & Athenaeum,* 1926, Vol. 39, pp. 206–7.

[Review of N. Bukharin, *Historical Materialism*]. *New Leader,* August 20, 1926, Vol. 13, No. 45, pp. 3–5.

"Physics and Metaphysics." *Sat. Rev. Lit.,* 1928, Vol. 4, pp. 910–11.

"Three Ways to the World." *The World Man Lives In.* New York: Van Nostrand, 1929, pp. 11–21.

"Physics and Theology." *Nation,* 1929, Vol. 128, p. 232.

"Religion and Happiness." *Spectator,* 1930, Vol. 145, pp. 714–15.

"Analysis of Mind." Charles W. Morris, *Six Theories of Mind.* Chicago: University of Chicago Press, 1932, pp. 135–38.

"Determinism and Physics." Durham, England, *Proc. of Univ. Phil. Soc.,* March 1936, Vol. 9, Part 4, pp. 228–45.

"The Problem of Universals." *Polemic* 2, January 1946, pp. 21–35.

"The Faith of a Rationalist." *Listener,* 1947, Vol. 37, pp. 826–36.

"Are the World's Troubles Due to Decay of Faith?" *Rationalist Annual* 1954, pp. 7–13.

"Do Science and Religion Conflict?" *J. Brit. Astron. Assn.,* 1954, Vol. 64, pp. 94–96.

"The Great Mystery: Do Men Survive Death?" London *Sunday Times,* January 13, 1957, p. 10.

"Mind." *Encounter,* March 1959, Vol. 12, No. 3, p. 84.

"Is the Notion of Progress an Illusion?" Malcolm Muggeridge, *Muggeridge through the Microphone.* London: British Broadcasting Corp., 1967, pp. 25–31.

"Bertrand Russell on the Afterlife." *Humanist* (Buffalo, N.Y.), September–October 1968, Vol. 28, No. 51, p. 29.

Bergmann, Gustav. "Russell on Particulars." *Phil. Rev.,* 1947, Vol. 56, pp. 59–72.

Bouwsma, O. K. "Russell's Argument on Universals." *Phil. Rev.,* 1943, Vol. 52, pp. 193–99.

Broad, C. D. Review of *Analysis of Matter*. *Mind*, 1928, Vol. 37, pp. 88–95.

Clark, Cecil H. D. *Christianity and Bertrand Russell*. London: Butterworth, 1958.

Dewey, John. Review of *Religion and Science*. *Southern Rev.*, 1936, Vol. 2, pp. 53–62.

Dwelshauvers, Georges. "Bertrand Russell et l' 'Analyse de l'Esprit.' " *Rev. Phil.*, 1926, Vol. 33, pp. 501–30.

Eddington, Arthur S. Review of *Analysis of Matter*. *Philosophy*, 1928, Vol. 3, pp. 93–95.

Eliot, T. S. "Why Mr. Russell Is a Christian." *Criterion*, 1927, Vol. 6, pp. 177–79.

Gotlind, Erik J. A. *Bertrand Russell's Theories of Causation*. Uppsala: Almquist & Wiksell, 1952.

Grelling, Kurt. ". . . Russell's Metaphysics." *Monist*, 1929, Vol. 39, pp. 501–20.

Hoernlé, Reinhold F. A. "The Religious Aspect of Bertrand Russell's Philosophy." *Harv. Theol. Rev.*, 1916, Vol. 9, pp. 157–89.

Kraus, Oskar. "Zur Kritik von Bertrand Russells 'Analyse der Geistes.' " *Arch. Ges. Psychol.*, 1930, Vol. 75, pp. 289–314.

Lovejoy, Arthur O. "Mr. Bertrand Russell and the Unification of Mind and Matter." *The Revolt Against Dualism*. Chicago: Open Court, 1929; New York: Norton, 1930, Chaps. 6 and 7.

Macdonald, M. "Russell and McTaggart." *Philosophy*, 1936, Vol. 11, pp. 322–35.

Morris, Charles W. "Mach and Russell." *Six Theories of Mind*. Chicago: University of Chicago, 1932, pp. 124–34.

Muehlmann, Robert. "Russell and Wittgenstein on Identity." *Phil. Q.* (St. Andrews), 1969, Vol. 19, pp. 221–30.

Niebuhr, Reinhold. Review of *Why I Am Not a Christian*. *The New York Times*, September 22, 1957, Sec. 7, pp. 6, 30.

O'Doherty, E. F. "Russell and the Great Mystery." *Studies* (Dublin), 1957, Vol. 46, pp. 27–33, 162–72.

Pringle-Pattison, A. S. ". . . Russell's Views on Religion." *Hibbert J.*, 1913, Vol. 12, pp. 47–63.

Santayana, George. Review of *Religion and Science*. *Am. Mercury*, 1936, Vol. 37, pp. 377–79.

Schiller, F. C. S. "Mr. Russell's Psychology." *J. Phil.*, 1922, Vol. 19, pp. 281–92.

Sparshott, F. E. Review of *Why I Am Not a Christian*. *Tamarack Rev.*, Winter 1958, No. 6, pp. 90–94.

Watkin, E. Ingram. "Bertrand Russell—Religious Atheist." *Catholic World*, 1923, Vol. 116, pp. 731–42.

Idem. "Religion Without Dogma." *Dublin Rev.*, 1927, Vol. 180, pp. 173–96.

Idem. "Religion Without Reason." *Men and Tendencies*. London: Sheed & Ward, 1937, pp. 49–92.

Watson, John B. "The Analysis of Mind." *Dial*, 1922, Vol. 72, pp. 97–102.

Wood, Herbert G. "Logic and Pessimism." *Expositor* (London), 1919, 8th Ser., Vol. 18, pp. 42–63.

Idem. Why Mr. Bertrand Russell Is Not a Christian. London: Student Christian Movement, 1928.

VI. ETHICS. SOCIAL AND POLITICAL PHILOSOPHY.

Authority and the Individual. London: Allen & Unwin; New York: Simon and Schuster, 1949.

The Conquest of Happiness. London: Allen & Unwin; New York: Liveright, 1930.

Freedom and Organization 1814–1914. London: Allen & Unwin; New York: Norton, 1934.

German Social Democracy. London: Longmans, Green, 1896.

How to Be Free and Happy. New York: Rand School, 1924.

Human Society in Ethics and Politics. London: Allen & Unwin; New York: Simon and Schuster, 1955.

Justice in War-Time. Chicago, London: Open Court, 1916.

Marriage and Morals. London: Allen & Unwin; New York: Liveright, 1929.

Political Ideals. New York: Century, 1917.

Power, a New Social Analysis. London: Allen & Unwin; New York: Norton; Toronto: McLeod, 1938.

The Practice and Theory of Bolshevism. London: Allen & Unwin; New York: Harcourt, Brace, & Howe, 1920; 2d ed., London: Allen & Unwin; New York: Macmillan, 1949. Title of 1920 New York ed.: *Bolshevism: Practice and Theory.*

Principles of Social Reconstruction. London: Allen & Unwin, 1916; New York: Century, 1917. Title of New York ed.: *Why Men Fight.*

The Prospects of Industrial Civilisation. London: Allen & Unwin; New York: Century, 1923.

Roads to Freedom. London: Allen & Unwin, 1918; New York: Holt, 1919. Title of New York ed.: *Proposed Roads to Freedom.*

"The Meaning of Good." *Independent Rev.,* 1904, Vol. 2, pp. 328–33.

"The Development of Morals." *Independent Rev.,* 1907, Vol. 12, pp. 204–10.

"The Philosophy of Pacifism." *Towards Ultimate Harmony.* London: League of Peace and Freedom, [1915], pp. 1–14.

"The War and Non-Resistance." *Int. J. Ethics,* 1915, Vol. 26, pp. 23–30.

"The Nature of the State in View of Its External Relations." *Proc. of Aristotelian Soc.,* 1915–16, Vol. 16, pp. 301–10.

"Two Ideals of Pacifism." *War and Peace,* January 1917, Vol. 4, No. 40, pp. 58–60.

"Liberty and National Service." *Tribunal,* February 22, 1917, No. 48, p. 2.

"The Position of the Absolutists." *Tribunal,* March 1, 1917, No. 49, p. 2.

"War and Individual Liberty." *Tribunal,* March 8, 1917, No. 50, p. 2.

"Resistance and Service." *Tribunal,* May 3, 1917, No. 57, p. 2.

"Democracy and Direct Action." *English Rev.,* 1919, Vol. 28, pp. 396–403.

"Democracy and Efficiency." *Athenaeum,* 1919, p. 204.

"Philosophy and Virtue." *Athenaeum*, 1919, p. 270.

"Socialism and Liberal Ideals." *English Rev.*, 1920, Vol. 30, pp. 449–55, 499–508.

"The Philosophy of Conservatism." *New Republic*, 1922, Vol. 32, pp. 309–10.

"What Is Morality?" *Nation & Athenaeum*, 1922, Vol. 32, pp. 254–55.

"Leisure and Mechanism." *Dial*, 1923, Vol. 75, pp. 105–22.

"Life as an Art." *Outlook* (London), 1923, Vol. 52, pp. 213–14.

"Does Ethics Influence Life?" *Nation & Athenaeum*, 1924, Vol. 34, pp. 635–36.

"The New Life That Is America's." *The New York Times*, May 22, 1927, Sec. 4, pp. 1–2.

"Ostrich Code of Morals." *Forum*, 1928, Vol. 80, pp. 7–10.

"On the Evils Due to Fear." *If I Were a Preacher*. London: Cassell; New York: Harper, 1929, pp. 219–30. Title of New York ed.: *If I Could Preach Just Once*.

"Disenchantment." *Nation*, 1929, Vol. 128, p. 428.

"Idealism for Children." *Sat. Rev. Lit.*, 1929, Vol. 6, p. 575.

"Politics and Theology." *Pol. Q.*, 1930, Vol. 1, pp. 179–85.

"How Science Has Changed Society." *Listener*, 1932, Vol. 7, pp. 39–40, 42.

"The Scientific Society." Mary Adams, ed., *Science in the Changing World*. New York: Century, 1933, pp. 201–8.

"The Essence of Law." *New York American*, December 28, 1933, p. 15.

"Is Euthanasia Justifiable?" *New York American*, January 1, 1934, p. 21.

"Pioneer Ethics." *New York American*, March 19, 1934, p. 15.

"Science's Goal." *New York American*, July 27, 1934, p. 19.

"Contemplation." *New York American*, October 26, 1934, p. 23.

"Power, Ancient and Modern." *Pol. Q.*, 1937, Vol. 8, pp. 155–64.

"Happiness." Martin Armstrong, et al., *What Is Happiness?* London: Bodley Head, 1938; New York: Kinsey, 1939; Toronto: Nelson, 1939, pp. 55–65.

"Do I Preach Adultery?" *Liberty*, May 18, 1940, Vol. 17, No. 20, pp. 57–59.

"Freedom and Government." Ruth N. Anshen, ed., *Freedom: Its Meaning.* New York: Harcourt, Brace, 1940, pp. 249–64.

"Dr. Russell Denies Pacifism." *The New York Times,* January 27, 1941, p. 14.

"Long-Time Advocate of Peace Approves Present War." *The New York Times,* February 16, 1941, Sec. 4, p. 8.

"A Philosophy for You in These Times." *Reader's Digest,* October 1941, Vol. 39, No. 234, pp. 5–7.

"Non-Materialistic Naturalism." *Kenyon Rev.,* 1942, Vol. 4, pp. 361–65.

"Citizenship in a Great State." *Fortune,* December 1943, Vol. 28, No. 6, pp. 167–68 ff.

"The Future of Pacifism." *Am. Scholar,* Winter 1943–44, Vol. 13, No. 1, pp. 7–13.

"The Outlook for Mankind." *Horizon,* 1948, Vol. 17, pp. 238–46.

"Toleration." *Listener,* 1948, Vol. 39, pp. 695–97.

"Boredom or Doom in a Scientific World." *U.N. World,* September 1948, Vol. 2, No. 8, pp. 14–16.

"The Way of the World." *World Rev.,* September 1948, Vol. 26, No. 9, pp. 11–15.

"Why Fanaticism Brings Defeat." *Listener,* 1948, Vol. 40, pp. 452–53.

"Values in the Atomic Age." *The Atomic Age.* London: Allen & Unwin, 1949, pp. 81–104.

"Unity of Western Culture." *World Rev.,* April 1949, N.S. No. 2, pp. 5–8.

"Living in an Atomic Age." *Radio Times,* May 4, 1951, Vol. 111, No. 1434, p. 5.

"My Faith in the Future." *John o'London's Weekly,* 1951, Vol. 60, p. 706.

"Are Human Beings Necessary?" *Everybody's Weekly,* September 15, 1951, p. 13.

"The Idea of Progress." Manchester *Guardian,* March 14, 1953, p. 4.

"Promoting Virtuous Conduct." London *Observer,* February 20, 1955, p. 6.

"Christian Ethics." London *Observer,* October 13, 1957, p. 8.

"Christian Ethics." London *Observer,* October 20, 1957, p. 15.

Review of G. Williams, *The Sanctity of Life and the Criminal Law. Stanford Law Rev.,* 1958, Vol. 10, pp. 382–85.

"Respect for Law." *San Francisco Rev.,* Winter 1958, Vol. 1, No. 1, pp. 63, 65.

"Civil Disobedience." *New Statesman,* 1961, Vol. 61, pp. 245–46.

"Civil Disobedience." Clara Urquhart, ed., *A Matter of Life.* Boston: Little, Brown, 1963; London: Cape, 1963, pp. 189–96.

"Die Pflicht zum burgerlichen Ungehorsam." *Friedensrundschau,* June 1963, Vol. 17, No. 6, pp. 16–21.

"The Ethos of Violence." *Minority of One,* January 1965, Vol. 7, No. 1, pp. 6–7.

Aiken, Lillian W. *Bertrand Russell's Philosophy of Morals.* New York: Humanities, 1963.

Bosanquet, Bernard. Review of *Principles of Social Reconstruction. Mind,* 1917, Vol. 26, pp. 233–34.

Dewar, Lindsay. *Marriage without Morals.* London: Society for Promoting Christian Knowledge, 1931.

Dewey, John. Review of *Education and the Good Life. New Republic,* 1926, Vol. 46, pp. 410–11.

Edman, Irwin. "To Bertrand Russell after Reading 'Why Men Fight.'" *New York Tribune,* February 28, 1917, p. 11.

Horowitz, I. L. "Bertrand Russell on War and Peace." *Sci. & Society,* Winter 1957, Vol. 21, pp. 30–51.

Kleene, G. A. "Bertrand Russell on Socialism." *Q. J. Econ.*, 1920, Vol. 34, pp. 756–62.

Knight, Frank H. Review of *Power*. *Ethics*, 1939, Vol. 49, pp. 253–85.

Lewis, John. Review of *Authority and the Individual*. *Modern Q.* (London), 1949, Vol. 4, pp. 341–65.

McCarthy, Donald G. "Freedom in the Ethics of Bertrand Russell." *Phil. Studies* (Maynooth), 1960, Vol. 10, pp. 100–32.

MacIver, Robert M. "The Social Ideas of Mr. Bertrand Russell." *Dalhousie Rev.*, 1926, Vol. 6, pp. 135–50.

McKenney, John L. "Concerning Russell's Analysis of Value Judgments." *J. Phil.*, 1958, Vol. 55, pp. 382–89.

Masaryk, Thomas G. Review of *Principles of Social Reconstruction*. *New Europe* (London), 1917, Vol. 2, pp. 342–50.

Nielsen, Kai. "Bertrand Russell's New Ethic." *Methodos*, 1958, Vol. 10, pp. 151–78.

Park, Joe. *Bertrand Russell on Education*. Columbus, O.: Ohio State University Press, 1963; London: Allen & Unwin, 1965.

Parris, Henry. "The Political Thought of Bertrand Russell." *Durham Univ. J.*, 1966, Vol. 58, pp. 86–94.

Perry, Leslie R. *Four Progressive Educators*. London: Collier-Macmillan, 1967.

Perry, Ralph B. "Non-resistance and the Present War." *Int. J. Ethics*, 1915, Vol. 25, pp. 307–16.

Stapledon, Olaf. "Bertrand Russell's Ethical Beliefs." *Int. J. Ethics*, 1927, Vol. 37, pp. 390–402.

Toynbee, Arnold. "Man and the Criminal Generation." London *Observer*, November 26, 1961, p. 25.

Woolf, Leonard. Review of *Power*. *London Mercury*, 1938, Vol. 39, pp. 74–76.